THEY DO THINGS
DIFFERENTLY THERE

THEY DO THINGS DIFFERENTLY THERE

*Stories from the International Division
of the British Geological Survey*

Compiled and Edited by
A. J. Reedman and D. G. Bate

They Do Things Differently There
Compiled and edited by A. J. Reedman and D. G. Bate

Published by Aspect Design 2016
Malvern, Worcestershire, United Kingdom.

Designed, printed and bound by Aspect Design
89 Newtown Road, Malvern, Worcs. WR14 1PD
United Kingdom
Tel: 01684 561567
E-mail: allan@aspect-design.net
Website: www.aspect-design.net

A copy of this book has been deposited
with the British Library Board

Cover image shows geologists at Silali caldera, Kenya (1992).
(Photograph by A. J. Reedman.)

Cover design copyright © 2016 Aspect Design

ISBN 978-1-908832-89-4

'The past is a foreign country:
they do things differently there.'
L. P. Hartley

CONTENTS

LIST OF ARTICLES BY COUNTRY

ACKNOWLEDGEMENTS

The editors are indebted to all current and past members of staff of the British Geological Survey who tendered anecdotes, reminiscences and photographs. Inevitably, it has not always been possible to include individual reminiscences in their entirety, and a few had to be omitted altogether. The editors take large responsibility for any perceived failings in the edited versions published here.

The following people graciously provided the material which appears in this compilation: R. Addison, D. T. Aldiss, P. M. Allen, R. S. Arthurton, J. W. Baldock, L. Baldock, W. J. Barclay, J. H. Bateson, W. Bauer, J. D. Bennett, J. P. Berrangé, K. B Bloomfield, H. F. Burke, N. R. Cameron, T. J. Charsley, M. C. G. Clarke, M. Clarke, M. J. Crow, D. P. F. Darbyshire, B. De Waele, L. J. Donnelly, R. A. Ellison, C. D. R. Evans, R. B. Evans, F. M. Fordyce, D. Greenbaum, D. Hackett, M. P. Hawkins, P. R. N. Hobbs, C. C. Johnson, R. L. Johnson, R. M. Key, M. Litherland, A. Macfarlane, D. I. J. Mallick, E. A. O'Connor, B. G. N. Page, P. E. J. Pitfield, J. H. Powell, R. Reedman, N. S. Robins, M. Smith, M. A. Squires, P. J. Strange, R. J. Thomas, P. Turner, C. N. Waters and B. C. Webb.

All photographs appearing in this book were either supplied by the above contributors or sourced by the editors from British Geological Survey archives. The BGS is thanked for allowing us to include those images which form part of its registered archive.

The assistance of Rob Evans, an early instigator of this compilation, is gratefully acknowledged.

We are also much obliged to Paul Turner for providing the map which appears on page xx.

FOREWORD

Working in the developing world is a hugely rewarding and at times challenging business for the geologist. There are hazards: from animals, the terrain, the equipment, the weather, and of course other people! The experience can be both invigorating and enriching, with strange and unfamiliar sights, cultures and colleague's odd habits being all matters for reminiscence.

Since 1965 more than 350 British Geological Survey personnel have worked on a truly global and varied programme of international development projects. This has resulted in many official publications and numerous papers in scientific journals, all available in the public domain. It has also provided its many individual participants with a host of unexpected experiences: some dangerous, some sad, and others (in retrospect) humorous. Such experiences are the subject of this book.

The compilers, both of whom are long-serving former officers of the BGS, have cajoled and harried past and present colleagues for their contributions, knowing that there are many gems to be preserved and savoured before they become lost. Told in their own words by the individual scientists (or their residential partners) and long suffering but essential administrative support team, these stories describe experiences that capture and convey the flavour of past and recent working lives overseas. As a testament to the resilience and ingenuity of field geologists, I hope this book will inspire others to follow in their footsteps.

Martin Smith
Science Director, BGS Global Geoscience

INTRODUCTION

The British Geological Survey, established in 1835, is acknowledged as the oldest national Geological Survey in the world. From as early as 1846 it had occasionally been called upon to furnish geologists willing to undertake assignments overseas, although such activities were not then part of its official responsibilities. The foundation for routine British involvement in overseas geology was laid with the opening in London of the Imperial Institute in 1893. Its prime purpose was to promote trade in natural raw materials in the colonies and dependencies, among which minerals were seen to be of significant importance. The Imperial Institute was renamed the Commonwealth Institute in 1958, by which time it had contributed much to our knowledge of the vast territories which then constituted the British Empire. The Institute's Mineral Resources Department, later to become a Division, was an important component of that establishment, and in its early years carried out a number of pioneering reconnaissance geological and mineral surveys in the colonial territories. These mainly involved one or two geologists, often traversing entire countries on foot without the aid of any but the most rudimentary of topographical maps.

By 1943 it was widely acknowledged that, while the Mineral Resources Division had achieved a great deal in terms of identifying the mineral potential of the colonies, there was still a serious lack of information about the basic geology of these extensive territories, and it came to be appreciated that a new organisation was needed to rectify this shortcoming. The Secretary of State for the Colonies thus accepted the recommendation of a committee set up to advise him on the need for an expansion of geological work: in 1947 a new organisation, The Directorate of Colonial Geological Surveys, was inaugurated in London. The Mineral Resources Division of the Imperial Institute became a Division of the new organisation and in due course Photogeological and Geophysical Sections (later Divisions), and an Age Determination Unit (initially based at Oxford) were established.

By the beginning of 1960 the 'wind of change' conceded by Prime Minister Harold Macmillan, whereby Britain would grant independence to its colonies, was already well underway. In this context, many overseas governments expressed a wish to retain, after independence, the services of expatriate specialised staff. The UK government therefore established an Overseas Service Aid Scheme (OSAS) aimed at assisting colonial and newly independent Commonwealth governments in meeting the cost of employing overseas staff before and after independence. At that time, in the geological sciences, these staff were largely under the administration of the Directorate of Colonial Geological Surveys, now renamed, in accordance with the times, the Directorate of Overseas Geological Surveys. The UK also agreed to continue its long-standing provision of specialist advice and services to less-developed countries, including those outside the Commonwealth.

In 1964 the UK government agreed a recommendation that the functions of the Geological Survey of Great Britain (GSGB) should be expanded to cover overseas work, and to this end the Directorate of Overseas Geological Surveys was to be amalgamated with GSGB to form the Institute of Geological Sciences (IGS), subsequently renamed the British Geological

Survey (BGS). The amalgamation took effect in June 1965 with the creation by Royal Charter of a new parent body, the Natural Environment Research Council (NERC). With the merger of GSGB and the Directorate of Overseas Surveys to form IGS, the new organisation found itself with a body of about 160 geoscientists dedicated almost exclusively to working on projects overseas. This was to be the basis for the Overseas (later, International) Division of IGS/BGS. With the formation of the Ministry of Overseas Development (ODM) in 1964, later renamed the Overseas Development Administration (ODA) and now the Department for International Development (DFID), most of the work of the Overseas Division of IGS/BGS would be undertaken as part of the UK overseas aid programme.

During the second half of the 1960s new projects were initiated in more than thirty countries around the developing world, several of which were funded under OSAS terms. These for the most part involved regional geological mapping, mineral exploration, water resource surveys and technical advice.

The pace of overseas activity increased during the 1970s: a decade which saw the initiation of almost ninety new projects in more than fifty countries. This can be compared with the sixty-three projects that were started in the previous decade. The scope and geographical spread of the Overseas Division's work continued to expand through the ensuing years. In the twenty-five years from 1965 to 1990, the Overseas Division implemented over 280 projects in more than eighty developing countries at a cost of over £100 million. This involved over 1,500 staff years of effort by IGS/BGS staff, who worked with over two thousand overseas counterparts. In the early years a significant number of projects involved the secondment of staff to fill established posts in the Geological Surveys of newly independent countries, many of which had previously been British colonies. Other projects comprised extensive geological mapping and mineral exploration surveys whereby, for example, large tracts of Bolivia, Sumatra,

Botswana and Kenya were mapped. Worldwide, a total of over two million square kilometres were covered. In 1990 the Overseas Division was renamed the International Division.

For much of the first thirty years of the Division's existence the majority of projects were classed as residential, with staff and their families living for two or three years in the recipient country. Shorter assignments were on a non-residential basis and this became increasingly common through the 1990s and into the new century. Also, as the amount of geoscientific work funded under the British aid programme began to decline, more contracts for overseas work were having to be sought from the European Commission and World Bank, among others.

This new climate (for BGS) of competitive tendering for externally funded work led eventually to a reconsideration of the role of overseas work within the organisation, and in June 2011 the radical decision was taken to create a spin-out company, International Geoscience Services Ltd, the role of which would be to pursue externally funded overseas thematic surveys and capacity building, and to do so at more competitive prices and with greater flexibility. International work is still very much on the BGS agenda but will in future focus more on pure science and less on the type of institutional strengthening which had become a mainstay of the organisation over previous decades. Accordingly, the last of International Division's projects and the Division itself came to an end. BGS international activities are now coordinated by a small Global Geoscience team under the direction of Dr Martin Smith.

It seemed therefore fitting at this time to celebrate the old Division's past glories in the form of an anecdotal history. The many scientific achievements of the organisation are well documented in numerous published papers, reports and maps, but the personal stories behind such achievements are less well known and a selection of these make up this volume.

When invited to contribute his memories to this volume, the now Reverend Canon Howard Bateson, a long time member of the Overseas Division, prefaced his contributions with the following observation:

> One of the major advantages of working within the IGS/ BGS Overseas Division was that it provided the opportunity to experience not only cutting edge scientific research but also different cultures and environments both at close hand and, crucially, not in the environment of the standard Thomas Cook holiday. Without the Overseas Division it is difficult to see how I would ever have become familiar and comfortable with working in the tropical rainforest of Burma, or been able to see a little of many different cultures: the Karen women of Kayah State with their brass neck rings, the over-the-top hospitality of the Burmese-born Gurkha folk in Shan State, and the mad wetness of the Buddhist Thingyan water festival in Mandalay; to say nothing of working with twentieth-century descendants of the Maya culture in Belize and having the opportunity of exploring with them the numerous centuries old pyramids and ceremonial buildings now overgrown in the forest; and again, experiencing something of the quite characteristic way of life of the Far East. Seeing the majestic scenery of the Andes, the Caribbean islands and all the other places we visited expanded our horizons, and it would be a pity if BGS staff were now denied those experiences—but it is a different world with different priorities!

Tony Reedman and David Bate
August 2015

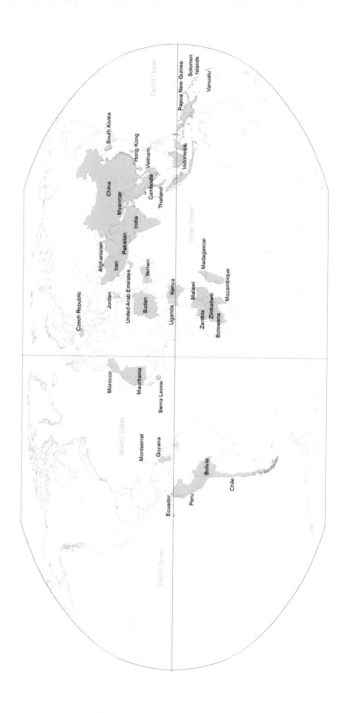

THE 1960s: WIND OF CHANGE

Operation El Dorado
Jevan Berrangé

Guyana gained its independence from Britain in 1965, and my first assignment on joining the then Institute of Geological Sciences in 1966 was to undertake primary reconnaissance geological mapping of all Guyana south of latitude 4° north, an area of about 77,700 km² (slightly smaller than Ireland). With the exception of the Rupununi Savannas that covers about 12,200 km² in the north-west of the region, the entire area is mantled with tropical forest and is virtually unpopulated. The only access to the project area from Georgetown, situated on the coast some 320 km away, was by air. A Douglas DC3 could use dirt airstrips in the savanna, and light planes with floats could land on stretches of calm water on the larger rivers flowing through the region.

Mapping the savanna required a Land Rover, which could be flown into the area in a DC3 that would just about accommodate the vehicle if one first removed its bumpers. In forested areas the only practical means of transport was by river, using canoes. At the start of each field season everything needed for a three-month expedition—men, food, equipment, outboard motor fuel and canoes—had to be flown to an airstrip in the savanna by DC3 or Twin Otter. It was then all transferred into a single-engine Beaver float plane and ferried to base camps at strategically located pools in the major rivers. The canoes had to be lashed onto the float struts of the Beaver as they would not fit inside the cabin, a practice I had learned when working in Canada.

Four annual expeditions were needed to map the region, and for the final two years Richard Johnson, a fellow IGS geologist, worked with me on the project. We each had five Amerindian field assistants and two outboard-powered aluminium canoes, mapping in separate river basins and meeting up occasionally as determined by the logistics of the field work. We traversed thousands of kilometres by canoe, usually moving camp daily: camp being a hammock slung beneath a tarpaulin.

Prior to setting off on a field expedition, I would spend a week in Georgetown checking all the equipment and buying provisions and fuel sufficient for the one hundred days I anticipated being away. Bookers General Stores were exceptionally well stocked in those early days following Independence, and I would go through the whole shop filling up trolleys with food and other items on my list. The Amerindian crew had separate rations provided by the Guyana government, so I was really shopping only for myself. This resulted in an amusing incident at the end of the first (1966) field season. I found I had quite a lot of surplus tinned food and other items, which I decided to give to my crew. In order to be fair I spread everything out on a tarpaulin and invited the men to choose items turn and turn about. We ended up with a couple of boxes of 'tissues' I had bought at Bookers which none of the crew seemed to want. When I asked who would like them the men looked rather embarrassed. I then looked more carefully at the packets and saw that they contained sanitary towels, not tissues! We all had a good laugh when I explained how I had bought them in error, since my foreman had been puzzling over why I needed such things. The ice having been broken, the men were only too pleased to accept my gift of sanitary towels for their wives.

Towards the end of the 1968 field season, while canoeing in the headwaters of the Kwitaro River, one of my crew met with an accident. We found our way impeded by a tree that had fallen across the river. In Guyana such an obstruction is called a 'tacouba'. My bowman, Christie, grabbed his axe and while balancing on the tacouba began chopping it with the intention of dropping the obstruction into the river so that we could proceed. As he brought down his axe I saw it deflected by an overhanging

Cutting tacoubas in the Essequibo headwaters, Guyana. (Photograph by J. P. Berrangé.)

branch and realised that he was going to land a blow on his foot or shin. Luckily the deflection was such that he only sliced the flesh off his ankle, which was left hanging by a piece of skin. I sat him on the bow of my canoe and with trembling hands proceeded to sew the flesh back in place. This proved to be difficult as his skin was tough and I was inexpert at sewing wounds. I had to use pliers from the outboard tool kit to help me pull the needle through. All of this was done without sterilisation or local anaesthetic, which in my haste I had forgotten to administer. Yet Christie sat impassively throughout the operation without flinching, although it must have been unnecessarily painful. He subsequently made a complete recovery.

The last of the four Operation El Dorado expeditions took place in 1970 and aimed to map the so-called New River Triangle in the far southeast corner of Guyana, which is the area between the New River and the Courantyne River that forms the border between Guyana and Suriname. Unfortunately the area in question was the subject of a long standing territorial dispute between the two countries, which in 1970 escalated into armed conflict. When Richard Johnson and myself arrived in Georgetown at the start of the expedition we learned that two of our four aluminium canoes had been requisitioned by the Guyana Defense Force (GDF). A few months earlier the Surinamese had established a military post and dirt airstrip at Camp Jaguar, near the confluence of the New and Courantyne rivers. The GDF had subsequently ejected the Surinamese garrison by strafing them with a light machine-gun mounted in a Twin Otter requisitioned from Guyana Airways. We were told that this had obliged the occupying force to flee to Suriname thereby enabling the GDF to make a 'tactical' landing on the airstrip and 'capture' the camp.

Before leaving Georgetown we had to commission a local company to make glass fibre replacements for the missing two canoes. All the canoes, together with equipment, food and fuel were then flown by DC3 to Apoteri, where the men were also assembled. On arrival I found that a drum of our fuel had been requisitioned by the GDF, and so there was further delay while I obtained a replacement. Our plan was to use a small single prop float plane to fly our respective two field parties to base camps on the New and Oronoque rivers along which we would undertake geological traverses. We were very fortunate to find a Beaver float plane stationed on the Demerara River near Georgetown operated by a British pilot, Barry Cliff, who was well experienced in bush flying under difficult conditions. He readily agreed to fly with a canoe strapped to the struts of his plane, and to attempt landing on stretches of river I had identified from the aerial photographs. This required quite an act of faith on his part as he sometimes had to land on relatively narrow rivers with minimal clearance on either side of the aircraft wings. When on the water he had to contend with river currents and on one occasion narrowly averted being swept over some rapids after losing his anchor. An account of his experiences will be found in his book *A Passion for Mountain, Sail and Flight* (2008).

De Haviland 'Beaver', with aluminium canoe lashed onto float struts, taxiing on the New River, Guyana. (Photograph by R. L Johnson.)

The boundary between Guyana and Suriname is the high water mark on the Guyana side of the Courantyne, not midstream as is usually the case. This meant technically entering Surname if one canoed on the Courantyne, which below its confluence with the New River is up to two kilometres wide. From aerial reconnaissance undertaken with Barry Cliff, I had observed a Surinamese camp on a large island in the Courantyne. I had no official permission to enter Surinamese territory, and given the state of hostility between the two countries, an element of risk would be involved in traversing the river. I explained the situation to my Amerindian crew and asked if they were willing to take me down (I could not have managed without them) and was gratified when they all readily agreed to make the trip. Some of the men had been with me on all four expeditions and I like to think that we had built up a measure of camaraderie and trust in one another.

I figured that we could either sneak past the camp unobserved at night or land there and talk our way through. I decided on the latter alternative as I did not fancy canoeing on a fast, rocky uncharted river at night, and in any event we would have to pass the camp again on the return journey upriver. As we approached the landing below the camp one of our outboard motors stopped working, and by the time we had got it running again a throng of men were assembled on the shore watching our approach and doubtless wondering who we were and what our business was. This was an isolated camp in the heart of the forest, the nearest 'civilization' being at Paramaribo on the coast hundreds of kilometres away. When I departed South Africa many years before, I never imagined that I would find my ability to speak Afrikaans of any further use—but I was about to be proved wrong. As we approached the shore I stood up in the prow of my canoe and in my most authoritative *Boy's Own*, *Sanders of the River* manner announced in Afrikaans that I represented the British government and demanded to meet the man in charge: 'Waar es die Kommandant?' He turned out to be friendly and after I had explained in Afrikaans why we were there he offered us a hut for the night.

While my Amerindian crew were cleaning out the hut and carrying up our gear I decided to take a walk around the camp, which turned out to be a hydrographic station on the site of a former military outpost. As I approached the commandant's hut I heard him talking on the radio to Paramaribo, explaining that an Englishman with five Amerindians had arrived, and asking what should he do. I quickly went inside and stood next to him in order to try and find out what was in store for us. Unfortunately a combination of radio background noise and my limited understanding of Dutch prevented me from making any sense of the advice from Paramaribo. It could not have been very good because the commandant began to look increasingly embarrassed and quickly stopped the dialogue by saying that I was standing next to him and that I spoke Dutch. In the event all the men at the camp proved to be very friendly and we spent the evening playing cards and shove-ha'penny.

We completed the traverse and got back safely to Camp Jaguar. Getting airlifted out of the forest however was not without incident. A canoe that had been poorly secured to the Beaver's struts came loose and nearly led to an air accident, which I think was the closest shave I had during all four expeditions. It illustrates that most accidents in the field result from human error.

Pidgin Post
Don Mallick

In December 1966, just before the start of the Christmas holiday, the head of the IGS Edinburgh office handed me a letter stating that I had been nominated to be seconded as Senior Geologist to the Geological Survey of the New Hebrides (now Vanuatu) and that I was to take up the position at an early opportunity. This came as something of a shock as I had been led to believe that my posting to Edinburgh, three months earlier, was likely to be for at least two years. What did 'an early opportunity' really mean, and where exactly was the New Hebrides?

That evening I went along with my wife, Sue, to Edinburgh Central Library and found that they had only one large old tome containing a chapter on the New Hebrides, from which we learned that it is an island chain in the western Pacific. However, the chapter began 'Nowhere have more missionaries lost their lives in following their calling than in the New Hebrides . . .' Not exactly the message we had been looking for!

This book also provided our introduction to the *lingua franca* of the New Hebrides, Pidgin English, which came in the form of a comparison of the announcement of the death of King George V and the accession of Edward VIII. The English version was a full paragraph beginning 'It is with greatest regret that we announce the death of His Majesty, George V, King of Great Britain and Northern Ireland . . .' listing all his titles. It then continued, 'He will be succeeded by his son . . .' with all his titles 'as King Edward VIII. Long live the King!' The Pidgin version was somewhat more direct: 'King George numba faef, emi ded. Son blong em, emi tekem job blong em.' A near perfect précis of the essentials!

After a preparation period of five and a half months, we set off in June 1967 for the Pacific. The first clear sign that we were moving to a new environment became apparent when we changed in Fiji from a large Boeing 707 to a forty-seat De Havilland Heron for the thousand-kilometre flight to the Anglo-French Condominium of the New Hebrides. Where was the hostess service? We were a bit taken aback half way through the flight when the co-pilot came out from the flight deck with his sextant to take a sun sight from the perspex blister on the top of the fuselage. He then sat in a spare seat, did a few calculations, and called out to the pilot 'Left hand down a bit!' This was a little unnerving since we were heading for a large bank of cloud which was about to hide our destination. However, we arrived directly over Port Vila, but could not see it until we were below the one hundred metre cloud base. The airport building did not impress: it was a two-room corrugated iron shed. It would keep passengers dry but offered nothing else.

We had our first lunch in the Hotel Rossi where there was also a lively party of about half a dozen people at one of the other tables. They soon departed, leaving behind a forest of bottles. The hotel owner explained that they were the UTA airline crew about to return to New Caledonia! Sometime later I was visited by a couple of geologists from Australia who had flown up via Noumea in New Caledonia. They warned me not to sit in the front right seats on the UTA DC4 plane, in which they had been obliged to travel in raincoats as it leaked! Later when we had occasion to return to the airport, to see off some friends on the same aircraft, we passed on the warning. The wife was very nervous of flying anyway, and this news did not help. But things got worse. The passengers boarded, and then had to disembark when one of the four engines refused to start. The flight engineer stripped off his shirt and began banging away with a hammer inside the engine cowling. Our friend was even more nervous when called to re-board. The fourth engine again refused to start. It soon became clear that this was not an unusual occurrence. The pilot passed out from the flight deck two long strands of rubber attached to a leather cup. The cup was placed over one propeller blade of the faulty engine and the rubber attached to a truck. The truck drove slowly away, the rubber stretched and then flicked the propeller and the engine started. How often is it that a large commercial airliner is started with an elastic band?

Of course, the French were losing face with this old DC4 of a government airline and arranged for it to be replaced by a Caravelle jet. When this first arrived in Port Vila it did so with a flourish, flying low round the town before landing at the airport. There it unfortunately sucked in some coral dust from the side of the runway, damaging the engine. It was immediately taken out of service for a while, and replaced by a small De Havilland Heron. Quel horreur!

Soon after settling in Port Vila I left to begin fieldwork on the island of Pentecost. Travelling on the Geological Survey launch

MV *Lopevi*, I first called in at the British District Agency on the island of Malekula to pay my respects, and to inform them that I would be working in their district. The District Agent was away on leave and so I was met at the wharf by the Assistant Agent, George Kalkoa (a New Hebridean who was to become President Ati George Sokomanu after independence in the 1980s). As we walked up to the Agency we passed a man with a large bush-knife, doing some weeding. George casually remarked 'He's one of our murderers'! It turned out that there had been an inter-village dispute on the neighbouring island of Espiritu Santo and one of the village headmen had ordered that some of their opponents be killed. More concerned to obey their chief than a national law with which they had little or no contact, several men were killed.

The killers were not particularly bad or vicious and the application of the law recognised this. Consequently the murderers were put in prison, by the District Agent, for a relatively short time by western standards, partly as punishment but with the aim of preparing them for return to their communities. They were given responsibilities, like unsupervised gardening. They were also called upon each morning to let themselves out of their cells to light the fire that would ensure that the Agency housing had hot water. They would return to their cells each evening. As a consequence of this approach, it was common in Port Vila to see an unarmed policeman leading a line of prisoners along the road, each carrying a large bush-knife—they were off to do the gardening at the government housing.

The Times They Were A-Changing [1]
John Bennett

Arriving at Lobatse in the darkness of a July winter's night in 1965, the only bright lights to be seen were those of the Cumberland Hotel, later to become 'the local'. Awaking next morning to a clear blue sky with the sun rising over the low hills that ring the town, I decided I could happily live with this situation, and indeed had some difficulty in appreciating the wish of folk in Lobatse for rain—not unreasonably after some seven years of drought.

The Geological Survey buildings were quite basic, but the petrological laboratory was air-conditioned, so microscope work became especially popular on hot summer afternoons. The inmates were friendly and an early experience that comes to mind was a field trip with the deputy director to the Molopo Farms in the south, where I witnessed his unsuccessful attempts (on that occasion, anyway) to bag one of many a guinea fowl for the pot. I then spent some days in the field with a colleague before starting my own mapping assignment in the north eastern part of the country, where it was known only that there are 'rocks in the east, Kalahari (Desert) elsewhere.'

It was a pretty idyllic life for a young bachelor. Six months or so in the field during the dry season, then back to town and the 'bright lights' (yes, Lobatse did have some!) during the wet season, when the rains came if the country was fortunate. A Chevy truck served as transport in the field, while a workhorse Bedford lorry laden with water and fuel drums, tents and

---

1 Botswana, previously the British protectorate of Bechuanaland, was granted independence on 30 September 1966. Prior to this date the professional staff in the Geological Survey Department, as in other British colonial territories, were recruited by the UK Ministry of Overseas Development in consultation with the Directorate of Overseas Geological Surveys. John Bennett's appointment as geologist in Lobatse was made under such an arrangement.

camping gear, towed my living accommodation. This last was a Public Works Department 'special', consisting of a corrugated sheet 'hut' with a bunk and some storage units within, mounted on an old truck chassis. One essential 'luxury' was a paraffin fridge. I had a generally amiable Motswana field crew of five, made up of two drivers (Samuel, who drove the Bedford and was the elder statesman of the team; and Lefty, until he was seduced by the private sector and a supposedly more civilised life-style in town); two assistants/ labourers (William, with a gravelly 'Satchmo' voice, and Phiri) and a 'camp keeper' named Joseph. Camp keepers had to be able to cook, but were so-designated because the Survey was not permitted to employ cooks for its geologists in the field. Monthly trips, mostly into Francistown, to collect the crew's wages from officious clerks in the local government offices, and to re-stock with supplies, might with luck include a civilised lunch at the hotel, and then a drive back to camp with the crew, now somewhat more lively and noisy after having blown at least some of their wages on maize beer.

Mapping in the field relied heavily on the use of air photographs of varying scales and ages, together with topographic maps issued by the UK Department of Overseas Surveys (DOS). Observations were made by traversing the ephemeral river courses that prevail under marginal Kalahari conditions. Field experiences that are etched on the memory include ice on the water in the wash stand of a winter's morning, the mopane or 'sweat' bees buzzing around one's eyes in the heat of the day, snakes lurking in the camp kitchen, encounters with elephant and buck, or lion kills in the more remote areas marked by circling vultures, and finally the scramble to catch the crew's hens before moving camp. These are treasured memories, as are those calmer moments: returning to camp for a welcome cuppa in the late afternoon, the brilliant sunsets, the starlit evenings in camp gazing in awe at the Milky Way, or just relaxing with the BBC World Service and Radio Lourenço

Marques for company. There was also the daily radio 'sked', officially to enable the Survey's groundwater team to maintain contact with the drillers, but also an interesting 'listen' enabling us to keep up to date with office politics and Lobatse scandals; but, thankfully, no 'micromanagement' from above, just monthly reports to submit, and an annual inspection visit from the director.

My three-year tour of duty (the normal period of appointment for expatriates) passed quickly, during which time I witnessed Botswana's Independence celebrations on a damp and cold September evening in Francistown. I also had the good fortune to meet my future wife, Margaret, on returning to Lobatse at the end of the 1967 field season. We married in Dublin while I was on leave in 1968 before returning to Botswana for a further three years. The former Bechuanaland had changed its status, and so had I. They were happy days![1]

1 At the conclusion of his first tour of duty John Bennett, like many other expatriate geologists who benefited from the UK government's 'Home-based Posts Scheme', was able to take up full-time employment with the Overseas Division of the Institute of Geological Sciences. His second tour of duty in Botswana, from 1968 to 1971, was on secondment from IGS.

Gardener's Question Time
Tony Reedman

The question might have been 'Who are you?' and 'Why are you in my garden?' In the event, however, and perhaps fortunately, neither question needed to be posed.

It was 1967 and I had just arrived with my wife in the town of Mbarara in Uganda, where I was to run the small regional Geological Survey office. It was my second tour in Uganda, now on secondment from the Institute of Geological Sciences to the Uganda Geological Survey and Mines Department. We moved into an empty Uganda government house and, as was often the case upon such a move, had acquired a dog from a fellow expatriate who was leaving Uganda for another posting. The dog was a large but friendly black Labrador ridgeback mongrel called Sam.

A day or so after moving into the house I heard loud barking from the garden. I went outside to find that Sam, jumping around in excitement while barking furiously and simultaneously wagging his tail, had confronted two large Ugandan gentlemen, both smartly attired in military uniform. Sam had successfully herded them into a corner of the garden where they stood apparently considering their predicament in some trepidation as rabid dogs were not uncommon in Uganda. I calmed down the over-excited Sam and approached the two intruders who were now standing, somewhat annoyed, with backs pressed against the garden hedge. The largest, most impressive and clearly the more important of the two 'trespassers' quickly demanded, 'Do you know who I am?' I confessed that I didn't know who he was, but I did know that he and his colleague were in my garden. 'I am Colonel Amin,' he announced and then added in a less aggressive tone and by way of explanation, 'your house has been empty for some time and our officers mess is in the house next door. We park our vehicles on the road in front of your house and have become used to taking a short cut through this garden.' This explanation completed, and Sam appearing suitably mollified and by now apparently friendly, Colonel Amin added, 'I will see it does not happen again.' With this we shook hands and my new military acquaintances disappeared back through the hedge into the garden of the 'officers' mess' next door.

It was only several months later that I realised I had been speaking to Colonel Idi Amin, Commanding Officer of the Second Battalion of the Uganda Rifles, who later was to become better known as the notoriously sadistic dictator of Uganda. We didn't encounter Colonel Amin again during our stay in Mbarara, but Sam enjoyed the proximity of the 'officers mess' next door. For the next few months his regular forays into their garden yielded large bones of some of the many animals from the nearby game park that the soldiers regularly slaughtered and which Sam struggled to carry into our garden and bury in the various large holes he laboriously excavated.

We left Mbarara and Uganda in 1969 with very happy memories and, luckily, before the coup which resulted in the beginning of the infamous reign of Idi Amin. Sam had been handed over to another expatriate living some distance away. The remaining career of Idi Amin has been well documented, but what became of Sam we shall probably never know.

Mapping and Mao
Peter Allen

My first overseas posting with the Overseas Division of the Institute of Geological Sciences was to Hong Kong, between July 1967 and the end of February 1969. I was there on a Technical Aid project with a colleague, Arthur Stephens (always referred to as Steve). This was at the height of the Chinese 'Great Proletarian Cultural Revolution', which lasted from 1966 to 1976 and spilled over into Hong Kong. The summer and autumn of 1967 was the most violent period in Hong Kong, but the impact of the Cultural Revolution was apparent for the whole time I was there.

Our main task in Hong Kong was to produce a new 1:50,000 scale geological map of the colony and the New Territories, with a land area of about four hundred square miles and comprising some two hundred islands. We were also to do some consulting. In the event, Steve chose to do the consulting and mapped a small area around Plover Cove. I mapped the remainder.

I flew to Hong Kong accompanied by my wife Joyce, and my two daughters, Sarah and Kathryn aged four and two. About ten days before we left, when I had given up the lease on our rented house and packed all our belongings, I had a phone call from John Pallister, Head of Overseas Division, rather diffidently suggesting that because of the civil strife in Hong Kong I should not feel obliged to go, especially with my family. There had been rioting there just before we were due to leave the UK, which I suppose caused the senior staff in IGS to have second thoughts about sending a young family out there. Joyce and I discussed it, but we had burned our boats by then and decided to go. On arrival we moved into the Merlin Hotel in Kowloon and stayed there for four weeks until a flat became available in mid levels on Hong Kong Island. There were forty-eight flats in the block, over half of them occupied by police families. Some of these became our friends and in the following months my wife shared some of the emotional burden with the families while their husbands were on the front line.

At this time there were about four million people living in Hong Kong, most of whom were either refugees or descendants of refugees from China. Even then, twenty years after the revolution, there was a steady flow of refugees arriving either across the land border or by boat. This huge influx of people caused a severe housing problem, which the government dealt with by building resettlement blocks as quickly as they could. They were pretty basic: tap water and bathroom facilities were communal and the amount of floor space per person per flat was minimal, but the millionth person was resettled in them while I was there. Many of the refugees were still living in squatter camps. There was a large camp on the north side of Hong Kong Island above the race-course. The houses were built of plywood, corrugated sheeting and anything else that could be found. Water was obtained from the streams that drained the northern slopes of The Peak. The squatters built a concrete dam across a stream and embedded the ends of blue alkathene piping into it. These pipes carried water to the houses. From across the harbour the slopes of The Peak looked like someone had thrown blue spaghetti over them.

That summer of 1967 was a particularly trying period for everyone. There was a much-reduced water supply to domestic properties with only four hours of water every four days in the flat, though the hotel had permission to provide water every day. The daily temperature was in excess of 30 °C and the humidity very high.

Riots, police raids and bombings characterised the high summer and we had only been in the colony a few days when we experienced our first riot. They tailed off during the summer, but in October there were fifteen to thirty bomb scares a day, most of them not hoaxes. At times on Hong Kong Island I had to make detours around road blocks in order to reach the mapping area. Towards the end of our first month, the first time-bomb, set in a paper doll, went off in a tram depot injuring eight people. A few weeks later a bomb activated by a trembler device was left on the tram lines on Hong Kong Island and blew up, killing one of the policemen who lived in our block. His daughter was the same age as Sarah and they were friends. Before long both of my girls were able to tell the difference in sound between a bomb and an explosive device that had been safely detonated by the army. They also learned to be wary of unattended packages left in the street, but they never became accustomed to seeing policemen armed with rifles. By mid October over 670 bombs had been dealt with by the police. By early November the terrorists had learned how to make pipe bombs. Perhaps the most significant event of this period occurred when a bomb in a rag doll left in a public playground killed two little children. Public opinion suddenly changed and the rioters lost a lot of friends.

The police raids were major events. As many as 518 people were arrested at one time and lots of guns and explosive, including gelignite, were recovered. Some of the raids did not go well. It took nearly three hours to get into one building using oxyacetylene burners. Each floor was barred by steel gates. While the police worked, concentrated sulphuric acid, oil and petrol bombs were thrown down at them. Eighty-one people were arrested on this occasion. During the summer several people were murdered, some of them selected for their well known anti-communist views and there were also deaths in custody.

My geological team consisted of a surveyor, who was my assistant and interpreter, a draughtsman, a driver and a labourer. They were all thoroughly urbanised people and had difficulty becoming accustomed to fieldwork. I had most trouble with the labourer. He was chosen from the labour pool held in the Crown Lands and Surveys department, others taking a turn when the one I had fell ill, injured himself or found some other way to avoid going in the field. After three had managed to escape such duties, the department recruited an eighteen-year-old lad especially for the job. He turned up, very unfit, wearing shiny black shoes and having never in his life walked on a surface that was not man-made. But he stuck it out and became excellent at his job. Twenty years later, when I met up with him, he was a police major in Hong Kong Central police station and was renowned for his ability as a criminal investigator.

I started mapping soon after I arrived and, despite the havoc going on all around me, I felt that I was not a target and most of the time did not feel unsafe. My family also went about their business without too much concern and they travelled all over the colony with me, spending time on beaches while I worked. The nearest I got to changing my mind was when my Land Rover, which was in the Public Works Department car park, was blown up. The police would not tell me if I had been selected for this treatment or if it was a random act of terrorism. I think probably the latter because this was the only successful one of many attempts to set a bomb off in that car park. The police, though, treated me with suspicion when a box of rock samples wrapped up ready for dispatch for laboratory thin sectioning was found by a staff member and reported to them. I was obliged to demonstrate that the samples were not bomb-making equipment.

I felt most anxiety when mapping around resettlement blocks. Many had been built in cuttings in weathered granite and needed looking at for safety assessment as well as for mapping purposes. Apart from being taunted by mobs of children, nothing significant ever happened. It was a different matter on the islands. On some of them the villages were communist controlled. They openly flew the red flag, and 'Long Live Mao Tse Tung' was painted on the pier. We knew we had to be careful around these. However, not all of them were overtly communist. In some places villagers would turn their back on us when we walked past and would not talk to us. On one occasion three of us were returning to our boat through a village where the men were openly hostile and they set the dogs onto us. We retreated through the village keeping the dogs at bay with our hammers until we reached the last house in the village. With our backs against the wall one of the dogs got through and bit the labourer. At that point the village men seemed satisfied and called the dogs off.

At some field locations I needed an armed escort. This became necessary when I worked on islands to the south of Lan Tau Island. I had to travel there in a police launch and was taken ashore in the police dory. When working anywhere near the Chinese border I had an armed police escort and was under orders not to go too close to it. There had been incidents when shots had been fired from the Chinese side. At Sha Tau Kok, a small village at the eastern end of the border, the line ran down the middle of the main street so that houses on the north side were in China and on the south side in Hong Kong. Incidents in places like this were hard to avoid in the hot summer of 1967.

The most unsavoury incident occurred in the summer of 1968. At this time the Red Guard had taken control in Canton (now Guangzhou) on mainland China, and a number of people had been executed: with their hands tied behind their back they were made to kneel on the water-front and were then shot in the back of the head and kicked into the Pearl River. The bodies of seventeen of them were washed up on the beaches of Hong Kong. While mapping on one of the western islands I noticed the smell of something decomposing and thought I had found one of the bodies. When I traced the source of the smell I was relieved to find that it was a pig, one of a barge-load that had drowned when the boat carrying them from Canton to Hong Kong had capsized. One of the odd things about this period is that trade between China and Hong Kong continued unabated. Chinese boats would come daily into the harbour loaded with fresh produce. After their cargo had been unloaded the boats would stay on, playing *The Red Flag* and *The East is Red* very loudly and well into the night using powerful amplifiers.

Despite these troubles, I departed at the end of February 1969 with the satisfaction of having brought the geological mapping of Hong Kong to a successful conclusion.

I Am Not Che Guevara!
Rob Evans

In 1967, as part of a British Aid Programme, I was one of a small team of geophysicists searching for evidence of mineralisation in the high Andes of Peru. We were working at an altitude of around five thousand metres above sea level in an area inaccessible by road, where horses were used for travel, and the survey base was a tented encampment.

After the first month of survey work in September our food supplies were beginning to run low, so I decided to go on horseback to obtain fresh supplies from the nearest village. I did not consider it necessary to shave before the journey, despite having a full black beard. The descent down the valley passed many isolated huts where the local shepherds waved at the passing foreign horseman with the greeting 'Che'. This was an Argentine Spanish term which roughly translated meant 'mate'. I politely acknowledged with a wave. By the time the village store was reached, and I had dismounted, I had attracted quite a following of locals. My Spanish was just about understood by the store owner, but I sensed some hostility and suspicion in the discussions that took place.

On leaving the store I found a policeman waiting outside who immediately demanded my identification. Fortunately I had

Rob Evans adjusting a proton magnetometer, near Oyon, central Peru. (Photograph by P. G. Greenwood).

on me some documentation provided by the British Embassy in Lima and the Peruvian Geological Survey. After much discussion amongst the local community, some of whom knew about our geophysical work in which some locals were employed, I was released. I then tactfully decided to employ a local man to guide me safely back to camp.

During the return journey my guide explained why I had aroused such suspicion amongst the local people. In late September 1967 the Peruvian police were looking for 'Che'

Guevara, the notorious Argentine guerrilla operating in the Andes. Che had a black beard, was six feet tall, and similar to myself in appearance.

A week later, in early October, Che Guevara was captured in the Andes of neighbouring Bolivia and subsequently shot by the CIA. If you see one of those posters of Che, so popular here in the 1970s—it's not me, honest!

Colour it Red
Keith Bloomfield

I reported for my first day of work at the Overseas Division of the Institute of Geological Sciences, Princes Gate, London, in 1968. Before this I had worked for fifteen years in the Geological Survey Department in Malawi. At Princes Gate I was given various desk jobs; but then quite unexpectedly in February 1968 I was told that my name had been put forward as an 'expert' in the location of raw materials for cement manufacture in the Sudan. I was to go there and sort out a local problem.

The Sudan government had been given a cement factory at Rabak [1] on the White Nile, south of Khartoum. It had been constructed for them by the Yugoslavs and was probably second-hand, having been moved there as a sort of aid project. So here was this factory stuck by the side of the White Nile, and the local administration had no idea where they were going to obtain the appropriate grade of limestone needed to produce Portland cement, although there were odd limestone outcrops nearby. The Sudan government made urgent requests to various governments. They asked the Czechs, the Germans, the French, and they may have asked the Americans. Most replied 'yes', they would send out a team—a chemist, a geologist and so on—in due course.

1 Today Rabak is an important commercial city in south-eastern Sudan on the eastern bank of the White Nile.

When IGS received the request they must have said something like 'we will send a man out in two weeks'. That's where I came in.

I flew out to Khartoum overnight and landed there in the early hours, about 5 am. I was met at the airport by a scruffy taxi driver and whisked off to the Grand Hotel by the Blue Nile. I had a couple of hours' sleep before breakfast at 7.30 am. Breakfast was hardly over before I was met by the Secretary of the Nile Cement Company and taken to their offices. I was only in Khartoum for a few hours. They had booked me on a train, a sleeper, to go south to the site of the cement factory that night. It was about ten hour's journey from Khartoum, travelling southward for about 180 miles on a very sandy, dusty train. The line first followed the Blue Nile to Wad Medani before turning due west to reach the White Nile at Rabak. I arrived early morning on the next day and was put up at a Rest House in the middle of Rabak. There was little to see apart from mud huts surrounded on all sides by hot, scrub-covered country.

The limestone deposit that I was asked to examine was situated at Nyefr Rugaiyiq, about forty miles south of Rabak, and soon a daily work pattern developed. I would be called for at about seven in the morning, sometimes much earlier, and taken on a bumpy journey southward across flat, black cotton soil to the area of outcrop. Here I was expected to show local counterparts how to make a geological map, how to sample the rock, and how to identify limestone possessing the qualities most suitable for Portland cement manufacture. In attempting to survey the area of limestone outcrop it was impossible manually to cut lines through the dense thorn scrub, so survey lines were made using bulldozers. In spite of it being the middle of winter it was still hot, and the air temperature would go up to about 45 °C at midday. The worst aspect for me, having just gone through an English winter, was the burning heat and intense sunlight.

In due course I developed a simple prospecting technique.

The limestone there is more correctly a marble, of which there are two principal types: dolomitic marble containing magnesium, and calcitic, or pure calcium carbonate marble. Only the calcium carbonate marble is suitable for Portland cement manufacture. The two types can't be distinguished by simply looking at them in outcrop, so I developed a way of differentiating between them by scaling-up a standard laboratory test. If you make a solution of the dye Alizarin Red-S with dilute hydrochloric acid and apply it to the limestone at a fairly high temperature, the calcium carbonate limestone will go red, while the dolomitic limestone remains

Nomadic Arabs, with Rabak cement works in the distance, Sudan. (Photograph by K. B. Bloomfield.)

colourless. So I got the Sudanese to make up large quantities of the mixture in jars, and we took brushes and painted wide stripes over the outcrops, which were fortunately quite smooth. Since the air temperature was so high there was a reaction at the surface, and after we had painted a few stripes across the limestones we could see a clear differentiation between the red bands, denoting calcitic limestone, and those without colour, which were therefore dolomitic. The local people thought it was magic!

The country around was dry and barren, being quite flat, with a thin sort of yellow seedy grass, packed with gum and Acacia bushes armed with thorns. It was the first time that I had seen so many Arab groups with their camels and cattle. These men, herding their animals across this country from the west, were probably genuine Nomads coming out of the Sahara. Although in appearance they seemed rather scruffy, one could imagine that they were probably quite wealthy.

I eventually managed to survey the area of limestone outcrop; but instead of then returning to Khartoum by train I was taken by car, an old fashioned Russian Volga. There were no very clearly marked roads in that part of the Sudan, so we set off from Rabak and drove in an almost straight line for Khartoum. Because the scrubby desert is flat it is possible to drive across open country. The driver would espy a rocky hill roughly in the direction we wished to travel, perhaps twenty or thirty miles away, and navigate by that. Once there, he would look for the next feature and carry on in the same way from one hill to another. We went through the big cotton growing area to the south of Khartoum, the Gezeira, and managed to get back to civilisation in one piece.

I was put up at the Grand Hotel in Khartoum by the Nile Cement Company for five or six days when I got back, and was able to submit a preliminary report recommending what immediate action needed to be taken by the company in order to begin cement production as soon as possible. The Sudanese were very hospitable people. The president of the Cement Company, Mergani Hamza, was a real Arab gentleman. He lived in Omdurman just across the river from Khartoum and took me to his beautiful house for tea one day, and he also showed me the famous Omdurman battlefield, where Winston Churchill had been present as War Correspondent. To get to Hamza's house it was necessary to go down a dirty sandy lane with mud walls on both sides. You then passed through a gate and suddenly found yourself in a garden with beautiful trees and bougainvillea, completely cut off from the rest of your surroundings. Most Arab houses were like that.

The Sudanese seemed quite happy with what I had done and asked me what I would like as a gift. I explained that being a government servant I couldn't possibly accept anything, so they said 'What would your wife like as a present?' The upshot was that I was given small gifts for my wife, son and daughter, and so came home fully laden. I returned to London about the middle of March, my first overseas job for IGS successfully accomplished, and awaited news of my next assignment. In October 1968 I found myself posted to Uganda, where I would remain for two years working on carbonatite complexes.

High Drama
John Baldock

In 1967, after three rewarding years working for the Geological Survey of Uganda and eighteen months completing a PhD with the African Institute of Geology at the University of Leeds, I joined the Institute of Geological Sciences (IGS). I was initially assigned to the North Wales Unit in the Leeds office, undertaking some detailed work at Capel Curig. Then, at short notice, I was re-assigned to the Overseas Division and informed that I was urgently required to join an IGS residential team in the Western Cordillera of northern Peru, where a geological mapping and mineral exploration project had been underway since 1963, funded by the ODA.

Frustratingly, given the implied urgency, I arrived at Lima to find that a complete lack of counterpart funds for fieldwork meant that the only tasks I could fulfil were a course in Spanish and some general background reading in the office. My wife, in the meantime, had been obliged to remain in the UK owing to complications in connection with the birth of our second child.

It was some ten weeks before she and the children could join me in Peru.

Later, when funds were finally available, John Wilson (ODA team leader) and I made some extensive 'orientation' advisory trips: a necessary prerequisite before undertaking a regional geochemical survey. On the first occasion, we left Lima (at sea-level) very early with our Peruvian counterpart and by evening had reached a small mine at a height of nearly five thousand metres. We were given a bare room usually allocated to a miner, and started to make our unappetising supper. John got up to stir the 'stew' and suddenly keeled over! His limbs were totally rigid; we could not bend his elbows or knees, nor could we prize the wooden spoon from his clenched fingers, and he could not speak! Neither I nor our Peruvian counterpart had any experience of this kind of seizure: was it a stroke/heart attack, exhaustion and/or oxygen deficiency, or what? What was to be done? The nearest local hospital was 150 kilometres away and 2,500 metres below us, but despite the tiredness and *soroche* headaches we quickly decided we had to take to the twisting roads again and get him down there. Yet it was a devil of a job to get his rigor mortis stricken body into the Land Rover! After a hectic night drive we eventually got John the medical attention he needed and he made a surprisingly rapid recovery—but it was a high-drama episode in my introduction to the high Andes!

On our next trip, somewhere near Ayacucho, we were in cloud and were unable to see any flat ground on which to make camp before dark. We finally reached a small triangular patch where we had a tin of cold beans and turned in for the night, choosing to get slightly damp outside in the mist. Very early next morning it started to rain hard and John decided to put up his tent. He was leaping around stark naked in the pouring rain with the dawn coming on, trying to put the poles and pegs in, just as hordes of local women appeared from all directions to set up their trading stalls a few metres from where we had decided to camp, which turned out to be their market square at the junction of three roads on the edge of a bustling village. 'What on earth were these idiotic gringos doing?' This was the question the bemused locals were clearly asking themselves. It was a rude awakening!

My next piece of orientation fieldwork was to visit some of the big copper mines in southern Peru. For this I booked a Faucett Airlines flight to Arequipa and deliberately chose a left-hand window seat to take in views of the Andes on the way. There was a bit of a commotion soon after take-off, but it seemed to quieten down quickly, so I thought no more of it—at least not until about fifteen minutes later when I could see only Pacific Ocean and no mountains out of the window. We were heading north! Were we going back to Lima? No announcement! We kept going north. Eventually the captain was permitted to announce that we had been hijacked and that he was being forced to fly to Cuba! However, it was all relatively civilised, though both the hijackers and some of the passengers were angrily brandishing hand-guns at one point.

We landed at Guayaquil and the women and children were released. Later, following intense negotiations, the men were also released and the crew took the plane and hijackers on to Cuba. Our plane returned the next day to pick us up and take us back to Lima, where we were made to return to the departure lounge 'to give evidence'. Then the real drama ensued—a massive and bad-tempered struggle between those who had been hijacked and were expecting to resume the previous day's interrupted flight to Arequipa, and those who were booked to fly that day. Eventually it was resolved with several badly bruised passengers and not too much bloodshed!

And a Wife's Eye View
Liane Baldock

After nearly three years in Uganda where whole families lived out in bush camps for three months or so at a time, I fondly imagined that in Peru I would be trekking up the Andes on a mule with a child in a pannier on each side! However, the altitude and extreme lack of water on the western flanks, where the fieldwork was mainly being undertaken, made this a non-starter: hangers-on were just a liability using up precious supplies unnecessarily.

We were in northern Peru when the dreadful earthquake of 31 May 1970 hit, causing a large part of the north side of Huascaran, in the Cordillera Blanca, to collapse. Some 2.4 million cubic metres of rock, ice and mud careered down the valley at speeds of up to 300 kmph (eventually reaching all the way to the coast) and obliterated the small town of Yungay completely. At least twenty thousand people died and thousands of children were left orphaned along the coastal strip. They had been playing outside after lunch, while their parents drank their coffee inside and finished the meal. Most of the houses were made of adobe with an upper floor of concrete, added as families became more affluent. When the adobe collapsed under the shocks, many inside were crushed by the upper floor collapsing on top of them. We wives spent many weeks and months knitting clothes and blankets—even whilst in the cinema—it seemed so wrong to be sitting and doing nothing to help.

A Tale of Thailand
Richard Johnson

Shortly after joining IGS I was assigned to a five-man aid team that was departing in early January 1968 for a three month field season in Thailand. It was led by Magnus Garson who had been recruited to the organisation after leaving the Malawi Geological Survey. This, like all the projects I worked on with IGS/BGS, was funded out of the overseas aid programme through the Overseas Development Administration.

The object of the project was to work with Thai counterparts to introduce new methods of prospecting for tin in the southern part of the country where the tin ore cassiterite was mined. We started in Phuket and then moved to Phang Nga and Krabi. Living conditions in Thailand were something of a holiday compared with my previous experience in Canada. We were accommodated variously in rented houses or small local hotels, and only once were we obliged to camp under canvas for a few days. Tourism had not penetrated into southern Thailand; very few people spoke English and signposts were incomprehensible as they were in Thai script. Bread was difficult to obtain but a wide variety of rice-based Thai food was enjoyed. Thai breakfasts were a little hard to get used to as they were based on soup containing bits of seafood such as squid tentacles—with visible suckers.

Fieldwork involved walking along streams, collecting samples from the sandy stream beds for later analysis, and making observations for a geological map of the area.

Compared with Africa, where I had spent much time previously, rural Thailand was highly organised at local level. The growing of rice in terraced paddy fields on sloping ground required a high degree of cooperation between individual farmers over irrigation and drainage arrangements. We crossed streams on bamboo footbridges that were clearly of local design and construction. Houses built of local timber were on stilts with slatted floors, except in the sleeping areas, giving much needed ventilation. We frequently were invited to eat our rice-based, packed lunches in such dwellings, where our crumbs would fall through the floor to be eagerly consumed by the chickens below.

On the one occasion when we camped, we hired, through our

Thai counterparts, a group of labourers to carry our gear to the proposed campsite. We had brought with us from London some ex-US army state-of-the-art backpacks with this eventuality in mind. Having filled these packs with our gear we gave them to the labourers. They took one look at them, went into the forest and cut bamboo poles, slung the packs on the poles and carried the poles horizontally on their shoulders one man at each end. So much for our high-tech packs. To save weight we took the minimum of food with us on this camping trip as our counterparts advised us that we would be able to purchase local

A typical house in rural Thailand. (Photograph by R. L. Johnson.)

produce at our destination. One of the items so acquired was a small pig. Our Thai cook was quite happy to roast it, but was unwilling to kill it, as the Buddhist religion has restrictions on the taking of life. After some discussion the cook agreed to kill the pig but using a knife belonging to one of the Christian IGS staff. A typical Thai compromise.

The area was quite well populated and we often came across parties of people, usually women or children, panning for tin from the stream beds. Wooden pans were used: the tin bearing mineral cassiterite being heavy, it could easily be separated from the lighter sands by this means. The resulting concentrate was taken to the local market where dealers would buy it for pocket money sums. One of the less useful findings of our project was that the amount of cassiterite in the streams was proportional to the distance from the nearest village!

A feature of working in a populated area was that at the roadsides, and even well off the beaten track, there were little stalls with seating where one could enjoy cold drinks, including a Thai speciality, *olieng*, or iced coffee. Such places did not have refrigeration but each day someone, usually a small boy, would go on a bicycle to the nearest town where he would buy a block of ice and bring it back packed in straw or sawdust. On getting out of the Land Rover at one such roadside establishment I saw what looked like oil dripping from the underside of the vehicle. Investigation showed a pool of blood in the driver's foot well; moreover, one of my shoes was full of blood. A *tark* or land leech had been attached to my ankle and had presumably dropped off when I got out. These beasts inject a combination of anti-coagulant and a local anaesthetic when they bite, hence the profuse bleeding from a painless wound.

We did not see any wild animals, though domesticated elephants could be a hazard to night driving as they did not have rear lights! As in Africa we carried snake-bite outfits containing ampoules of anti-venom and a syringe. The kits we carried in Africa and elsewhere contained a polyvalent anti-venom, effective against any poisonous snake we might encounter. Those in Thailand carried a series of ampoules each for a different species of snake: thus on being bitten by a snake one was expected to have a good look at it and then refer to the illustrated identification booklet provided. Fortunately no-one was bitten.

Our field-season came to an abrupt end with the onset of the monsoon. Rain that was heavier than any I had seen in

Africa or elsewhere made travel difficult and fieldwork along streams impossible.

One of the pleasures of living and working with our Thai counterparts was that we gained a deeper insight into the local culture than would the average tourist. One rather surprising custom emerged when we were given a farewell dinner at the end of the trip. Our counterparts concluded proceedings by singing folk songs to which we were expected to respond. We tried a variety of such songs, and much to our delight they particularly enjoyed 'On Ilkla Moor Baht 'at'. While they liked the tune and especially the rhythm, the circularity of the story is in keeping with the Buddhist belief in re-incarnation. After we had 'translated' the Yorkshire dialect into standard English, the Thais sang the line 'Then us'll all ha' etten thee' with gusto!

On the Beach
Martin and Madeline Clarke

On being recruited by IGS in 1968, I was seconded on OSAS terms for two years to the Mines and Geological Department of the Ministry of Natural Resources, Kenya. I had previously obtained a good introduction to that country while completing a post-graduate degree by mapping a carbonatite complex in Western Kenya.

The Mines and Geological Department at Nairobi was at that time housed in a wooden building with a veranda, standing on stilts and covered by a corrugated iron roof. It was said to have been the HQ of General Jan Smuts during the First World War campaign against von Lettow-Vorbeck, and it looked the part. In fact, old military debris was sometimes revealed locally after heavy rain. In charge of the department was chief geologist John Walsh on whom responsibility had fallen when David Sanders, the director, had arrived one morning to find a letter on his desk relieving him of his post. John and David had joined the department long before Kenya achieved independence in 1963. Another old East Africa hand was Joe Mason who had worked in Somaliland with J. W. Pallister. Other posts were occupied by two young Kenyan nationals and a Canadian, Mark Mloszewski. Support staff included very efficient Goan draughtsmen and chemists.

There was an ongoing mineral exploration project in the Coast Province to which I was assigned, and as this entailed continuous field work it was decided to rent a base on the coast rather than commute the three hundred miles each way to and from Nairobi. John Walsh was an enthusiastic supporter of this initiative as he liked visiting the coast, not least because he had a son working as a harbour pilot in Mombasa. A spare staff house on the beach at Vipingo, some twenty miles north of Mombasa, was rented from a Swiss-owned sisal plantation for £35 a month. To this I returned most weekends, and Madeline, my wife, clearly enjoyed our coastal residence.

In the late 1960s the Coast Province of Kenya had a very different feel to up-country Kenya where there were still echoes of white settlerdom and a patronising attitude by some. Coast Province with its ancient Arab town of Mombasa had a distinct character and language. The Swahili spoken in most of East Africa was a crude lingua franca while that of the Coast was the first language of the area. In the Old Town area of Mombasa Island, with its adjacent dhow harbour, many of the Swahili and Arab inhabitants still dressed in white flowing robes, while the women wore black *buibui* with little more than their eyes visible. Arab coffee hawkers strode the pavements dispensing coffee into small ceramic cups from slim conical pots with long beaked spouts, the apparatus resting on a small charcoal heater.

In the old harbour one could see many dhows drawn alongside or anchored in the nearby estuary. Trading by these iconic twenty to fifty ton single lateen-rigged sailing vessels from the Gulf and along the East African coast had existed for over a millennium. This form of trade was virtually brought to an end in the 1970s because of piracy emanating from Somalia. We were lucky to witness their last expression with many such boats visible from our house sailing southwards during the north-east monsoon that lasts from November to January. In mid-year the monsoon wind blows from the south-east and at that time the dhows would return northwards mainly carrying wood and charcoal.

At this same time I became aware that in neighbouring Uganda the Geological Survey would be marking its fiftieth anniversary in late July 1969 with a conference and field trips mainly organised by fellow IGS personnel on secondment there. At very short notice I applied for leave and together with Madeline and our four week old son, Tom (born in Mombasa on 16 June), set off for Entebbe in our trusty Mark 2 Cortina. After a tough three day drive we arrived in Entebbe to meet the incumbent IGS folk attached to the Geological Survey there, including Keith Bloomfield and Tony Reedman. Kingsley Dunham, the then director of IGS, was a guest speaker at the conference, and having realised my visit to Uganda was self financed, kindly sanctioned it to be official! We stayed with Bill Morton, who had been a year ahead of me at Manchester University. A sombre memory is that several years later, in 1977, our host was killed working in Ethiopia when he got caught up in that country's hostilities with rebel groups.

Back at the coast in Kenya a very busy time ensued with exploration boreholes to be sited at a lead-zinc prospect, core to be logged, and in due course workable reserves to be calculated and a report written. At this time one of the difficulties encountered was fierce competition between the local driller, Joe Thadee, and the expatriate contract driller Clarrie (Clarence) Berkholdt. The latter worked strictly by the book with five nine hour shifts per week, while Joe, who probably correctly realised that there was nowhere near parity of income, would come on-site for about one week in three, drill night and day around the clock and usually outdo the footage of Clarrie when the monthly totals were calculated. Both men and their crews were excellent workers, but the varied approach typified their completely different backgrounds. I spent a great deal of time with each, but never with both at the same time!

Joe, a tall rangy Seychellois Creole, who had been born on the coast, had hunting rifles and a game licence, so we occasionally went up-country, legitimately, to a hunting block where we camped for a few days with three of his drill crew, drank a few beers, yarned and came back with a large haul of meat butchered from the carcasses of two or three antelope shot by Joe. Clarrie's relaxation was, on Saturday morning, to go down to Mombasa's Kilindini road, which had many bars frequented by sailors, and return, refreshed, by dusk on Sunday.

As the only 'professional' member of the Mines and Geology Department at the coast, it was occasionally necessary to put on different hats. One such was that of Inspector of Explosives, or in this case, fireworks. A shipment of the latter had to be inspected and verified by the inspector of explosives, a post temporarily vacant within the Mines Department. So my job it was. Armed with the relevant papers I located the quite large shipment and opened and ceremoniously ignited several different examples much to the astonishment of the agents receiving them.

My time in Kenya was one of the most rewarding and instructive periods of my career, and being virtually the only geologist involved, allowed a welcome degree of freedom of action.

Prague Spring
Jevan Berrangé

In 1968 I was one of a handful of IGS geoscientists attending the International Geological Congress in Prague, Czechoslovakia (now the Czech Republic). After an interesting few days spent on field excursions I was ready to attend the plenary sessions, but on stepping out of the hotel doors on the morning of 21 August I found myself facing two tanks with soldiers sitting on top of them. The Russians had invaded and the so-called Prague Spring and the Geological Congress were abruptly ended. I hurried back to my hotel room to fetch my camera and spent the next twenty-four hours prowling the streets taking pictures of the Soviet occupation of Prague.

By the following morning I had run out of film and so decided that it was time to leave. At the hotel a motor convey was being arranged to take visiting geoscientists out of the country, this being considered the safest plan. I had decided to make my own way home by rail, and in order to reach the station it was necessary to take a tramcar, but after a few blocks it could go no further as the overhead tram lines were down. However, whilst standing in the tram I had befriended a man carrying a bag of groceries and a dead rabbit. He had been shopping and was trying to get back to his home near the railway station. He said he knew another circuitous route that would get us to our destination, so I decided to go along with him. After a long and devious ride this tram also could go no further. My companion suggested that we take a taxi, and did I have any money for the fare? We tried to hail a couple of passing taxis but they would not stop. We then spotted a stationary cab at some traffic lights and my companion ran across the road and threw his rabbit onto the taxi windscreen to make sure it did not drive off. I produced a few $10 notes and the driver agreed to take me to the station and my companion, with his rabbit, to his house where we parted company. As the taxi neared the station the presence of debris on the road made it impassable and eventually the driver pointed me in the direction of the station saying he could take me no further.

I managed to buy a ticket for a train that was leaving for Austria a few hours later. I don't remember much of the journey except that it was very slow and halting, that I befriended a German girl and that I managed to hold on to my rolls of film and souvenirs (leaflets etc.) of the invasion by putting them in my umbrella where they were not discovered when the Russian troops examined our luggage. Other passengers were not so fortunate.

Russian tanks in occupied Prague, 21 August 1968. (Photograph by J. P. Berrangé.)

Back in London I sold the copyright of my photographs and my story to an agency, Camera Press, and had the satisfaction of seeing some of the photographs appear in various publications including *Time* magazine. In 2011, I showed my Prague photographs and memorabilia to the director of photography at the Imperial War Museum, who was keen to have them, so I donated everything to the museum.

Suspicious Minds
Tim Charsley

In May 1968 I arrived in Malawi with my wife of four months, Tricia. Malawi (formerly Nyasaland) had been independent since 1964, but under Dr Banda little had changed as he was adamant that the Civil Service should remain 'colonially' run until there were Malawians sufficiently qualified to replace the Europeans. I had been seconded from what was then the Institute of Geological Sciences. Therein lay my troubles, since I was at this time one of the first permanent IGS geologists to be seconded to this ex-colonial Geological Survey, then staffed by directly contracted expatriate geologists. Of course the existing staff realized full well what this might mean for their future. They suspected that IGS was looking to take over so that new posts and renewals of existing ones would become the fiefdom of IGS.

So, what to do with the new boy from the feared IGS? Well, there was that job of having another look at the potentially mineralised area around Nsanje in the south, map it in more detail and carry out a geochemical survey. Did anyone mention 'arsehole of Africa' at this stage? Of course not; it would be an interesting, challenging and necessary piece of work for a fit, twenty-five-year-old IGS man.

Now, what about equipment? Unfortunately, all the caravans which geologists use as field accommodation are allocated, so he'll need a safari tent. They are a bit tatty as they haven't been used for a while, but that's life. Oh yes, unfortunately there are no Land Rovers available, but then it's not that far south and a vehicle will come out of the Public Works Department soon enough. In the meantime, there is a good condition Bedford truck to take him and his field equipment to Nsanje.

'What's it like in Nsanje, where Malawi narrowly tails off into Mozambique,' we asked?

'Well, it's malarial, so you need to take prophylactics; there's a food shortage, so you'll need to take a lot of supplies; and be aware that Frelimo are active in Mozambique and there have been cross-border raids!' (Mozambique had not yet gained its independence from Portugal and Frelimo were fighting a guerrilla war.)

So, totally ill-equipped, but with the determination to prove myself, I headed south at the beginning of July. Nsanje was a sorry place, run down and with a very poorly-nourished population. The so-called market had very few vegetables and little meat, and the pathetic line of freshly-killed mice for sale probably best summed

Local recruits, packed up and ready to move camp, Malawi. (Photograph by T. J. Charsley.)

up the dire state of the area. I established a camp at the foot of the Lulwe Hills, and the men I'd brought from Zomba, along with local recruits, dug a waterhole nearby. Camp established, I did a few traverses to get to know the geological units that Keith Bloomfield had mapped at 1:100,000 scale several years earlier. Of the rocks, I was pleased to encounter nepheline syenites as I had been co-author of a monograph on nepheline and phonolite for the IGS Mineral Resources Division. The Basement rocks were rather baffling to me as my structural geology had been moribund since John Ramsay's lectures at Bristol University. However, at this period sorting out polyphase deformations was mainly done by a handful of academics and not by many field surveys, who lumped everything as 'Basement, undivided', so specialist knowledge couldn't really be expected of me.

All in all I enjoyed my first forays into African geology, but back at camp I had to contend with swarms of mosquitoes and a paucity of water. Even at midday when the critters were supposed to be lying low I had to work under a mosquito net, and at night make sure I didn't let my flesh touch the edge of the net or they'd suck away. When I'd covered the southern part of my field area I moved camp up into the hills beyond the Lulwe Mission, and there at least the mosquitoes observed a proper day-time curfew.

What about the geology? There was no obvious major extension of the small occurrences of copper and lead mineralisation, however much I and a local prospector, who had extracted some galena and produced some copper from malachite, might have wished it. With some guidance from Ray Cannon, the regional geologist, and Tony Hopkins, I managed to get my Ds, Fs and Ms sorted up to, I think, five generations in the high grade gneisses. Otherwise, I got some satisfaction in laying to rest one of the geological conundrums of the area. This was an inlier of sediments termed the Nachipere Series, previously regarded as metamorphosed post-Basement, pre-Karoo sediments. However, on close inspection no evidence was found of metamorphism and the sediments turned out to consist of basal tillites, sandstones and siltstones passing upwards into shales and thin coal layers. In other words, typical Karroo, which was later confirmed by spore analysis.

Tricia had joined me in the bush, and we were finally given a Land Rover and caravan. Our last camp was in the hills a few hundred yards from the Mozambique border, and where, one evening, we were summoned by two heavily bearded and armed Portuguese soldiers to visit their guard post, a blockhouse, about half a mile from our camp. My field assistant, Tom Gibbs, warned against going as he thought this would be the last he'd see of us, but as it turned out they wanted us to take a heavily pregnant African woman to the Lulwe Mission hospital. This I did with much trepidation that the baby would be born somewhere along the very rough bush track with me as midwife, but fortunately all went well. The reward came a few days later when we were invited to a meal to meet the Portuguese Regional Governor and his wife in the famous blockhouse. The lady was in her finest clothes and wearing high heels, making a nice contrast to us in our well-worn khaki bush-clothes. We were obviously the entertainment, described as the Malawian Armand and Michaela Dennis!

My baptism of fire over at the end of the field season, I didn't look back and we enjoyed our time in Malawi enormously. Two jobs gave me the greatest satisfaction. The first was working with Ken Wilderspin siting water supply boreholes, eventually so successfully that the department was able to offer a 'no water, no charge' scheme to all customers, and during this time I personally sited over 350 boreholes. Secondly, I carried out a nationwide survey, including drilling programmes, of the limestone resources culminating in the publication of a memoir. Of that time my greatest memory is of surveying Basement marbles in the centre of the country, camped for several weeks on the shores of Lake Malawi with its beautiful fresh water, and eating barbecued lake fish every day. A difficult beginning had come to a happy ending.

The Captain
Barrie Page

It was February 1969 and I was a member of a group of geologists who had completed a four-month geological reconnaissance survey of Navarino Island, at the eastern entrance to the Beagle Channel, just north of the Cape Horn group of islands at the southern tip of Chile. It is, of course, an area renowned for its violent storms.

Our team included four geologists from the Chilean government's Instituto de Investigaciones Geológicas: Ricardo Fuenzalida, Alfredo Cruzat, Manuel Suárez and Vid Stambuk—all later to become distinguished geologists, although on this trip our fate was to come very close to being extinguished geologists. A fifth team member was Rodrigo Bustos, a technician, and I was seconded to the group from the Institute of Geological Sciences.

Our transport was the cutter the *Rayo*. It was about thirteen metres long, wheelhouse at the stern, and powered by a diesel engine which failed but once—unfortunately when we were on the rocks and starting to break up! The cutter also had a mainsail and a jib. These were used only once, and that was just to see how she sailed in a following wind up the Beagle Channel. In order to survey the coastal rocks and to land on the islands we had two three-metre aluminium boats with outboard motors. They were a bit flimsy for the conditions. When killer whales surfaced next to them they felt even flimsier, since killer whales have been known to hole and sink much larger craft, such as the nineteen-ton schooner the *Lucette* in the Pacific in 1972.

The cutter had a cook, engineer and deckhand, all in the form of an absolutely splendid man, Mondaca. On Wednesdays Mondaca made bread—the only day his hands were free from engine oil; and we had grey bread—some correlation here I feel. The captain was Santiago Johnson, somewhat differently splendid but no less interesting, and the focus of this story.

My first acquaintance with Captain Johnson occurred when we were on the jetty in Punta Arenas loading the *Rayo* with supplies for our voyage south through the Chilean Archipelago. To reach the starting point of our work at Puerto Williams on Navarino Island we would have to wend our way some three hundred kilometres through narrow rocky channels and past desolate gale-swept islands to work in a region with forbidding names, many in English: Bahía Desolada, Ras Furias, Isla Deceit, Seno Ladrones (Robbers' Inlet); the canals Cockburn, O'Brien, Keats and Beagle; the peninsulas Brecknock and Hardy; the islands Gordon, Stewart, Londonderry, Smoke, Burnt, Lennox, and Wollaston. This journey and subsequent coastal operations in a small vessel required a high level of seamanship.

Captain Johnson certainly had one of the requirements—the sailor's roll—well demonstrated as he came alongside the cutter. Perhaps the bottle of whisky he held in his hand contributed to this aspect of his seamanship. He made his introduction along the lines of 'Shipmates, we are going on a long voyage. Let's go down below and have a party!' To our reply that, at that precise moment, we were a little too busy for this, he continued, 'Well, shipmates, do you mind if I go below and have a party by myself?' Not without character was our Santiago Johnson, though it was, in fact, the last party he was ever to have. The captain was of Scottish descent, very amiable, had reddish hair and a somewhat grizzled appearance which went well with his noticeably deep, sonorous and (I suspected) bottle-nurtured voice.

We left Punta Arenas and after a few days of sailing through the Magallanes Archipelago reached our survey area. We accomplished the work without too many difficult incidents. An encounter with killer whales surfacing within touching distance of our little outboard was dealt with, I like to think, with a measure of calm alacrity. On that occasion I released, in record time, the lock, so that the propeller could ride up over obstacles, gunned the motor, shot over the kelp and ran the boat straight onto, and some distance up the beach—no panic there then! The porpoises were much nicer. I have driven the outboard at top speed with a porpoise racing alongside me with my arm round its dorsal fin. Its corresponding method of bonding was to leap in the air, come down sideways and try to fill my boat with a quantity of the Pacific Ocean. We also got held up by a storm in a small bay on one of the islands, not an infrequent event, and food supplies ran pretty low. Making one tea bag last several days meant making the tea more an act of faith than actual brewing. And never try to eat a cormorant.

We used the small boats, two men to a boat, for mapping the coastal area and made several traverses across Navarino Island. We made the traverses lightweight and in somewhat Spartan fashion—bivouacs rather than tents. Our objective was to see if this part of Chile was as rich in minerals as its northern region. It wasn't.

The accommodation on the cutter was not exactly five-star. The two bench seats in the saloon, just forward of the engine, and one alongside it, converted to three beds. Mondaca and the captain had their bunks behind the engine, a further bed could be slung across the wheelhouse. Alfredo and I had the small forward cabin where we slept on two bunks—usually, that is. The exception was the night the captain anchored the *Rayo* in a small bay on the west of Navarino Island. He selected the anchorage a little too far up the beach at high tide, a small tide, but nevertheless significant. As the tide ebbed the *Rayo* touched the bottom and gradually started to keel over, as did all the occupants in their bunks. And the ebbing tide, followed by the rising tide, meant a sleepless night, with a gradual shift for the occupants of the bunks, slowly out of the bunks, up the side of the ship, and back down again. Fun all round. Perhaps this was an indication of errors to come.

On completion of our work we left Puerto Williams, the small naval establishment on the north side of Navarino Island, to sail the three hundred kilometres or so to back to Punta Arenas. The weather was not bad, a brisk breeze coming up the Beagle from the west. We sailed into the breeze, down the Beagle alongside the peaks and glaciers of the Darwin Cordillera to our north and Isla Hoste to the south. At the eastern point of Isla Gordon the Beagle splits into its northern and southern arms. We followed the northern arm, found a tiny bay in the fjord wall, anchored for the night, and the next day continued our voyage west, no longer into a breeze but a markedly stiffening wind.

About thirty kilometres further west the northern arm splits into two narrow channels around the Isla O'Brian, with the Canal O'Brien to the south and the Canal Pomar to the north. We took the northern passage in the hope that, with the weather rapidly getting worse, we would have more protection. But the northern passage, thirty kilometres further on, opens out into the Ballenero Channel which itself is fully open on the west to Bahía Desolada, the Pacific Ocean, and the full force of the westerly gales that give to this part of the world its fearsome reputation.

The *Rayo* rode out into the Canal Ballenero. We were now in open waters, the wind was a howling gale, the waves hitting us with ugly force, the skies dark, while the gale-driven spray meant we could hardly see where we were heading. The *Rayo* was taking a beating, and so were we. And then we glimpsed a naval vessel. It looked like a very fast torpedo launch, barrelling its way at high speed in the opposite direction to ours. Perhaps they knew something we didn't—they did! The winds were going to rise to hurricane force and we were heading straight into them. At this point Mondaca struggled up on deck (we were all crammed into the little wheelhouse) to dip the Chilean flag, as is obligatory in these waters. The act went unacknowledged by the naval vessel, and we later heard that when our story became known the captain of this vessel was severely reprimanded by his commanding officer for not warning us of the impending storm.

So, we were left to face the hurricane. The *Rayo* was hitting the oncoming sea hard. It was customary for all of us to take our turns at the wheel. The buffeting, even in modest gales, meant you got a bruised chest as you metronomically lurched into the wheel to the tune of the waves. But this sea was up a league or two in ferocity. Captain Johnson was at the wheel as we ploughed along the Ballenero Channel and he appeared to be in a manic phase. As the cutter rose and fell into horrendous troughs he turned to me, weirdly smiling, and then, with a laugh, shouted, 'I love this!' Well, we didn't. The captain's mighty struggle at the wheel to keep the boat straight seemed, with a heavyweight orchestra at top decibels outside, rather Wagnerian. However, Santiago's version of *Götterdämmerung*, did not feature in our plans—no twilight for the rest of us if we could help it.

The waves were sweeping green all along the length of the boat and washing over the wheel house. With visibility limited to just about seeing the next wave, and the navigation chart showing many small rock reefs, we were, as they say, in very dangerous

The *Rayo*, with small launch in tow, Beagle Channel, southern Chile (Photograph by B. G. N. Page.)

waters. We would shudder against a wave which would jar the boat to a standstill, so that she could barely rise to meet the next oncoming wall of green. It seemed that at any moment we would disappear under the next wave. I went below to see what could be wrong. Why did the boat feel so heavy and leaden?

I found Mondaca kneeling by the engine, which was set in a well slightly below the deck level of the saloon. He was bailing like a man possessed. He said that if the water reached the plugs on the diesel the engine would fail, and we would go down. I could see water coming under the door of our forward cabin. I went to investigate, opened the door and was greeted by a wall of water flooding out. In passing I noted that my best shirt came floating out with it, but thoughts on suitable attire for my demise was the least of my problems. I found that the hatch cover above the cabin had been ripped off by the storm and the water was now pouring in. We were virtually sinking. Another few minutes on this course and we would have gone under.

I went back up to the wheel house. Captain Johnson thought our position was near Isla Burnt. We were convinced we were near another island, Isla Smoke. In any case we had to turn the boat around and try to find some shelter, which we sought to do, in effect taking over the captaincy of the ship.

Turning the boat was going to be a very critical manoeuvre. I think Santiago Johnson had the wheel and was persuaded we needed to turn. Trying to read the waves correctly we powered into a 180° turn immediately after getting over the crest of one wave and just managing to complete it when the next wave hit the stern and hurled us onto our reversed course. If we had not turned quickly enough we would have been rolled over and gone to the bottom.

We ran before the wind and sheltered behind the island for a while but even this gave small respite. Somewhere better was desperately needed if we were to survive. We got across a stretch of water to what appeared to be a headland and anchored under a small cliff. Up on deck we could not hear each other speak above the screeching wind. The waves sweeping past us did not appear to be too large but that was because they were being flattened by the hurricane, and really all you could see was a mad and chaotic storm of white spray racing by in a piercing scream.

We went below and played bridge. Not much else we could do really. We were there for some hours, continuously buffeted, and then the cutter gave a huge lurch and was swept helplessly out into the channel and into the teeth of the storm. The anchor chain had broken.

When we broke from the anchor the cutter wheeled around 180°; the two outboard motor craft were lashed to the davits on the sides of the boat and were acting as sails and spun us round back into the wrath of the storm. We keeled over so far on the turn that I remember seeing the tip of our wireless aerial touch the water. We started the engine as fast as we could and headed into the fjord known as Seno Ladrones (Robbers' Inlet), the wind hurling us along, the motor barely controlling the boat. We had just over ten kilometres to go to reach the head of the fjord.

The storm was still raging, but as we got deeper into the fjord the wind had changed so that it was now coming down the fjord straight at us. If we could get to the head of the fjord there would be no fetch for the wind to whip up the sea and all we would have to contend with was the wind itself—or so we thought. But the wind, although not continuous, was blowing in screaming gusts as it swept down the glaciers into Seno Ladrones from the highest mountain in the Darwin Cordillera, Sarmiento, 2,234 metres high and some twenty kilometres inland—plenty of downhill for the wind to pick up speed. I do not know what wind speeds we experienced but I've been in 100 mph winds before, and these seemed worse.

As we got to the head of the fjord we looked for an anchorage. Fjords, being what they are, offer few of these. I climbed on to the front of the bowsprit of the jib sail holding a coil of rope, one end attached to me, the other to the boat. I guided the helmsman, with hand signals since you couldn't hear yourself speak, to steer the boat towards a very large boulder in the water at the cliff edge and near a tiny wooded embayment a few square metres in area.

I was quite familiar with leaping from boats onto rocky coastlines from my time as a commando. My demise then might have been a possibility, but here it was upgraded to a probability. As I was preparing to jump I distinctly remembered what my grandmother used to say to me as a small child when confronted with some disaster—spilled porridge or something equally distressing: 'Worse things happen at sea.' Little comfort here, given the circumstances!

I jumped and I stuck, otherwise you would not be reading this. The boat was made fast as best we could and we went below and resumed our game of bridge. It could have been monotonous, but for the odd diversion, and one of these now occurred. The boat started banging on the rocks. These great gusts of wind—you could not stand up in them—were still coming at us and were driving the boat to destruction. We were starting to break up.

Mondaca tried to fire up the engine and we found that the starter motor had broken. We had no motor—the boat was dead in the water—which raised the question, would we too soon be the same? Disaster on top of disaster, could this place throw anything else at us? We were now in danger of losing the boat and having to try to make our escape either by using the two aluminium boats—if we could get enough fuel in them to get us to safety, which was a few hundred kilometres away—or by walking out over the Darwin Cordillera, a similar distance.

We embarked on three courses of action. I got one of my climbing ropes. We looped it around the flywheel of the engine and led it out through the wheelhouse onto the deck where it was pulled by two or three of the lads running along the deck trying to get the flywheel to turn and the diesel motor to start. Endless runs were made. It was very hard work. At the same time Mondaca and the captain were at the stern (I had made the bow fast) hurling a small kedge anchor into the fjord to get it to hold so that we could pull the stern off the rocks where it, and the propeller, were getting smashed. Small hope really, given the nature of a fjord, but Mondaca in particular worked heroically to try and save us by this method.

Given that if the boat went down we would need the right supplies to make our escape, I started the third action, to transport essential gear—ropes, ice axes, fuel, food, etc.—to the tiny embayment using one of the aluminium boats and a rope to pull it back and forth over a few metres of water from our stern to the shore. As I was doing this an enormous gust of wind came screaming down from the glacier, made its hit, and blew the aluminium boat into the air. It came down and sank to the bottom, along with our supplies.

But this was relatively shallow water and I could see some of the supplies. I went below to get into my wetsuit in order to dive and retrieve the gear. As I was struggling into the wetsuit trousers, I saw a pair of legs come dangling into the saloon over the three steps down from the wheelhouse. The rest of the owner of the legs gradually descended. It was Captain Santiago Johnson being lowered by some of the deck party. He had collapsed on deck.

We laid the captain on the bunk in the saloon. He had suffered either a stroke or a heart attack. Our medical kit contained a heart stimulant for injection and I was left with the decision of whether to use it or not. Using it might accelerate Santiago's end or, on the other hand, somewhat delay it, depending on the nature of his illness. It was not the ideal time for making such decisions, and we were still breaking up. I decided not to use it and in any case Santiago now appeared to be very close to death.

He made a last request—respect due here—he asked for a whisky, totally unafraid and true to his principles to the end. Santiago was preparing for his exit with something approaching heroic dignity. I thought a final dram would really finish him, so I found some cold tea, put that in a glass and tried to give him a sip. Then he had some last words. They were muttered in Spanish and I could not catch them. I asked Alfredo what they were.

Apparently the captain said he fancied me. A slight dent in dignity perhaps. My companions were of course convinced that this was evidence the captain had truly lost his moorings. I prefer to think, naturally, that it was the kindness of the offer of the (disguised) whisky that prompted the words with which he left this world. We put him in his sleeping bag.

Meanwhile, back at the shipwreck, the lads were still trudging up and down the deck trying to turn the flywheel with the climbing rope. We needed to get the stern off the rocks so I had to improvise another plan. We got the other aluminium boat into the water to try and get a rope across to the other side of the head of the fjord, here narrowed to just over a hundred feet. Manuel and I got into the boat. A small generator gave us some light, as darkness had now descended.

We knew the frequency of the gusts and needed to wait for a gap in them to try to get across the water before the following one hit us, remembering that a previous gust had produced an airborne boat. We had to row the boat as we could not manage to get the outboard onto it in these conditions, and we rowed with some vigour. Halfway across the fjord the generator failed (water in the fuel) and we were in pitch black night. But we had to continue, the next gust was on its way. We made it to the other side and fixed the climbing rope. At last we could pull the boat off the rocks. Suddenly, over the noise of the wind, we heard the roar of the diesel motor—the lads had got the flywheel to move, started the diesel, and we were going to make it—all excepting one of course.

We repositioned the cutter off the rocks and settled down in the saloon. The cards came out and another game of bridge ensued, two players on one side of the little saloon table, me and another on a bench on the other side. Not much room there, since we were sharing it with the captain.

At some time during all of this frenzied activity we had actually sent out a Mayday call. We had no response save one from a tanker in Hawaii. The connection was not good but we did, I think, receive the information from them that the weather there was very nice. A great comfort to us all.

The storm gradually abated and we turned in for what was left of the night. At some point Vid suddenly woke us all up. He was on one side of the saloon, the captain on the other. Vid claimed the captain was moving and making noises. I checked, but Santiago had assuredly remained dead. Nevertheless, Vid and I exchanged berths and we all managed some sleep.

The next day was calm. A thought then came to us that if the captain's body were allowed to remain below, the oncoming rigor mortis would make it very difficult for us to get him out of the saloon, through the wheelhouse, and onto the deck. So we immediately shifted the body onto the foredeck near the hatch opening and secured it to the deck. We then set sail to return to Puerto Williams, our nearest port. We had of course kept the diesel running all night and indeed did not switch it off until we got back to Navarino Island.

We had just got out of Seno Ladrones into the open bay and I was in the saloon when Mondaca came rushing down from the hatch to switch off the gas on the galley stove. At the stern of the boat we had two man-sized butane gas cylinders strapped vertically to the rear of the wheel house. The valve on one of them had finally failed, no doubt due to the strain of the storm, and butane gas was leaking all over the ship. If the conditions here couldn't sink us, they were going to blow us up!

We managed to release the wildly hissing cylinder. It was heavy but we lifted it to the deck rail, careful not to make any sparks, and pushed it overboard. I watched it speed to the bottom like a torpedo with a propelling stream of butane gas bubbles. We pressed on.

At the western end of the Beagle we anchored for the night and the next day headed east. As we were reaching Puerto Williams we were rather dismayed to see an Argentinean gunboat bearing down on us. It seemed they had spotted the body on the deck and had come out from Ushuaia to investigate.

I had to stay below out of sight since the presence of a British scientist on a Chilean boat, in an area of unresolved border dispute between Chile and Argentina, and with the UK as an appointed arbiter, could have taken some explaining. They did seem serious, indeed there were half a dozen machine guns pointed at us. After explaining our position we were allowed to continue, and the gunboat left by cutting sharply across our bows at very close quarters, nearly swamping us. But at long last it was the end of our problems at sea.

Back at the naval base of Puerto Williams I was asked if I wanted to attend the autopsy. I was of the opinion that the only autopsy I could ever possibly attend would be my own, and I would try to avoid that if I could. It was found that the captain had died of a massive brain haemorrhage. Obviously the administering of the heart stimulant when he had collapsed would, I imagine, have been pretty disastrous, and we would have missed his memorable last words.

We returned to Punta Arenas—eventually. The flight from Navarino to mainland Chile was actually a scheduled route even though the airline was a one-plane outfit. It came two weeks late—not even Heathrow at its worst could manage that. When we finally got away the weather was again typically grim. It was so bad that the Dakota DC3 had to land on a grass strip on the north of Tierra del Fuego to wait for a break in order to get across the Magellan Straits. Over Punta Arenas the cloud was solid. We flew around for a while—rather bumpy—and then dropped like a stone, met the runway, and braked to a rather quick stop. Later in the airport bar we saw the pilot, one Bocatti, having a stiff drink. We asked him about the landing. He said that when we had circled the airport he had suddenly spotted, through a hole in the cloud, a bit of the runway beneath him and had taken the plane down as fast as he could. We then asked how he had known which part of the runway it was. He said he hadn't. Excellent! When he got the wheels on the tarmac he hoped there would be enough runway ahead of him to stop the Dakota before we left the airport unofficially. Bocatti needed that drink. On learning this, so did we.

In Punta Arenas we held a dinner to celebrate the end of our survey adventures. I remember, indeed it is about all I can remember, that during the course of the dinner, we all rose to our feet many times, with ever decreasing facility, to toast 'Mondaca!', the hero of the *Rayo*. But in truth, in the terrifying white maelstrom of those monstrous seas, screaming winds and deadly rocks, not one of my companions was found wanting.

And the *Rayo*? A storm eventually claimed her. She sank in the Magellan Straits, not many miles from the grave of Captain Santiago Johnson.

THE 1970s: BROADENING HORIZONS

A Ghost in Africa
Mike Crow

My first IGS project (Sierra Leone) and my last BGS project (Sumatra, Indonesia) were the two most satisfying assignments of my overseas career, but the first was the most formative. I joined IGS in November 1971 and two weeks later my wife and I were in Sierra Leone. The IGS Sierra Leone team consisted of John Arthurs and myself and was led by Sandy Macfarlane. I had replaced Al Wilkinson and in due course Al was to return when John left for a posting in the IGS Belfast Office.

On my first day in Freetown, Sandy showed me round the Geological Survey compound, which was composed of Nissan huts dating from when the site had been a Royal Air Force headquarters. Particularly memorable was the toilet, a small rectangular hut which stood in solitary splendour in the centre of the sloping car park area. Close inspection reinforced Sandy's advice not to use this facility even in an emergency. Next we visited the thin section laboratory. Here one of the operators was fast asleep, draped over the thin-cutting apparatus. He was delighted to have visitors but he told us that unfortunately he could never make a thin section as his cutting blade was broken. We would have to speak to the director.

The director was Mr Abdul Gabisi, a large man with a presence that filled his roomy air-conditioned office. His desk was empty, a common feature of Geological Survey directors of his generation, indeed Mr Gabisi, a Sierra Leonean, had been appointed on expatriate terms which involved lengthy overseas leave each year. Mr Gabisi welcomed me with a polite manner of toleration of a necessary evil which in due course he hoped would go away. Our project had political clout as it had been fixed up, it was said, following a conversation over drinks between the president of Sierra Leone, Siaka Stevens, and Mr Harold Wilson, our prime minister. Mr Gabisi was a past-master of the art of saying 'no' and could give endless, inventive and varied reasons why things could not be done, even though sadly they were in our project agreement. Occasionally Mr Gabisi would say 'yes'. Mr Gabisi had a weakness—he was an opera fan. Sandy had exploited this failing with the occasional gifts of operatic long-playing vinyl records.

One of the contentious issues concerned the availability of local counterpart geologists. Unfortunately, it transpired, they could not go into the field for personal reasons (some of them were relatives of the director), or because of their required presence for headquarters duties. I had read that following independence Sierra Leone had amalgamated the former Crown Colony, comprising the Freetown Peninsula, with the Protectorate, which covered the rest of the country. Freetown was dominated by the Krios, a well-educated elite, who were the descendants of slaves released from slave ships captured by the Royal Navy. The Protectorate was populated by the indigenous tribes, where domestic slavery had been outlawed only in the 1950s. Our project area was Sierra Leone north of latitude 9° north, deep in the 'interior' as it was called by the Krios.

It took two days to drive to our field areas, including an overnight stay at our forward base in a former Agricultural Officer's house situated on a small hill at Musaia. There Mr

Abu Day, chief technical officer, reigned, looking after our field equipment and the field teams. Messages here tended to get lost until Sandy introduced a simple management technique for checking that people did what he wanted them to do. He issued everyone with duplicate books. Instructions were written on the original and the evidence that the message had been sent was in the duplicate. The system worked.

The field teams were superb, apart from the drivers. The teams could improvise almost anything out of jungle creepers. They were not issued with camping equipment but instead were billeted on the local people. This meant geologists always had to pitch their tents next to villages. My field team, which I inherited from another IGS colleague, Al Wilkinson, was led by Pa Amadu, a grizzled Survey veteran Technical Officer who was assisted by Tommy Aruna (headman). The team had taken to the 'integrated' survey methods promoted by the IGS geologists which used aerial photos for navigation and plotted the geology and sample localities on the recently published 1:50,000 scale topographic maps. This method of field work was welcomed as being less strenuous in the heat and humidity than the chaining surveys which they were accustomed to do. The remit of each IGS geologist was to survey and sample as much as possible of a 1:50,000 sheet during each month of field work.

Field work was tough because of the heat, humidity and absence of roads. Traverses had to be planned to include as many streams as possible in order to collect the stream sediment samples. Fortunately there were numerous paths, but the air photos were not always reliable for navigation as the villages tended to move location, a custom dictated by the 'slash and burn' agricultural method used. Many villages had orchards of orange trees. The oranges were a green drinking variety and full of juice. Each tree had a label with the owners name on it. Areas inaccessible by road were traversed by porter treks. Pa Amadu and Tommy Aruna were experts at recruiting and managing the local people as porters. It was a surprisingly efficient and fast method of surveying and not without interest as we visited remote village communities living in a traditional tribal manner and unaffected by modern life. This was Africa as visited by the Victorian explorers. We occasionally came across villages full of lepers. We had to move on then as the men could not be billeted in such villages. Subsequently the Leprosy Project based in Freetown was able help these forgotten and isolated communities.

Some villages had huge round huts with little bedrooms and tall conical grass roofs. All the structures and furniture were made of wood tied up with creepers. The cleanliness of villages depended upon the leadership of the headman. There were always masses of children who would sometimes put on a singing and dancing display for me. Children would surreptitiously touch my hands to see if I was real. It was well known that ghosts were white and their mothers told them that if they were naughty the white men would come and take them away. In one village I was warmly welcomed as no official (district officer) had visited the village since independence, and there was a long list of disputes to be resolved. I had to decline judgement on grounds of absence of legal experience.

It was dangerous for white men to be about when the local people undertook their nocturnal ghost hunts. This generally involved heavy drinking followed by shooting at anything coloured white using home-made muskets. During the ghost hunting season I was advised not to leave my tent during the night, for any reason. Another potential source of danger were the 'secret societies'. We met one such society during a traverse, which consisted of scores of men wearing loin cloths and little crowns made of twisted grass. Their leader wore a wood mask and an impressive grass costume. Tommy Aruna told me that the society members were made to eat dogs and crows, but what exactly they did and why they did it, was secret.

The wild life was elusive and enthusiastically hunted by the village huntsmen clothed in animal skins and armed with home-made muskets. They were invariably successful and brought home bush meat varying in size from small antelopes to huge pythons carried by several men. I was once offered for sale a baby chimpanzee.

Field work was suspended during the wet season, at which time the team members would go on leave or write up their reports in Freetown. My first wet season was spent recovering from a bout of hepatitis during which my eyes turned a bright yellow, and my

Summit of Bintimani (or Bintumani), Loma Mountains, NE Sierra Leone, with geologists Sandy Macfarlane (left) and John Arthurs (right). (Photograph by M. J. Crow.)

field team were convinced that I would die. However, it was not to be and I survived even the recovery period of months without beer. On another occasion I developed a spectacular red network beneath the skin on my arm. Dr Aboud, our Lebanese physician, identified my complaint as a sub-cutaneous worm. The cure, which was simple and successful, was to immerse my arm in a bucket of ice-cold water.

Our Freetown home was a bungalow on Juba Hill, with a distant view of the ocean. Later another bungalow rented by the project, next to the giant water pipes of the Freetown water supply, was allocated to Hugh Rollinson, who had been posted by ODA on contract to the Geological Survey. Our landlord was Sir Bangkole Jones, the former chief justice. He would visit us occasionally on a Saturday afternoon driven in a car with white upholstery and accompanied by one of his nieces. He would entertain us over tea with anecdotes of his judicial career. He told us how on one occasion he agreed to suspend a court hearing so that workmen could replace the court clock. He never saw the clock again as the 'workmen' he said, were 'thiefmen'.

An expedition was arranged to climb Bintimani, which at 1,945 metres is the highest peak in Sierra Leone, located in the Loma Mountains in the eastern part of the project area. Sandy Macfarlane, John Arthurs, Malcolm D'Ath (our Aid Officer at the British High Commission) and myself assembled at a camp at the foot of the mountain, where we enjoyed a convivial evening prior to the climb. Unfortunately Malcolm had to return to Freetown urgently, so he missed climbing out of the tropical heat to the cool summit of Bintimani and the view of the forested topography stretching towards the borders with Guinea and Liberia.

It is regrettable that few photographs survive from my time in Sierra Leone. My camera was damaged when our plastic boat capsized travelling over some rapids. It was one of the hazards of surveying the river sections provided by the Rokel and Great Scarcies rivers, in which we had the advantage of following in the paddle strokes of IGS geologist Peter Allen, whose PhD field sheets we were field checking. Besides the occasional rapids, another hazard of traversing by boat was the local technique of fishing using dynamite which was readily available in the local shops.

Towards the end of the project a general election was held. The ruling party had determined that no potential opponents should be elected to Parliament. As Nomination Day approached all the main roads were blockaded by drunken mobs of party supporters determined to prevent political opponents from serving their nomination papers. These road blocks slowed the journey back to Freetown and involved heated exchanges with drunken, weapon waving political activists.

The Sierra Leone project (1970–73), for all its negative aspects, has happy memories for me, not least because our eldest son was born in Freetown. A great deal of credit is due to Sandy Macfarlane whose dry sense of humour injected an atmosphere of normality into experiences that could only be described as surreal.

Cannibalism: Public Asked to Co-operate
Sandy Macfarlane

In the previous contribution, Mike Crow has related an excellent and amusing account of the IGS Sierra Leone Project. Much of what he recounts I remember vividly, although he has omitted, perhaps out of delicacy, to mention another even more awful Geological Survey toilet than the one he chose to describe. It was sited directly outside the director's office, a small hut enclosing a wooden thunder-box above a long-drop full to the absolute brim with the ordure of a long line of eccentric directors. Its use was forbidden to all but himself although, my office being next door to the director's, I was granted partial exemption—an equal share of the ever-present olfactory delights.

The Geological Survey Rock Store, a rackety, windowless shed at the back of the compound, also deserves a mention. It was an edifice that the local staff seemed most reluctant to approach, and on my initial inspection I was soon to find out why. First the key had to be located and then several layers of rust removed from the lock. Eventually with great difficulty and after much hammering the key finally turned. At that point the door appeared to open of its own volition and an avalanche of rocks, the entire Survey collection, swept out into the compound—only a quick step backwards preventing my being taken with it. One would have expected crestfallen looks from the local staff, but no, their faces were suffused with pride—every specimen could now be examined at one glance. But how was this irreplaceable national archive, collected and catalogued over many years at considerable expense and under difficult field conditions, to be returned systematically to the Rock Store? No problem: shovels were brought and like stokers charging a ship's boiler in the days of steam the job was done. With much pushing and shoving the door was finally shut and ceremoniously locked, and to the best of my knowledge has remained so ever since.

But what of the 1972 front-page headline in the Freetown newspaper, *The Daily Nation*, as quoted at the head of this account? The practice of voodoo and witchcraft as well as ritual cannibalism was ingrained in Sierra Leonean society and there were frequent reports in the local press of senior government officials accused of the abduction and dismemberment of young children. The ritual drinking of human blood was seen as a potent means of guaranteeing a successful political career. My cook lived in continual fear that his young son would be taken and indeed all of our field staff without exception believed in the supernatural. So it came as no real surprise when an accusation of attempted cannibalism was raised against one of the IGS team.

The project field base was at Musaia, a former Agricultural Station in the far north of the country. There we had set up accommodation, field laboratories and storage facilities to supply three independent field mapping teams each led by an IGS geologist. It was the custom for us all to meet up there at weekends for rest and relaxation and to discuss progress, pool ideas and so on. Well, after one very convivial Saturday night I was roughly woken early on Sunday morning by a delegation of our headmen with the news that John Arthur's Land Rover driver had fled for his life claiming that John (a member of the IGS team) was planning to eat him. A pretty serious charge you will agree. At that point John himself appeared, bleary-eyed, his Ulster accent even thicker than usual and with chin and thick black beard on a horizontal trajectory—a sure sign that a Northern Irishman has perceived a slight—real or imagined—and is anxious to do something about it, preferably with violence. He was quick to refute the charge of premeditated cannibalism, rather too volubly I thought.

Anyway, after considerable discussion it emerged that the driver in question had overindulged on palm wine, notorious in its fermented state for having hallucinatory powers, which led him to believe that he was destined for the cooking pot, courtesy of John Arthurs. So first voicing his fears to all and sundry he had apparently then high-tailed it for Freetown to lay his complaint before the director. The unanimous decision was that I, as Team Leader, should proceed forthwith to Freetown to acquaint the director of the 'true' facts.

It was a day's drive to Freetown and on the way I stopped off at every small village that had some form of local authority to inquire after the driver and his state of mind. I found that he had indeed passed through and with each stop his story had become wilder and more extraordinary—white men running amok in the north with machetes and suchlike. So on arrival in Freetown that evening I called on Malcolm D'Ath, our 'case officer' at the British High Commission. Malcolm was a man ever able to calm the fevered brow of a stressed-out geologist and after a few beers and much laughter it was agreed that a 'straight bat' and a 'stiff upper lip' were the best stratagems to bring to my meeting with the director.

Next morning in the director's office it took but a moment to realize that I was talking to a Sierra Leonean who had already heard the driver's story at first hand and fully believed every word of it. Eventually, much later, we came to a compromise: we agreed that Ireland was indeed a strange country preoccupied with the supernatural, where witches, elves and leprechauns roamed at will and where the locals were known to commit unnatural acts with both man and beast. But as John Arthurs was from Northern Ireland where nothing worse than extreme religious bigotry was the norm, it was therefore unlikely, although not beyond the bounds of possibility, that he had planned to eat his driver. And there the matter rested.

The driver, after all the fuss and bother he had caused, was eventually transferred out of the project and given a five-ton truck to play with. As with all good government practice the tried and true method of promotion outwards and upwards was deemed the best method of punishing defaulters. And what of John Arthurs? He subsequently had a distinguished geological career in both the public and private sectors which included a posting to the South Pacific. As you may be aware, the Melanesians were previously known, and still are on occasion, for their weakness for human flesh roasted whole in large earthen ovens: *long pig* as it is known in the pidgin language. Was it pure coincidence that took John there? I have often wondered.

Matters for Negotiation
Howard Bateson

An Uncertain Start

Generally speaking, throughout my overseas career I found relations with the 'local' administration to be good and helpful— we all wanted the job in hand to go well. Occasionally, however, there were exceptions. My biggest reversal of the normally good relationship occurred at the beginning of our project in Burma. In 1971 we were to investigate the mineral potential of an area of the Shan States to the east of Pyinmana across the Sittaung River. As was the normal custom, an early visit was arranged, via the British Embassy, to meet with the senior management at the Geological Survey headquarters.

After the usual pleasantries with the director, who wore military style uniform adorned with much gold braid, and our introduction to the staff who were to be our counterparts, conversation turned to the 'modus operandi' of the task ahead and some indication of the protocols that were to be in place— mainly regarding the financial arrangements and the supply of some essential items of equipment. It was apparent that the

Crossing the Sittaung River on a bamboo raft, near Pyinmana, Burma. (Photograph by J. H. Bateson.)

administration of the fieldwork was going to be complex and many layered, which was not a good omen! But that was the system in place and we would work with it. Things became somewhat less cordial when I reminded the director that the Burmese government had promised in the inter-governmental agreement to provide us with all the necessary maps to use in the surveying. When, I enquired, might I expect them? 'Not at all', was the immediate response. Apparently it was not possible for any maps to be handed over as they were strictly confidential. Both I and the second secretary from the British Embassy were somewhat taken aback at this state of affairs and no amount of diplomatic sweet talking was able to change the situation—we were expected to operate without maps—it was as simple as that.

The two senior counterparts, an engineer and a chemist, who spoke good English, had sat quietly through all this and were clearly embarrassed. I didn't improve things much when, undiplomatically, I declared that without maps there could be no survey and I would return to London as there was no point in proceeding. The meeting was abruptly concluded and I received a reprimand of sorts from the diplomats—one did not give ultimatums for fear of upsetting the officials. Nevertheless, upset or not, the maps appeared at my hotel within a couple of days! I never met with the head man of the Survey again, but my relationship with the Burmese counterparts was excellent. They were supportive and worked with the complex administrative systems to our mutual benefit.

Medicine Man

In my experience there often is a tendency for the 'hosts' to have elevated expectations of the 'experts' in their midst, usually unexpected and almost always unwarranted. The area of our work was quite remote: a walk of several days away from the trappings of civilization. Not too many Europeans ventured or were allowed into this sort of area, which meant that we were from time to time regarded as miracle workers with the 'know-how' to deal with any eventuality.

One   afternoon   a   young

Palaung girls at a remote village in central Burma. (Photograph by J. H. Bateson.)

teacher from a village a few miles from our base walked into camp. He had heard on the 'grape vine' that we had amongst our equipment a medical box from which knowledge he surmised that I would be able to assist his young niece whom he had brought that afternoon to see me. She was about ten or eleven years old and had badly cut her arm with a cutlass she had been using to cut firewood. The accident had occurred two or three days earlier and the wound had gone septic and was by now very swollen, hard, discoloured and obviously very painful. Her uncle 'thought it didn't look too good' and 'had I medicine to get it better?' It was clear that this was a hospital job, but that was not going to happen as it would have been a couple of days walk for a fit person to get to the nearest clinic and this girl was definitely not fit for such a journey. I was, according to the uncle, the last hope—so I set to with hot water, antiseptic and bandage to clean the wound and cover it against further infection and with considerable trepidation I decided to give the poor girl an ampoule of penicillin by injection. Somehow I got this done, having previously practiced on oranges. The girl and her uncle, suitably impressed, left to walk back home and I took refuge in a pre-supper gin and tonic. A couple of months later, as we prepared to leave our base *en route* for Rangoon and home, the young lady (with arm healed), her uncle and other villagers came to say farewell.

On another occasion, we were sitting enjoying our 'tiffin' (afternoon tea) when a messenger arrived in the compound and went straight to the counterparts where much chatter took place before one of them came to find me. Could I go down to the village as 'there was a bit of bother in the temple.' I had no idea what was up but agreed to go. The situation was 'interesting' to say the least. One of the three or four monks in residence had gone berserk and armed with a machete was now holding a young man captive in the temple. I had no idea what lay behind all of this but 'could I get the guy freed and the situation calmed down?' Of course it was obvious that I was the ideal candidate for the job, not speaking the local language, with no idea what lay behind the situation and never having done such a thing before and, to top it all, being more than somewhat terrified. In short, I had all of the necessary qualifications.

I spent the next couple of hours in the company of a crazed monk who was threatening a villager with a large knife. I was equipped only with an unwilling interpreter who, nevertheless, stayed with me, a little behind and much nearer to the door! After a while, by some miracle, I managed to get the captive handed over to me unharmed and further, in the fullness of time, the monk even gave me his knife and we got him secured. Within hours he was on his way to Pyinmana and the doctor, which I guess may well have taken a couple of days to walk. I never did find out what it was all about or what happened to the monk—the other fellow, his erstwhile captive, was happy with my efforts, so I gathered.

Fred Kano's Army

We had been briefed by the Embassy that there was military action between China and Burma across their borders and we were advised to keep clear of these areas. This wasn't too difficult since our area of investigation did not go too close to the international border. Nevertheless, we could hear the sounds of artillery not too far away from at least one of our camps. This was a situation that made for understandable caution.

Of more immediate concern was the reported action between the Burmese Army and a whole variety of groups and gangs operating in the Shan State. Some of this was related to the drug industry, we being on the western borders of the 'Golden Triangle' where the struggle for territory between rival drug barons could flare up unexpectedly at any time. Some of the angst was derived from the long-standing and deeply held antipathy between the peoples of the Shan and the ethnically different and more populous Burmese groups of the central plain. We were working well within the territory where such conflicts occurred. Most of this I did not know at the beginning, but it became clearer as time went on.

One of our senior counterparts was an engineer who had served in the British Army in the Second World War and been awarded the MC for action near Mandalay. It transpired that he was in negotiation with a powerful local warlord in order to guarantee our safety and safe passage while we were in the area. This had apparently been going on, in secret, for months prior to our arrival and was closely allied to the desire of the Burmese Department with whom we were working to bulldoze a drivable single track road, suitable for four-wheel drive vehicles, through this part of the Shan. This was specifically for our benefit.

Some couple of months into the field season I discovered that the ten to twelve miles of road had been agreed with the local military chief subject to the proviso that a couple of the bridges that had been constructed across streams would be destroyed immediately after we had departed at the end of the field season. It seems that the fighters of the Shan were afraid that our new road would afford the Rangoon government and its army improved access to 'their' territory. Much later, when we were back in Rangoon just before we left for London, I discovered that the bridges had indeed been blown up within twenty-four hours of our leaving the field area.

All of the above is background to the security precautions that were put in place during our field season and why, through our interpreters each evening, we had to let our 'security' know the plans for the following day so that they could decide how many of them went where and with whom. Our 'security' at this time was a group of ten or so policemen all of whom appeared to be very close to retirement. Fred Kano's army, indeed.

Our day began early: out on the line by 7 am, then walking/working all day to return by 4 pm or thereabouts. To give them their due, the elderly cops were usually ready to depart when we were, but within a few days it was very apparent to us all, including our Burmese counterparts, that these guys were far too unfit to keep up the pace. They began to go down like flies.

The real crunch came one day when working in one of the boulder strewn stream systems in the area, one of them was so tired that he fell over a boulder and his ancient 303 went off. I hadn't, till then, realised that they walked with the things loaded and cocked. I was not impressed and as 'The Boss' of the outfit I raised the matter with the Burmese suggesting that, for their own sake, it might be better if they were all sent home. They quickly departed and I gathered later that there was something of a row in their HQ and a certain amount of loss of face too.

I thought this would be the end of the matter and for the remaining time on the project we would be left unencumbered by security. How wrong I was. Not only were we to get replacements but until they arrived we were ordered by a very senior military commander not to go out of the immediate environs of the village. The replacements for the policemen appeared quickly, within a couple of days, and were a rather different kettle of fish—a couple of dozen or so heavily armed soldiers from a commando style regiment of the pukka Burmese army. I guessed that things were going to be very different, and I guessed right!

The officer in charge of this mob came to see me each evening to hear where I thought we would be working on the following day, which he had to OK with his superiors. It was also his duty and responsibility to obtain appropriate military permission if we wished to work further afield. This was a bit of a brake on last minute changes to the schedule and in one or two cases we had to postpone work in a particular area because we couldn't get the appropriate clearance.

Our military detachment took their job seriously; they were always ready to move out before us and always deployed their men in what I took to be a 'real' military formation, some working the forward point and others on the flanks as well as 'sweepers' at the rear. If they came upon any 'suspicious' or uncertain situation, an isolated hut for example or folk working in the fields, we were corralled by several heavily armed soldiers and 'asked' (made) to sit down while others of the force investigated, even resorting to kicking in the odd door and interrogating any unsuspecting farmer who happened to come along. This certainly was doing geology in a very different way.

Apart from the security aspects of the operation these chaps were tough, willing and able to go anywhere and do anything despite their heavy armament. After a hard day out in high temperatures and sometimes hacking through difficult and thick bush it was back home, me to sit for a while exhausted, they to drop armaments and play volleyball until the light failed!

There were from time to time some practical administrative difficulties that stemmed from the local security situation. The area of the Shan was apparently divided up into a number of autonomous military zones each with their own commanders and command systems and their own ideas of how the security was to be maintained! And of course, as it would, Murphy's Law applied and our area of investigation cut across at least one of the zonal boundaries, which just happened to be a river. This meant that when we wanted to work across the other side of this stream we had to get prior permission from the commander of that area, as not to do so left us open to being fired on. Unfortunately like much else in Burma then, and perhaps even now, getting this permission was easier said than done and it could take our Burmese counterparts several days to locate the authorising military and even more time to negotiate just when and where we could go and who was going. Much revision and modification to the mapping plan was necessary causing not a little frustration.

On my return to Rangoon I learned that the reason for some at least of the high profile security measures was because a Russian attached to the UN, doing what, I do not know, had been abducted by one of the warlords in our area and held to ransom. This event, to say the least, greatly embarrassed the Burmese and they were not too keen to have the event replayed with a bunch of Brits, and in hindsight I wouldn't have been too thrilled either.

A Rhino's Right of Way
Eugene O'Connor

These days it is common to see adverts in the press for safari-type holidays in Africa, each costing several thousand pounds, with southern and eastern Africa amongst the popular destinations. In the early 1970s, as a young and rather green geologist, I was posted to Zambia on what would be my first overseas assignment for IGS. Coming from a relatively non-colonial background in southern Ireland, this was going to be a challenging undertaking.

Having quickly settled into the capital Lusaka, in what seemed a post-colonial setting, I was assigned a field area in the eastern part of the country. This turned out to be a forest reserve and was only sparsely populated. The geology comprised a vast sequence of high grade gneisses similar to rocks I had seen previously in County Mayo in western Ireland. But it soon emerged that the forest contained more than rocks, trees and dense bush, for I was informed by my civil servant assistant that the large earthy droppings littering the narrow paths were those of elephant. It was not long before we heard the presence of elephant groups, and on at least one occasion I became a David Attenborough-like witness to a robust male elephant altercation, presumably over a female partner lurking nearby. Gradually other animal species made themselves known as we traversed the bush observing rock outcrops and collecting samples. These were guinea fowl, hyenas, occasional snakes, and numerous monkey and baboon species.

On one memorable day we set out early in our pick-up Land

Rover to a traverse starting point, utilising tried and trusted aerial photographs, because reliable topographical maps had not yet been published for all the map sheets in Zambia. There were five members in the group including our driver. Suddenly out of nowhere a large and inquisitive rhino emerged onto the open ground. My Zambian colleagues, in a frenzied panic, immediately abandoned the vehicle. I thought frantically about joining them but something instinctively told me to stay put. The rhino steadily approached and clearly did not like the unusual grey metallic creature, our vehicle, trespassing on its terrain. Then, advancing at a gallop, it headed at my door and rammed it. The unexpected resistance of the metal skin startled the burly animal. Momentarily stunned, it decided against engaging further and slowly retreated into the bush. After a while I alighted nervously to see a substantial dent in the door. One by one my colleagues emerged from the surrounding bush and returned to the metallic intruder which had so offended the rhino. My civil servant colleague, surveying the damage, said that I would have some explaining to do to the director of the Geological Survey.

We continued on our way, sampling and mapping in more remote areas and staying in simple overnight bivouacs, where large fires were lit and maintained during the night to ward off potential visits from lions and hyenas. Expatriates were no longer given licence to carry arms, even in risky places like game reserves.

On another occasion during the same field season the driver and some workers went to fetch firewood in the vehicle. When they returned the driver came to me rather sheepishly to admit another incident. One of the headlights was smashed and he genuinely claimed that yet another rhino had dashed out of the long grass onto the track and hit the Land Rover head on. When I eventually reported both incidents over the radio to the director—a crusty Afrikaner—he was not best pleased. We were allowed one return visit per field season to the capital to re-stock with provisions, and after a chastising interview with the director I was called to the minister's office with the director in tow. Again I was reprimanded for allowing damage to government vehicles and it seemed that my stories were considered scarcely credible.

With the director's support, however, I survived and was allowed back to complete my map sheets in the Eastern Province. They were very memorable field seasons for a variety of cultural, wild life and personal reasons. Our eldest son was born in the high and safe ground of the plateau region during the second year and we remain thankful to the staff and support team of the Lundazi District Hospital. The Lundazi area was also quirky in that it is the only known former Colonial region where the District Commissioner built himself a scaled-down version of a Scottish castle. It became a hotel after Independence and my wife and I spent several pleasant evenings there at the end of field seasons.

In retrospect it was an amazing experience for a young geologist and his young student wife to work and live amongst the 'big five' and other animal species in the forest reserves and I am grateful to the Geological Survey in Lusaka for giving me the opportunity to experience an extended personal safari whilst simultaneously improving my geological knowledge.

An Ill Wind
David Greenbaum

I joined the Overseas Division of the Institute of Geological Sciences early in 1972, shortly after completing my PhD at Leeds University. To me, geology had always meant 'seeing the world' and I was not to be disappointed. My first overseas posting was to the New Hebrides (now Vanuatu), a British-French Condominium in the South Pacific consisting of eighty or so islands, lying about a thousand miles off the coast of eastern

Australia. After a few weeks induction at IGS's Princes Gate office in London, I was packed off on a two-year secondment to join another IGS employee, Don Mallick: Senior Geologist with the New Hebrides Geological Survey. I arrived into the tropical heat and humidity of Port Vila with a wife and baby son.

The New Hebrides Geological Survey was just about as small as a geological survey department could be. Besides myself and Don, it comprised a cartographer, a secretary, a Peace Corps volunteer and three or four technical assistants. Our remit was broad: to complete the mapping of the island group, monitor its volcanoes, reconnoitre for minerals, and investigate the geothermal potential—in fact, we were the 'experts' in just about everything geological, with the exception of groundwater and seismicity, which were the responsibility of the French!

My first experience of fieldwork in the New Hebrides came a week after our arrival and turned out to be something of a baptism of fire (or less than holy water). Leaving my family to settle into the small government house we had been allocated, I set off on a three-week field trip with Don Mallick. This was to involve a short visit to the island of Ambrym followed by the geological mapping of Espiritu Santo, the largest island in the New Hebrides (and the original setting of James Michener's *Tales of the South Pacific*). Ambrym is a volcanic island formed around a spine of older vents with an active centre inside a large, classical caldera. Our mission was to check on its recent activity. Don had visited the island before and, as it later turned out, was not exactly to be welcomed back by the inhabitants. His previous visit had been closely followed by a large eruption, and there was a strong suspicion in the minds of the local chief and villagers that Don was somehow responsible for making the volcano 'angry', though we only learnt that much later.

Travel between the islands of the archipelago was usually by light aircraft but the Survey also owned a launch used to transfer camping equipment, supplies and the team around the coast. The *Lopevi* was an old thirty-foot motor launch of wooden construction with a small central cabin/galley which also housed the engine. It was seaworthy, but hardly ocean-going, and one wouldn't want to spend too much time under cover breathing in diesel fumes. On this occasion, Don and I had flown to the island of Malekula where we rendezvoused with the *Lopevi* which had set off from Vila a couple of days ahead of us. The plan was to steam to the south side of Ambrym and to camp ashore overnight.

As we approached the island the weather, which had been unsettled all day, began rapidly to deteriorate and by the time we arrived, around mid-afternoon, it was blowing quite a gale. Having found what seemed reasonable shelter, we dropped anchor and set about establishing camp. Our sole dinghy with two field assistants and some camping gear was launched but as it approached the beach a freak wave (a harbinger of things to come) hit and overturned it. Fortunately, no one was hurt but the rowlocks were lost and in the mounting seas it was impossible for the dinghy to return in order for the rest of us to go ashore. Over the next half hour the wind increased and whipped up the sea, and it soon became apparent that we could not remain where we were. However, in the mounting swell, the anchor would not budge, and there was a danger that the bow would be pulled under. It quickly became obvious that our only option was to cut the anchor and run out the storm.

Moving out from the shore and leaving our two stranded assistants to fend for themselves, we were met by huge waves and force nine winds. To everyone on board other than me it was apparent that we were in the middle of a tropical cyclone but, not having experienced anything nautical, I had little idea of the seriousness of our situation and somehow imagined that this was all a normal part of fieldwork in the South Pacific! In fact, apart from some slight sea-sickness, I was quite enjoying the adventure. Stupidly, I had complete confidence that all would be well. As they say, ignorance is bliss.

The crew were admirable and for the next fifteen hours remained calm whilst they steered the boat through mountainous seas, at first seeking shelter along the Ambrym coast but eventually, as the winds veered, running to the neighbouring volcanic island of Lopevi (after which our launch was named). At some point the boat's aerial was ripped off so that radio contact with Port Vila, which had anyway been virtually non-existent all day, was now completely lost. The next disaster to strike was that the small hatch above the wheel was torn off its hinges. Though seemingly of minor importance, the loss of the hatch was potentially very serious since waves breaking over the boat might easily flood the engine compartment—and were we to lose the engine, we would be at the mercy of the seas, the reefs and the rocky shoreline. Fortunately, this danger was not lost on the captain who without hesitation attached a rope around his waist and dived in to recover the hatch before it was swept away.

I still vividly recall the driving rain, the noise of the wind, and the huge waves rising high above the boat and crashing down around us. I spent the entire night wedged across a small fridge and side table, life vest on, happy enough now to breathe in the diesel fumes, half dosing, half holding on, as the boat rose and fell in the enormous seas. There were moments when the *Lopevi* seemed to hit a wall of water and shuddered as if she would break in two but she was solidly built and survived everything that was thrown at her.

Finally, towards morning, the cyclone passed, the seas quietened and the crew could at last relax and inspect the damage—which amazingly was slight. We had been lucky, more so than I had realized at the time, but the crew took it in their stride. There was much relief in Port Vila when radio contact was finally re-established. Unbeknown to us, we had, in fact, caused a good deal of concern—not least of all with our wives! We had not been heard from since the cyclone first struck, some twenty-four hours before. Vila had been battered too and, when contact with us was lost, there was a real fear that the *Lopevi* might have sunk. I remember being most surprised that we had made the local 'news'!

Washed Away
Rob Evans

In mid-1972 I flew to Seoul, Korea, for geophysical field work with Korean counterparts as part of an IGS Technical Cooperation project with the Korean Geological Survey. On arrival I was taken to see the field area (Hwanggangni) by the already resident IGS team members, Dave Workman and Tony Reedman. They were the 'Anglo' element of our 'Anglo-Korean Mineral Exploration Group'—on reflection an inappropriate name as I was unashamedly Welsh. I was shown the team's idyllic tented field camp, established on a high sandy bank beside the gently flowing Han River. The site was shaded by a fine stand of poplar trees which had been earmarked by the local people to be felled and sold in order to finance the construction of a local community centre. However, as old Africa hands sensitive to the need to preserve the precious shade provided by these trees, our team had persuaded the local villagers to accept a cash donation in return for leaving the trees *in situ*. The local newspaper duly carried the story of this odd transaction between the villagers and the eccentric foreigners who apparently enjoyed living in tents beneath trees, like refugees, on the banks of the river.

A couple of weeks after my arrival, Dave and Tony left for two months leave back in the UK, leaving me the only remaining British member of the team. A few days later I drove with my Korean counterparts to the field area, just as heavy rain started to fall, making driving conditions difficult and dangerous, particularly because the British built vehicles were right-hand drive Land Rovers in a country that drove on the right. We returned to the camp site late at night, where I bedded down while my Korean colleagues opted to stay in a small village inn just over a nearby ridge.

The next day, although it continued to rain heavily, I took my counterparts out to conduct a geophysical survey on the nearby ridge. As the day progressed the rain got much heavier and my Korean colleagues politely suggested that we should

Farmhouse used as a camp store on the banks of the Han River, Korea, with Tony Reedman (seated) and Mr Bae, the owner, holding Paul Reedman. (Photograph by R. Reedman.)

abandon field work. I, also politely, suggested we continue, stating that where I had previously worked in west Wales it was always raining. Of course I couldn't know that this was to be the start of the worst monsoon period in the country for decades, though the normally sedately flowing Han River was by now rapidly expanding into a swollen torrent. As dusk fell the counterparts returned to their village inn while I slept beside some very damp geophysical instruments beneath a canvas that was being pelted by increasingly heavy, driving rain.

As dawn broke the next day I was woken by river water encroaching on the groundsheet inside the tent; the camp had now become an island in the expanded river and many of the prized riverside trees had been washed away. Fortunately I had tied the project's rubber dinghy, used for ferrying us across the erstwhile gently flowing river, to the tallest, strongest tree in the camp, and I now began a rapid evacuation. Geophysical instruments and camp material were loaded into the boat which I rowed to the rapidly receding 'safe' bank of the Han River, giving thanks along the way for my past teenage experience in rowing against the flow at Henley-on-Thames. On reaching the shore the equipment was taken up to the nearby mud- and wattle-built farmhouse of Mr Bae, our kindly Korean neighbour who had let us use one room of his house as a camp store and office. Situated across the nearby local road and several metres above river level, we agreed that the rescued camp equipment should be safe in Mr Bae's farmhouse. As it continued to rain heavily I finally agreed to join my Korean colleagues, together with the geophysical equipment, in the village inn for the following night. Apparently, because of my boating escapade, they were worried about my safety—and possibly my sanity!

Surprisingly, the next morning dawned bright and clear. I roused everyone to restart surveying and drove with difficulty on the rain-sodden and damaged track back to the ridge. There we were met by Mr Bae, the owner of the farm where we had left all our recently rescued equipment. He was clearly upset as he told us that he had lost all the said equipment, as indeed I was on hearing this news—until we drove over the crest of the ridge and started to descend. There we were met by the sight of the swollen Han River occupying the entire valley with no sign of the farmer's house or much of the nearby village. Not only had our camp been entirely washed away together with its picturesque grove of trees, but the newly constructed village community centre had disappeared as well. Sadly, poor Mr Bae had lost his farm and livelihood but he had appeared more concerned about losing the foreigner's belongings!

This was the worst flooding of the Han River in decades with, tragically, hundreds of lives lost and floodwaters affecting the capital Seoul, many miles away.

Underdogs in Underpants
Tony Reedman

Sport was popular in Korea in the 1970s, particularly baseball in consequence of the many thousands of US troops still stationed in the country. Football, both soccer and some rugby, were also played by Koreans at that time. Soccer would become immensely popular in later years when Korea, together with Japan, hosted the 2002 World Cup finals at which the Republic of Korea reached the semi finals after eliminating both Spain and Italy. Today there is a thriving professional league in South Korea, but this was not so in 1972 when Korea was one of the fifty poorest countries in the world.

At that time my family and I were living in an apartment block in Seoul and got to know the English coach of the Korean national football team who lived in the same block. Knowing of my interest in football he suggested that I might like to organise a team from the Geological Survey of Korea (GSK) and that he could arrange suitable opponents from amongst the small number of British troops who at that time served as a modest attachment to the UN Forces in Korea—a hangover from the Korean War in which British troops had served with great heroism and as a result were much admired in that country. I consequently, and with some difficulty, raised a team of volunteers from my Korean geological colleagues, and a football pitch and 'kick off' time were arranged. It transpired that our opponents were to be a team from the current British Forces contingent in Korea, comprising members of the Irish Guards on secondment from Hong Kong and mostly, it seemed, consisting of wiry young Yorkshiremen from Huddersfield.

Being winter it was typically cold and frosty on the day of the match, much the sort of day made famous by the Korean War of some twenty years earlier. We arrived at the ground and I assembled my makeshift team in the spartan changing rooms and went out to size-up our rather too professional-looking opponents, all kitted out in their smart team apparel. When my team somewhat reluctantly emerged from the changing rooms and shuffled out onto the pitch I was amazed that they were all attired in smart white track suits; amazed because in making preparations we had barely managed to assemble eleven pairs of ancient and decrepit football boots and matching pairs of socks. As we sorted ourselves out into an approximate imitation of a football team, ready and willing to engage with the British enemy, the penny dropped—those were not white tracksuits my team were wearing, they had all merely shed the outer layers of their normal winter attire and were now dressed solely in their underwear, which at this time of year consisted of white long johns and long sleeved vests. This definitely showed initiative but needless to say, their 'track suits' were not removed for the game. When the whistle blew it was downhill all the way as we were no match for our well drilled and suitably attired opponents. Surprisingly, to us at least, we only lost thirteen–nil and afterwards, following several bottles of Seoju in a local bar, bravado was restored, if not pride, and we unanimously decided that the team should be disbanded and the long johns should be employed only for normal use.

I was to encounter the contingent of the Irish Guards again some months later on the occasion of the British Embassy party held to celebrate the Queen's Birthday. The British Ambassador, as was usual, was to make a short speech and propose the loyal toast. He climbed several steps up the impressive staircase in the Embassy residence and in this commanding position turned to address the assembled audience of mainly Korean guests, British residents and the soldiers of the British 'Honour Guard'. Following the usual formalities, the Ambassador chose to comment on a recent meeting of the Korea-British Society in Seoul. Apparently, following the recent general election in Britain, in which the Conservatives gained power, the special guest at the meeting had been the newly appointed Foreign Secretary. Why then, wondered the Ambassador, in a tone of surprised admonishment, did so few of the British residents attend the meeting to hear their new Foreign Secretary? The answer came immediately in a loud stage whisper from one of the Irish Guards of Huddersfield, 'We all voted bloody Labour.'

Land of Contrasts
Rosalind Reedman

It was the late spring of 1971 when Tony, myself and our three-year old son Paul arrived in Seoul for the first time. I really didn't know what to expect, though I knew from previous reading that South Korea was listed by the UN as one of the fifty poorest countries in the world. I wondered how our life there would compare with that in Uganda where we had previously lived for five years. On arrival in Seoul I remember being very surprised by the heat, by the size of the bustling city, the smart hotel we were to stay in for the first few days, and the business men in smart formal suits. I was amazed too by the position of the city, surrounded by spectacular craggy mountains, and elsewhere the beautiful public gardens. However, I had not anticipated the interest that a European child with blond curly hair would create until we emerged from our hotel and wandered around the centre of the city. Old ladies would seize him and stroke his hair, arms and legs as though they could not believe he was real. However, he didn't seem alarmed by this unusual introduction to his new home!

After a few days we settled into our apartment by the Han River and began our new life. Most of our neighbours in the apartment blocks were members of the American forces, over forty thousand of whom were still stationed in Korea. They all had access to duty free supplies flown in from America, which we did not. We would have to rely on the local market— so even ordinary shopping became an experience. At first, trying to find familiar food items was frustrating and it was a while before we got used to doing without fresh milk, cheese and English-style bread; but we began to appreciate the local food and to try the many different new vegetables we saw. We especially loved the beautiful persimmons, large crisp pears and locally grown sweet black grapes, which we had not expected to find in Korea.

We were introduced to Korean style food by Tony's colleagues in the Geological Survey. Tony and Paul liked it straight away but I took time to get used to the high chilli content of most dishes. In fact, *kimchi*—a fermented cabbage with garlic and chilli, designed to provide a vegetable during the long cold winters, and a staple diet of Korean meals—is still a problem for me, but the rest of my family love it. Being a great coffee drinker, I was very happy to see the number of 'tea-rooms' that existed in every village, town or city in Korea and in which coffee was actually the favoured beverage. In the 1970s a visit to a tea-room was made even more interesting by watching businessmen making phone calls and having meetings over their coffees. Few people had phones at home or televisions, or even privacy in their apartments, which often contained an extended family rather than just a couple and their children. The privacy of an office was expensive so for many the local tea-room became their place to meet clients and discuss deals. I spent many happy hours in tea-rooms in small towns waiting for my husband and the other geologists to return from fieldwork, while the tea-room girls working there would feed Paul and keep him constantly amused.

We spent weekends in Seoul visiting galleries and museums or enjoying the Secret Garden adjacent to one of the old royal palaces—a haven of peace in the midst of the crowded and busy city. Sometimes at the weekend we went to the nearby countryside where we saw how Koreans enjoyed their time outdoors: the picnics in the woods and the drinking and singing that Koreans are so good at. At first I was surprised that men and women usually celebrated their leisure time separately but always in large groups, while westerners usually prefer small mixed-sex groups; but there was always a good time for everyone to enjoy. This accepted form of segregation has changed quite dramatically over the years as the country has become more westernised.

I began to learn about the long cultural history of Korea and to appreciate the high quality of its music and folk culture. Attending concerts in Seoul was surprising—it seemed to me that western classical music was far more popular than I remembered at the same period in my own country. More young people played instruments than in the UK and the standard was very high. On the slow, local trains in which we travelled to the field area, young people would play guitars and sing, often with considerable skill. I joined an oriental art class and worked hard at the disciplined technique but could never achieve the effortless artistry of the Korean ladies.

We took our first long trip soon after our arrival in Seoul, travelling on the 'Blue Train', an express from Seoul to Pusan, to pick up our own car from the port. The luxury, cheapness and efficiency of the train, as well as the attention of the female attendants, was a revelation for those of us who were used to the old-fashioned, uncomfortable and often dirty train system of the UK at that time. It was a beautiful ride through the summer countryside and showed us for the first time something we would always love, the rural beauty of Korea, the mountains and valleys, the temples and hillside tombs, the local people in their traditional costumes, the thatched villages with their beautiful walls. Train travel in Korea is still my favourite way of travelling through the country, although nowadays the cities seem much larger and closer together with little countryside between them. Indeed, the only way to see the picturesque villages of our time in Korea is to visit the popular Folk Villages and theme parks, scattered throughout the country.

Of course, at that time, the hillsides were bare with very few mature trees after deforestation during and after the Korean War. There were narrow, unpaved roads winding away from the main, and only, highway. The small towns we visited at that time, which had few shops and little activity in their centres, are nowadays huge cities with their own universities and concert halls. Many Arbor Days of tree-planting have created lovely wooded hillsides, while dams have changed the landscape and created cool lakes with summer holiday homes and hotels scattered along the lakesides.

On our return trip to Seoul from Pusan we drove our own car (shipped out from home) up the then only highway in Korea and saw only a few lorries, buses and army vehicles, but no private cars. Driving in Seoul was easy with only buses and taxis to worry about and after curfew at midnight we, as foreigners with semi-diplomatic status, could drive anywhere in total peace and quiet. The curfew was strictly enforced for Koreans and ran from Midnight to 4 am. I remember the pre-curfew rush for the local people to get home, usually men leaving bars and clubs, as I seldom saw another woman when I went out with Tony and our friends and counterparts, not even their wives. Sometimes the only women I saw on evenings out would be the hostesses in the restaurants or bars but they were invariably very kind and would play with Paul while I relaxed and enjoyed my meal. They would also feed the foreign men (literally!) with special food and I got used to the fact that in Korea, looking after the men and their needs was the female's main role in society and in the home.

I was puzzled by the position of women in Korea at that time. I learned that Korean women who were university graduates could not work after marriage although they were often required to have a high level of education to be an acceptable wife and to enhance the status of the men they married. When I taught English for a while at Korea University in a mixed group of male and female undergraduates, everyone seemed very liberated and easy with each other, but I could not persuade the girls that they could be successful in their own chosen subjects—they seemed to think this would be an unfeminine thing to do. I eventually understood that they either didn't want to work or were unable to do so because of family pressure to marry. I also discovered that married women had their own sort of power in controlling the family finances and running the household, organising the children's education, and so forth, and that divorce at that time was very rare, certainly much rarer than in the western world.

Soon after we arrived in Korea, we adopted a baby daughter and named her Joanne Sungwon ('spring garden') and she made our little family complete. Some people in Korea (not our close friends) were puzzled and kept asking us 'why?' And again I learned something new, about how important family name and family tradition is in Korea and how hard it was to be successful in any area without a strong family background. Now Joanne is a successful accountant working in London and has her own half-Korean sons whom she is determined to take back to Korea and show them their origins sometime in the future.

We spent a lot of time doing fieldwork in Korea, taking the children with us, which was very unusual then and virtually unknown amongst the Korean geologists. I have so many happy memories of our field camp by the Han River surrounded by mountain slopes and terraced hills with rice paddies and

Members of the Reedman family at camp beside the Han River. (Photograph by A. J Reedman.)

Traditional Korean farmhouse near the Han River field camp. (Photograph by A. J Reedman.)

scattered traditional rural dwellings. Next to our camp was an old farmhouse where our 'camp store' was situated and where the farmer, Mr Bae, would provide *makkoli* (rice beer) for Tony and his counterparts when they returned from a hard day's field-work. The farmer would play with Paul or they would row in a tiny boat on the river, each happy with the other's company, though neither spoke the other's language. The nearby river was at that time a relatively narrow strip of water, but following the construction of a dam several years ago, has now become a huge expanse of water which covers our original campsite, the farmer's homestead and the nearby road. Indeed, a few years ago we went with Tony's counterpart, Yoon Kern Shin and his wife, on a river-boat which sailed right over the area he and Tony had mapped! When we were camping by the Han River, Joanne used to play with her toys in a playpen where I felt she was safe from falling down the bank into the river. However, the country women passing by the campsite, would ask me why I kept my child in a cage instead of carrying her around on my back! Now, ironically, in the UK many people carry their young babies in special backpacks, so Korean customs have followed us home.

During the summer holidays, when Seoul became a furnace to escape from, the children and I spent weeks at the beach and I noticed that most Koreans could not swim but just stood in the sea water, or crowded pool, to keep cool. Now when I want to swim on my visits to Korea I am amazed by the high standard of the many pools and the expertise of the swimmers, especially the younger generation.

I think, in summarising this short description of how I found life in Korea in the 1970s, I would say that there were some contrasts that I found surprising: I felt that the intelligence and ability of the female population was not reflected in their position in society at that time; also the lifestyle difference between city and country was enormous, especially the sophistication of Seoul compared to the rest of the country; but the energy and work ethic of the country was inspiring and I will always be glad that we were lucky enough to be able to watch Korea develop and see its people, our friends, reach the highest levels of success all over the world.

Those Were the Days
Roger Key [1]

I arrived in Lobatse, the headquarters location of the Botswana Geological Survey, at midnight on 24 March 1972 on the Cape Town to Bulawayo train. This was the end of a hectic fortnight starting with my PhD examination on 8 March (passed, just) in Liverpool, followed by a rush to the south coast of England to catch the *Pendennis Castle*, sailing on 10 March for Cape Town. We arrived there in the early hours of 22 March, and after wandering around the city I caught the evening train for Bulawayo. My first sight of African 'wildlife' on the train journey was of what I thought was a herd of buffalo grazing in the moonlight. They were in fact cows. This was the start of my African adventure where I expected everything to be different. My previous life consisted of a childhood in rural Wales and six years at Liverpool University. When the train arrived in Lobatse, just about the entire expatriate staff of the Survey was on the platform waiting to meet the latest recruit from the UK. I was whisked off to the inappropriately named Cumberland Hotel for my first taste of South African lager and, eventually, bed.

The next morning I was driven to the Survey offices to be

1 Roger Key has spent most of his career working in Africa. He joined the Botswana Geological Survey in 1972 as a government of Botswana employee working alongside a team from the Institute of Geological Sciences (seconded under OSAS terms). He formally transferred to the IGS in 1974 and continued working in Botswana on secondment.

In 1998 Roger was awarded a Distinguished Service Medal by the government of Botswana, and an MBE in the following year.

formally introduced to the director, John Hepworth, and deputy director, Clive Jones (both on secondment from IGS), who briefed me on my duties before I was given a tour of the offices and introduced to all the staff. In 1972, the professional members of staff were exclusively expatriate and were mostly from the UK. There was a mixture of seasoned veterans including ex-colonial officers as well as 'wet-behind-the-ears' youngsters such as myself. The set-up was in every respect that of a typical African Geological Survey Department: concerned with those aspects of geology directly related to the development of the country. This included producing good quality regional geological and geophysical maps, investigations of industrial mineral occurrences, helping and monitoring mineral exploration companies, and most importantly for a dry country like Botswana, carrying out groundwater studies. I was assigned to the regional geological mapping division and my first task was to recruit a field team.

Geological fieldwork in Botswana traditionally started immediately after Easter to coincide with the start of the 'dry season'. The field teams were expected to spend six months continuously in the field area, so the selection of a good team was very important. By the time I arrived in Lobatse everyone else had their teams organised, so I was left with a selection of characters who nobody else wanted. I had to acquire two drivers (one for a five-ton lorry used for collecting water, diesel and fire-wood, and one for a Land Rover/one-and-a-half-ton Bedford truck used by the geologist for mapping), two field assistants and a cook/campkeeper. The drivers and assistants were found but as no cook was left the word was spread around the local town that a new cook was needed. One of my field assistants then came to me to say he had a friend who worked in the local fish-and-chip café and he would like to join us. An interview was organised and the friend (Tom) was appointed as our cook.

I then had four weeks to get organised for my first field season. The scientific work involved reading previous accounts on the local geology and interpreting air photographs of my mapping area to prepare a draft geological map. The logistics were the main challenges: acquiring surveying equipment, water and diesel drums that did not leak from the Survey stores and making sure that the field vehicles were well equipped with spare tyres and the necessary tools. The tradition in the Botswana Survey was for the geologists to sleep in caravans in the bush. The caravans were galvanised iron huts mounted onto the chassis of a five-ton Bedford lorry. They did not look much, but were ideal for Botswana as they could be driven along the sandy tracks that made up the country's road system in those days, helped by following the grooves made by the lorries that transported cattle all across Botswana (the country's main economic activity). The lorries could also be parked under large shade trees, an absolute necessity in Botswana's hot climate. The caravan that I was given had previously been used by John Bennett, a married IGS colleague, and had the benefit of a double bed as John's wife accompanied him on his field trips. I also had to buy a six-month supply of food and this involved a trip to the nearest large supermarket, which was in Mafeking across the border in South Africa.

Just six weeks after leaving the UK and having previously not had a lot to do with non-white people (apart from playing league cricket against the Liverpool West Indians) I set off for the field area in charge of five older Africans who expected me to control their lives for the next six months. Fortunately they could all speak some English and they seemed to accept it as normal to be told what to do by a complete stranger. The first day was a very long day. The drive north from Lobatse to my field area initially involved travel along the country's main road to Francistown and only the first sixty kilometres of the over four-hundred-kilometre journey was on a tarred surface. The rest of the journey was on a corrugated sandy surface and we arrived in Francistown just as it was getting dark. Although my crew wanted to stop off in

Francistown we continued on into the night until we reached the field area. The next day was spent sorting out the camp and my equipment, and collecting firewood from the surrounding woodland. Several mission pots were filled with water and set on the camp fires ready for the evening meal. As was the norm, I had my own private camp fire and was expected to eat on my own away from the crew. I asked Tom to make me chips, at which, based on his reference, I assumed he would be a dab hand. After waiting about an hour for the chips I decided to see how he was getting on and found him making the chips one at a time in his frying pan. It then came out that he had actually never cooked before in his life. This was the inauspicious start of his eight (happy) years as my field cook.

The ensuing days followed the established routine of fieldwork in Botswana. I set off at about 7 am in the smaller vehicle with a driver and one field assistant to a drop-off point, and then traversed on foot down a dry stream or river bed to an agreed pick-up point at a specified time, usually mid-afternoon. The lorry was used to collect diesel and water from the nearest town or to collect firewood from the surrounding countryside. Evenings were spent 'inking-in' the day's geological observations and updating the draft geological map. What could go wrong?

Well, firstly, vehicle break-downs. My one-and-a-half-ton Bedford truck had a bent chassis which meant it went crab-like along straight roads. This was normally OK in Botswana with its flat landscape and lack of road traffic. It only became scary when we had to cross narrow bridges over the few large river beds. Also, poor fuel commonly prevented the vehicles from starting in the mornings.

Then, language problems. There were misunderstandings about the locations and times of the meeting places at the end of traverses. It didn't happen very often but having to walk an extra ten kilometres back to camp after a long traverse along a sandy river bed was not a lot of fun.

Thirdly, field fridges. Most field teams had small gas fridges that were notoriously temperamental and were forever going out. As with the caravans, the fridges were also handed from one geologist to another and were commonly very old. Lighting the small flame at the back of the fridge required almost inhuman dexterity and the designer of these fridges had his name taken in vain by many geologists. The alternative method of keeping food cold was the charcoal fridge which had a compartment surrounded by charcoal enclosed in chicken wire. Water was sprinkled onto the charcoal and as it evaporated it got the compartment cold. This worked very well until the charcoal started to disappear as it was used for cooking.

Finally, crew fights. My first field crew had two characters not wanted by anyone else. One was the driver of the five-ton lorry and the other his assistant. In camp they were fine; but trips into town, where they were exposed to women and drink, could lead to serious problems. It was a general rule that no women or alcohol were allowed in the field camps. And after one very late arrival back into camp I sacked both the driver and his assistant and sent them back to Lobatse. This was a major problem for both of them and for the rest of the field party. The other assistant was promoted to driver (and remained my driver for the rest of my time in Botswana) and two new assistants recruited. I did try to teach my cook to drive but gave up after he drove into a tree at the field camp.

Once a month we went into town so that the field crew could be paid and for all of us to do some shopping and have a drink. One of my duties was to complete the pay slips for all the crew and to take these to the local pay office. In 1972, Botswana had only been independent for six years and there was still a lot of anger among some of the town people against Europeans. Unfortunately the paying clerk in the Francistown revenue office was one such person and he did his best to be as slow and obnoxious as possible to all Europeans. The upshot was that paying the crew took a long time and required a good deal of self-control not to lose your temper. Indeed, on one occasion my colleague Martin Litherland, who was mapping the area adjacent to mine, did lose his temper and had a go at the paying clerk. Inevitably this landed Martin in the local jail and I had to go there and explain the situation. Our crews came along to support my plea and Martin was duly released. Fortunately the clerk was moved to another job after this incident. The visits to the local bars were more fun.

Health and safety issues revolved around not being bitten by either a snake or a scorpion, or dying of thirst or sunstroke. Before one field season we were given a morning's instruction by a Dutch doctor on where to inject anti-venom if we were bitten by a snake. We were told to draw an imaginary cross on one of our buttocks and that it would be safe to inject ourselves anywhere within two of the resultant quadrants. Unfortunately, once in the field we all forgot which of the four quadrants were the safe ones. However, in all the time I was in Botswana none of the field crews were ever bitten despite seeing snakes on almost every traverse, and I actually stood on puff adders on two occasions.

Twice a day, in the morning before fieldwork and in the evening after fieldwork, there was a radio link between the field camps and Lobatse. This was to check on the well-being of the field teams and to keep them informed of local news. Marsden Jones controlled the radio schedule and he was a very popular Welshman who had spent his whole career with the Bechuanaland Survey before staying on after independence. The daily radio schedules were the only communication with the outside world and everyone could hear the talk between Marsden and all the field teams.

At the end of the field season it was a tradition to go into the local town for a major drinking session with the crew to thank them for their work and to talk about all that had happened. They were happy times.

A major responsibility of the expatriate geologists in the 1970s was to train newly qualified local geologists. In my case, Tafliani Machacha joined my field team mid-way through my first field season and remained with me until he went off to Leeds in the autumn of 1972 to successfully complete his degree. Tafliani eventually became the first local director of the Botswana Geological Survey in the mid-1980s, taking over from Colin Clarke. The training of counterpart geologists was one of the major successes of the IGS (and later, BGS) Overseas Division. Many of these geologists eventually became the heads of their respective Geological Surveys, as well as permanent secretaries and ministers, or professors in local universities.

For some unknown reason national Geological Surveys in some British colonies were often placed next to the national prison or lunatic asylum in towns well away from the main administrative centres. Such was the case in Botswana. One of the tasks assigned to the prison inmates was to cut the grass verges and they were often to be seen outside the Geological Survey office. They would commonly request cigarettes from passing pedestrians. On one occasion one of them asked Ernie Milner, who was in charge of the geophysical equipment at the Survey, for a cigarette. In making his request the convict happily enquired 'Do you remember me Mr Milner? I was the one who stabbed you last Christmas'! The stabbing had nearly killed Ernie, and it was only the quick work of the local doctor that had saved his life.

Postscript. My second period at the Botswana Survey, from 1992 to 1998, was the culmination of over thirty years of IGS/BGS support for the regional mapping division of that Survey. When I first came to Lobatse in 1972 the regional geology division was wholly staffed by British geologists without any local (Motswana) geologists. There were no trained local geologists and Botswana's university (University of Botswana, Lesotho and Swaziland) did not have a geology department. When I returned in 1992 the director of the Botswana Survey was my first counterpart from twenty years earlier, Mr Tafliani Machacha, and the regional geology division was made up entirely of local geologists. Many of these young geologists had received on-the-job training from IGS/BGS geologists seconded to the Botswana Survey, before going to the UK for post-graduate training (MSc and PhD level). My new job was to lead the regional geology division and to train Dr Read Mapeo when he returned from completing his PhD at Southampton University. By the time of my departure at the end of 1997 he was able to take over the reins.

Field conditions had changed dramatically since 1972, when Botswana had only a rudimentary infrastructure. Thanks to its stable and honest government, revenue earned from diamond mines (Orapa, Jwaneng and Letlhakane) had been used to build a network of tarred roads across Botswana as well as clinics and schools in rural areas. Mapping teams were no longer cut off when they went into the field. Now everyone, including the field assistants, drivers and cooks had a mobile phone as well as their own car. There was no need for the twice-daily radio contact with Lobatse and trips home at weekend were allowed.

The availability of hand-held GPSs, high-resolution airborne magnetic data and satellite images also changed the mapping methodology. Things had moved on considerably since the 1970s when mapping was done using air photographs and 1:50,000 topographical maps, and a compass was used to locate field positions. However, the geologists still had to complete the traverses along dry river beds and scramble up thickly vegetated hills and ridges.

Over the Hills to the Caspian Sea [1]
Russell Arthurton

The very thought of the juicy *chelo* kabab with its bowl of rice, raw egg and sumac that we habitually enjoyed in Qazvin (northwest Iran) on our way to our field area in the hills still brings a rush of saliva to my mouth. From there on, any gourmet delights would be those that we prepared ourselves. Fortunately our driver was a resourceful cook, so we usually ate well before setting off over the Alborz Mountains with a string of mules, camping kit and rations strapped to their saddles.

Nowhere is the climatic divide formed by a mountain range more apparent than across the Alborz (also written Elburz). Every

Mule pack about to set off across the Alborz mountains of northwest Iran. (Photograph by R. S. Arthurton.)

1 Between 1968 and 1975, IGS provided technical assistance, in the form of field training, to the Geological Survey of Iran. During the second phase (1972–75), from which the following account arises, a team completed the survey of the Qazvin and Rasht 1:250,000 map sheet, straddling the Alborz Mountains between the Qazvin Plain and the Caspian Sea.

traverse of those lofty ridges and deep valleys started in the dry
heat of Iran's dusty interior and finished in the soggy dampness
of the Caspian plain, our kit and selves often wet through with
unrelenting rain.

Camping at villages was the norm, though occasionally,
when the weather was settled, we would pitch under the stars,
watching shepherds on distant slopes burning thorn bushes to
warm themselves. Dinner mostly came out of tins. There was
a range of Persian recipes: these when served in a wrapping of
lavosh unleavened flat bread made for a sustaining meal. The
ghormeh sabzi—a green *khoresht* or stew with herbs and dried
lemons—was one of the best. Sometimes we struck lucky with
fresh chicken or sheep's liver and *doogh*—the last a sort of watery
yogurt. Lunch was also lavosh, folded on crumbled white cheese,
panir, and ice-cold water from gushing springs.

Hospitality was the order of the day in the mountains. No
stranger would pass by without offering to share whatever food
he might have. No shepherd's encampment would allow us to
proceed on our way without plying us with tumblers of well-
stewed tea to be sucked through rock-hard lumps of *ghand*
(sugar). There was little we could offer in return. Perhaps it was
our company that the shepherds valued; or perhaps they were
simply fascinated that anyone from the great city should choose
to make such a journey into their territory. It is sad to relate that
on the one occasion when these mountain people really did want
something from us, we failed them in their need.

It happened that there had been a terrible accident in a village
on our route. A little girl, maybe two or three years old, had
slipped and fallen into a hot bread-oven causing extensive and
serious burns. Word had spread that there was a doctor on his
way across the mountain. In Iran at that time all professional
people such as ourselves were referred to as doctors irrespective
of any medical skill. Of course, we had no option but to visit
the child. Never have I felt so appallingly impotent. Basic first

aid was all that we could supply. Our tube of ointment for the treatment of burns was woefully inadequate. We offered to carry her at day-break to a clinic in the main valley but the family insisted she stayed where she was, her fate to be as willed—we could do no more.

On descending to the Caspian coast, our routes tracked through dense forest. Oh for a GPS! Overnight stays were in comfortable, tin-roofed timber dwellings—a far cry from the flat-roofed, mud-brick village stacks to the south. But the same welcome prevailed, with on one occasion the offer of inhaling something very out-of-bounds through a shared bubble pipe. Such was the lot of an IGS field geologist on a technical assistance project in Iran in the early 1970s.

Between the Lines
Nick Robins

Working in the midst of a civil war was at best character building, at worst dangerous. I was a salaried employee of the Overseas Development Administration and at a loose end in January 1974, when a call came through to go to the Yemen Arab Republic to stand in for an IGS staff member, John Chilton, who had been repatriated with hepatitis. I was met at the tiny airport at Sana'a by members of the Montane Plains and Wadi Rima Project, an interdisciplinary team in which IGS hydrogeologists formed a small part. I was sent into the field to supervise an extensive drilling and groundwater testing programme; indeed, it was here that I learnt my trade, working alongside Italian drillers from the Rome office of George Stow & Company, whose main base was at Henley in the UK. My ability to speak Italian within a short time far exceeded that of communicating in Arabic, and I learnt how to eat spaghetti with just a fork and to dilute my wine with water.

Working in the field was an enjoyable challenge and day to day work was divorced from any acknowledgement of the civil war going on around us in what was then the Republic of Yemen, or North Yemen as it was sometimes called. Shortly after my arrival I was asked to transfer my allegiance from ODA to IGS, being thus probably the only IGS employee to have neither applied for a job in the Survey nor to have been interviewed for one!

The trick in Sana'a was not to be out and about in the afternoons when a hanging was scheduled. If insufficient numbers had turned up in the square to witness the hangings the army would gather up strays from around the town centre to bring the numbers up to par. Not that I was often in town as my job was in the field with the drilling rig.

The civil war didn't really become an issue for us until the time that the water bowser came back from loading at the well to discharge water into the mud pits. The driver opened the valve and a trickle of water followed and then stopped. It was only then that we noticed the array of bullet holes in the back wall of the bowser. That was a difficult time because the following week we were working at a site furthest from base and the most northerly of the drilling sites, adjacent to anti-government held territory. We spudded in and began drilling about mid-afternoon. It was hot and dry, perhaps 35 °C, and very still apart from the noise we were making at the drilling site. There were two villages either side of us at the edge of the flat alluvial floor of the Qa Jahran (Montane Plains) adjacent to the basalt uplands. Suddenly, rifle shots rang out almost simultaneously from both villages. Our distance from each village was such that very soon we were conscious of their spent rifle bullets falling on us from the sky; not that they would kill you, but they would certainly give you a headache. The late afternoon was spent sheltering under the drill trailer while two of the drill crew were dispatched, one to each village, bearing a gift of Black Label whisky for each respective Sheikh and asking that they cease fire while we retreated.

The gifts were accepted gratefully by our teetotal neighbours but the firing continued until long after bed time. The message had come back that we were to continue working while the two Sheikhs battled it out as to which village would then take over the completed borehole for its village water supply. Silence fell about midnight. We crept quietly about the site greasing down everything that could be greased. In the stillness of the night, blessed by the dim light of a small crescent moon, we tripped up the drill pipes and gently lowered the mast while other crew members filled in the mud pits. By day break we were nowhere to be seen. I was subsequently told off by the project hydrogeologist, Brian Morris, for not completing the drilling schedule. But I was eventually to get my own back for this untimely reprimand!

My ex-British Army Adeni driver, Ahmed, like all other drivers in the country, had a powerful faith in two aspects of the Highway Code. The first was, that for fear the car battery should get overfull, it was necessary to drive around in the bright daytime sunlight with the headlights on full beam. I had no problem with that and I suspect our battery never did get overfull, not that it would have been that easy to tell! But the second act of devout faith concerned the hair-pin, blind corners on the mountain roads. The corner was there to be cut, so that instead of sticking to the right hand lane on a left hand bend, Ahmed would come over to the left half of the road to negotiate the bend directly in the path of any oncoming vehicle. It was a terrifying experience, repeated time and again, with the explanation that Allah was protecting us, and that even the Infidel passenger was under Allah's protection. 'But', I would always respond, 'surely he is protecting the guy coming the other way too, so which of you is he going to save?' The faith was obviously very strong because near misses were all that ever happened to us, and Ahmed would then swear at the other driver in perfect Army-style English!

One very sad incident shocked me to the core. Ahmed was driving me slowly through a narrow street across a village on the way to the drilling site. We felt a bump and he stopped. We ran to the back of the car to find the head of a small child squashed beneath the offside back wheel. Without thinking, adrenalin pumping, the two of us lifted the tail of the long-wheel based Land Rover, complete with logging unit (probably about a ton and a half in weight) off the child while a villager eased the body away from the car. The child had run out from a narrow gap after the front of the car had passed—the driver without any chance of seeing her—the little girl knowing that a car would only pass though her village perhaps once every few days, although traffic to the rig had greatly increased this statistic.

Suddenly we were confronted by a shouting angry mob of people. Instinctively we ran the length of the village and could see the rig only a few hundred yards away. The crowd ran after us throwing stones and any likely projectile they could find. As we ran onto the drilling site the Arab drill crew closed ranks around us while debate ensued with the villagers. Ahmed was later arrested and gaoled without trial for his alleged traffic offence. I never saw him again.

The comparative safety of the next part of the job, drilling in the coastal wadis beneath the mountain front—the Wadi Rima part of the project—was a welcome relief from the mountains. Here the climate was a bit aggressive: 40 °C in the day, 30 °C at night, and unlike the dry air of the mountains it was humid as well. However, most of the hard work on the rig was scheduled for the relatively cool hours of the night shift and tripping out and logging always took place at night. If nothing much was going on I would curl around the spare tyre on the Land Rover bonnet and sleep, safe from the creepy crawlies that took command of the ground at night, until the driller wanted me.

The job was eventually almost completed and my work in Yemen nearly over. I had a ticket to London in my pocket and one week to go. We were over one hundred metres down in the last borehole and all was going swimmingly. Brian Morris had instructed us to prove a sandstone at 120 metres and to complete the hole three metres beyond the break (we only had 128 metres of serviceable drill rods). At 120 metres we were still in the mudstone, at 123 metres there was still no sandstone, then without warning the drill rods started jumping and the whole rig made the most incredible noise. Bruno, our Italian driller, shut down the rotary table and uttered a few silently spoken oaths that obviously had been passed down from the Romans. At night we tripped up to see what had happened—the final rod came out and then the tricone bit minus one of its cones. Bruno ran a line and a fishing catch down the hole in the vain hope of recovering the cone so that we could carry on drilling with a new bit. Two days later the cone was still at a depth of 123 metres and my plane was taking off in only a few days. Like a pair of naughty schoolboys, Bruno made out the completion certificate, '128 metres wadi deposits over mudstone, sandstone not penetrated,' and complicit in the deal, I signed it off. There was just enough time to do the geophysical log which remarkably bottomed at 123 metres, 'Five metres at bottom lost to soft infill material,' read the log notes. Many years later I confessed my sin to Brian Morris. My guilt was pardoned with a wave of the hand, 'I guessed as much,' was all that I got from Brian! But I had got my own back, and I caught my flight with a day to spare!

A Royal Visit
Don Mallick

In 1974 the Queen, with Prince Philip, Princess Anne and her husband, Captain Mark Phillips, visited the New Hebrides as part of a tour of the South Pacific aboard the royal yacht, HMS *Britannia*. The Queen, as head of the Commonwealth, was visiting one of her colonies, but the New Hebrides was a Condominium run jointly with France, who treated the territory as part of metropolitan France. A very limited franchise of French civil servants, planters and business people, together with those on New Caledonia, elected a deputy who sat in the Assemblée Nationale in Paris. The French, however, accepted the Queen's visit, remembering, perhaps, the earlier celebrations surrounding a visit by French dignitaries.

The Queen had indicated that she wanted the minimum of preparations for her visit, so of course there were weeks of cleaning and painting of anywhere that she might see. It was decided that she would visit a few places in Port Vila and, of course, there would be a gathering on the British Paddock with dancers brought in from many of the other islands. There would also be a half-hour motorcade around the town (using most of the very limited number of tarred roads that were in existence at the time). This decision caused a problem. There was only one decent British saloon car in Port Vila—the British Resident Commissioner's Jaguar—and that had to be reserved for the Queen and Prince Philip. How were the others, the Princess and her husband, ladies-in-waiting and equerries, the Resident Commissioner, and the British and French judges, to be transported? The answer was to borrow cars from the French! (the French Residency had several Citroens, and French citizens had various Peugeots and Renaults).

The reason that the two judges were involved goes back to the 1907 protocol which set up the administrative arrangements for governing the New Hebrides jointly by Britain and France as a Condominium (also known as the Pandemonium). There were to be separate British and French administrations, schools, hospitals and police, and jointly run services like PWD and communications. The legal system was complicated with British and French nationals each being subject to their metropolitan laws and overseen by the relevant judge, with anything involving the native New Hebrideans being subject to joint (Condominium) law and jointly under the British and French judges. The protocol recognised that the two judges might disagree and so provided for an arbiter who was the president of the Joint Court. Unfortunately, however, the president of the Joint Court was defined in the protocol as being the nominee of the king of Spain! Of course, Spain had no king for many years until 1975, and so the two judges acted together as president of the Joint Court and were paid to reach decisions where separately they disagreed! The judges argued, not very successfully, that together as president of the Joint Court they outranked the British and French resident commissioners. Consequently, there was no way that they were not going to have a prominent involvement in the Queen's visit.

The planning for the drive around town was like a military operation. It was decided that British Residency heads of department would act as drivers for the motorcade. I was allocated to head the procession in the protocol car, a Peugeot 405 belonging to a French planter. There was a rehearsal of the route where we learned to drive at constant walking pace.

When the day of the visit arrived I was accompanied for the motorcade by the British Residency security man and by the Queen's policeman. On one part of the route our security man became a bit worried when we reached a small demonstration with some New Hebrideans shouting and holding up a banner saying 'You are not our Queen'. To our relief the Queen's policeman seemed quite relaxed about it, saying that the Queen did not regard it as a proper visit if there was not at least a bit of a demonstration.

Not to Be Continued
Jevan Berrangé

In the early 1970s, David Bleackley, then in charge of managing IGS overseas projects in Asia and South America, had learned that in the 1930s French geologists had suggested that the deep lateritic red earth overlying Quaternary basalt lava flows, widely exposed in Vietnam, might be bauxitic: bauxite being the primary ore of aluminium. As the Vietnam War had officially ended in January 1973 with the signing of the Paris Peace Accords, and most of the US troops had left by March of that year, the time seemed ripe for the UK to launch some technical cooperation with Vietnam, and I was charged with undertaking a feasibility study to appraise the situation and determine whether or not IGS could effectively assist the Vietnamese Direction des Ressources Naturelles in a bauxite exploration programme.

After arrival in Saigon in 1974 I soon discovered that the country was not quite as peaceful as one would have liked for a Technical Cooperation project. In Saigon there was a night-time curfew, and on some nights the thump of guns across the

river could be heard quite distinctly. Many of the cafes and bars where the Americans liked to congregate had diamond mesh screens to stop any passing Viet Cong motor-cyclist throwing a grenade amongst the patrons.

I was warmly welcomed by all the staff at the Direction des Ressources Naturelles and a Miss Tan was assigned to me as my counterpart geologist. She was a Vietnamese of ethnic Chinese origin and some days after my arrival she invited me to lunch. We hailed a trishaw and after a disorientating ride lasting about half an hour

Roadside section in lateritic earth, Vietnam, with Miss Tan. (Photograph by J. P Berrangé.)

through a maze of small streets and alleyways, eventually arrived at a Chinese restaurant. Miss Tan was obviously well known to the management and we were immediately ushered into a plush private room that had been prepared for us. The menu was in Chinese and so I had to leave it to my hostess to do the ordering. A multitude of bowls containing different dishes and sauces soon appeared on our table and Miss Tan set about blending and mixing the various ingredients. She then invited me to try the food, but instead of having me help myself to the different dishes she proceeded to feed me with chop-sticks. So all I had to do was sit with my hands in my lap (not hers), open my mouth and make suitable comments about how delicious the food was. When I remarked that being fed by a woman was a novel experience for me, she explained that in her culture the woman's role was to do everything possible whilst indoors to attend to the needs of the man, but outside it was the duty of the man to look after the woman. She did no more than feed me.

Most of the Quaternary basalt areas were in the Central Highlands of South Vietnam, precisely those areas still controlled by the Viet Cong. Although the American troops had mostly left, a local airline, Air America, said to be a CIA outfit, was still flying from Saigon to various towns in the interior. I figured that their aircraft were probably better maintained and safer than the local Vietnamese planes, even taking into account the possibility of being brought down by a SAM7 surface-to-air missile that the Russians were giving to the Viet Cong. So I decided to use Air America to fly to Buen Me Thuot and Pleiku.

On arriving at a town we had to report to the local military HQ in order to get a vehicle and to ascertain whether or not the roads we wanted to travel along were 'safe'—that is, free of Viet Cong. Some were and some were not. It soon became apparent that government forces only controlled part of the countryside and then only during the day, so we had to be back at base by 4 pm for the night curfew. I remember going along one particular road and the driver going slower and slower as we went into what he considered Viet Cong territory. I figured we were safer if we went faster but psychologically he was unable to do this, and eventually he stopped altogether and said that we must go back.

The field work consisted of sampling the lateritic red earth exposed in road cuts to determine whether or not there was any enrichment in aluminium. I quickly noticed how the Vietnamese counterparts were only too keen for me to get out of the vehicle and do the sampling and measurement of the road cuttings, and wondered whether this was why they parked the vehicle on the tarmac because of the danger of land mines in the earthy hard shoulder.

The results of our sampling were somewhat encouraging but nothing further ever came of the project as in March 1975 the Viet Cong launched a massive assault that quickly culminated in the fall of Saigon and surrender by the South Vietnamese government. I was not really surprised. My excursions into the field had showed quite obviously that the government forces had never really controlled the countryside and the towns were ripe plums waiting to fall.

Scam!
Howard Bateson

In early 1974 a US American individual had outlined a proposal to the Bolivian government with a view to their approval and participation. It was claimed that there was sufficient geological and mineralogical evidence to suggest that in a certain area of the Altiplano there existed substantial deposits of silver and a host of other metals which could be won by a large open-cast extraction process. It appeared that the Bolivian government was sympathetic and also that at least one international bank had been approached for the necessary financial support. This was all apparently based on recent new work by the author of the proposal who claimed to have been responsible for examining a number of old (sixteenth century) Spanish conquistador mines in an area where local folklore and place names suggested that a large amount of silver had been extracted. Of course the proposal claimed that more of such minerals remained to be won by using up-to-date mining methods.

Was this a credible proposal? IGS was duly called upon to advise. We had a copy of the proposal in all of its detail, and our remit was to check the validity of the science and replicate the analyses of mine material by re-sampling from the places that were identified in the documentation. An ODA economist was assigned to the team to look at the very detailed costings provided and the general economic health of the proposed project.

Once in country, we devised a plan of action before leaving La Paz so that we knew more or less which locations mentioned in the report we wanted to visit. Some were easier to find than others but all were situated in or very close to old mines of the Spanish conquistadores period. These were in their own right quite fascinating: some were entered through a horizontal portal and tunnel and others via a vertical shaft. Clearly they were built and operated at a time when labour was plentiful. The entrances were most often beautifully constructed corbelled arches which were also to be found deep underground where local rock conditions made them necessary. We re-sampled all the sites, or at least those that had not mysteriously caved in—a feature that we soon recognised coincided with the best sampling results mentioned in the project proposal; so the real nuggets could not easily be checked! We wondered why?

It was during a descent into one of these mines that I observed just what the effects of suffering from vertigo could do. We had had the foresight to bring with us several lengths of climbing rope as we anticipated the need to descend some of the many shafts. The method of going down a shaft was normally by means of a spiral of cut steps around the walls of the circular shaft—a way down that was extremely daunting, even with the safety of a top rope secured at the surface, as the four-hunded-year-old steps were in places badly eroded by a mix of use and antiquity. I recall that the deepest shaft we descended involved a vertical drop of thirty metres, just short of one hundred or so feet. I descended first, as I normally did, with the Mining Engineer following. On arriving at the bottom I checked that the horizontal tunnel was accessible and called for the Mining Engineer to come down. He got about halfway and then froze, physically unable to move in any direction. Fortunately he was held safely by the Bolivians hanging on to his top rope. The problem was how to get him out. Simply talking to him had no effect at all, his ability to make any movement having completely gone, and it was surprising just how someone could cling so tightly to small finger- and hand-holds. Eventually the only solution was for me to climb up alongside him and physically push him off to leave him suspended in mid air so that the lads on top could pull him out. He didn't try any more descents!

Our work done, we got back to La Paz to find that we were expected to give an informal report, ahead of the written submission for ODA, to a meeting of local government ministers and officials on a date that had already been arranged through the British Embassy and at which we would be supported by the Embassy's Second Secretary. All of our Bolivian counterparts were also to be there.

We got our heads together over a few *pisco* sours and outlined our three statements on the geology, mining and economics respectively, the content of which we relayed to our Bolivian friends. We did not then quite understand why they were so diffident about agreeing to stand up and speak in support of our joint conclusions, the gist of our conclusions being that the whole idea was a scam. The data supposed to be the basis for the proposal could not be reproduced and the engineer was highly suspicious of the already implied tie-up between the US author and a large heavy machinery manufacturer in Germany.

At the appointed time we three turned up with the diplomat and met with our counterparts to be ushered through the front door of a large government building and, after being relieved of our passports at the door, on into a reception room where the meeting was to take place. The room was large with a big central table around which there were seated a number of people, some in military uniform, and a couple of stenographers. It was instantly clear that this was no simple chat—it was to be recorded for posterity. At the head of the table were three empty chairs which looked ominous, and after a few minutes these were occupied by three gentlemen in full military garb with epaulettes and much 'scrambled egg' and lanyards. There was some sort of welcoming remark translated to us and then, having been introduced by the diplomat, I was asked to make my statement. In effect this was a brief run-down of the geology, a résumé of the claims made in the project proposal and a short summary of how we didn't feel the thing stacked up. I remember that although I was not on my feet for very long, the temperature got distinctly cooler and our Bolivian counterparts appeared very uncomfortable, particularly when asked to corroborate my less than supportive views. The damage had been done by the time the Mining Engineer had his say and this was reinforced when the three top men brusquely upped and left the room and it was indicated to us that the meeting was over.

Afterwards outside I learned that the gents in the army gear were displeased since they as private individuals had been some of the would-be backers of the scheme and were trying to promote the business with the government. We also learned that a major British banking house had been approached to help finance the venture to the tune of several millions and it was they who had asked ODA for a second opinion—ours!

Subsequent to our departure from Bolivia the Mining Engineer traced the author of the proposed project and discovered that his only claim to fame was that he had designed and installed the air con system for a couple of large multi-story buildings in Chicago and he had never been involved in any form of mining enterprise! As we had thought, it had all the hallmarks of a confidence trick and the hoped for financial backing rapidly evaporated.

Silence for Safety
Jevan Berrangé

The Pailin ruby/sapphire deposits in Cambodia, discovered by Burmese pedlars in 1874, had long been exploited by local and foreign 'diggers' using primitive techniques. As the Khmer government was deriving virtually no revenue from this rich gem field, they formed a company, Société Nationale d'Exploitation et Commercialisation des Pierres Précieuse (SONEXPIEROR), to mine gems in their concession area and buy gems recovered outside it. Following a visit by IGS's David Bleackley to Pailin in 1973, it was agreed to send an Overseas Division team to Cambodia with a remit to make a study of the geology, gemmology, mining methods and economic potential of the gem field. I was to be the team leader, Alan Jobbins the IGS gemmologist and Eric Davies the mining engineer. Eric was an old Southeast Asia hand, having been a POW in Japan during the war, and had worked on alluvial tin deposits in Malaya during the Malayan Emergency (1948–60). The team was assisted by a Burmese counterpart geologist, Siv Chlay Eng, and several local field assistants.

On arrival in Phnom Penh in November 1974 we found it surrounded by Khmer Rouge forces who would from time to time shell the town. The same applied to most of the other major towns in Cambodia. The surrounding countryside was essentially under the control of communist forces, and as the overland route to Pailin was deemed to be unsafe, even to armed convoys, the only relatively secure way to travel to Pailin was by air. This necessitated flying in an ancient DC3 to Battambang from where the military flew us in a helicopter gunship on to Pailin. Besides carrying the four of us and our gear, the helicopter was loaded with ammunition and a large bale of banknotes about the size of a hay bale. I was told that

Women panning for rubies and sapphires, watched by concession holders (shaded by black umbrellas) to prevent pilfering. Pailin, Cambodia. (Photograph by J. P Berrangé.)

these were being brought in to pay the garrison troops and to restock the bank—not that I recall seeing a bank.

We were warmly welcomed by the governor of Pailin, Colonel Houl Tuan, who at our first meeting asked me how many troops I would need to do the job. When I told him that I didn't want any, he then asked what arms we wanted. I had the impression that, if requested, we would have been issued with AK47s, grenades and maybe the odd mortar. We didn't want these either, but in the end had to settle for an armed escort of two soldiers. Much more helpful was a small Vietnamese man who asked me for a job and whom I engaged as my personal 'bat-man'. He had been attached to the French army and had lived through the battle of Dien Bien Phu after which he had made his way to Pailin to try his luck in the gem field. He must have had a Vietnamese name but he introduced himself as 'Bon Sambo', probably a nickname given him by the French. At the time I don't think either of us realised its racialist connotations.

Whilst Alan and Eric spent most of their time working in the gem field, which was relatively secure, I had to go further afield into the surrounding forests, so the two soldiers usually accompanied me. They didn't offer what might be called close protection and much of the time seemed to be either ahead of me and Bon Sambo or lagging far behind. On one occasion after I had not seen them for some time, I went back along the trail and found them in a field picking cannabis leaves. On another occasion, whilst walking up a small creek in the forest with Bon Sambo, a shot rang out some distance ahead of us. As our escort was nowhere to be seen I assumed that they had been ambushed by the Khmer Rouge. Hiding in the undergrowth we waited to assess the situation and were relieved when our two soldiers showed up grinning from ear to ear carrying a little squirrel-like animal which they had just shot for the pot. Whilst I sympathised with their need for meat, I had to tear them off a strip as I had previously made it clear that we were to make silent traverses into the forest so as not to alert any Khmer Rouge troops to our presence. Gun shots were definitely to be avoided. This was the advice that Eric had given us based on his experiences in Malaya. He had been horrified when, on the evening prior to my first traverse, I had told our local field assistants where I planned to go next day. Eric quite rightly pointed out that I should be wary of the possibility that the local staff might inform the Khmer Rouge of our movements and that I could be in danger of making a trap for myself. There certainly were Khmer Rouge forces in the vicinity as evidenced by a battle between government and Khmer Rouge forces that took place about twenty kilometres outside Pailin whilst we were in residence.

We used to eat every night at a local restaurant, always being sure to get back to our house by the 9 pm curfew. The food was a blend of French and Southeast Asian cuisine and utterly delicious. One night, much to the disapproval of both Alan and Eric, I decided to try a soup made with some cannabis leaves I had confiscated from my escorting soldiers and given to the restaurant. A 'steamboat' (a large bowl with the central chimney filled with glowing charcoal to keep the soup hot) with chicken/cannabis broth was duly produced and devoured by myself. This is the one and only time in my life that I have taken a psychedelic drug. The effects during the night were weird. I felt as if I was lying on a bed of cotton wool or clouds but with a tremendous weight pressing down on me. As the night wore on, I became increasingly concerned that I would not be able to attend an important meeting, scheduled for noon the next day, with representatives from Shell and the two French managers of the Société des Plantations de Pailin (coffee and pepper). However, after numerous mugs of strong black coffee and a cold shower I was back in the real world and, according to both Alan and Eric, was able to give a lucid account of the potential of the Pailin gem field.

One night Alan fell worryingly ill. His temperature rose to dangerous levels and he became somewhat delirious. The curfew meant that I could not go and look for a doctor and as I could not make a diagnosis, I decided to treat him with aspirin, wide spectrum antibiotics and anti-malarials and keep his temperature down by cooling him with a wet flannel. He was still very poorly the next morning so I went to find a doctor. No doctor or even a paramedic could be found in Pailin—a town of perhaps 200,000 people, and with wounded government soldiers in a compound. I was told that all medics had gone to Phnom Penh and I therefore decided to evacuate Alan back to the capital. The only means of contact with Phnom Penh was via the radio transceiver at the coffee plantation and eventually after anxious hours a helicopter gunship arrived in the late afternoon to pick up Alan. I had to send Eric with him in order to make sure he received proper medical attention, and our counterpart, Siv Chlay Eng, to translate. Before being left alone in Pailin with various Khmer assistants, none of whom spoke any English, I realised that I would have difficulty ordering food at our favourite restaurant. So I had Siv write down the names of a selection of foods in Cambodian script opposite the English equivalent. Then all I had to do was point to the name of a dish and the cook would know what to serve me. In the event Alan's illness was never specifically diagnosed, he recovered quite quickly and was able to return to the project along with the others. He has since claimed that I saved his life. I think this is a bit over the top, but it was a worrying time.

Screwed and Unscrewed
Poul Strange

In the mid-1970s the Institute of Geological Sciences undertook a two-year photogeological mapping project in the eastern Andes of Bolivia, which involved three months of field checking in the Vallegrande area where Che Guevara had been captured and killed some eight years earlier.

My IGS colleague, Howard Bateson and I each had a GeoBol (Bolivian Geological Survey) counterpart and driver and British Embassy Land Rovers for the survey work. In the remote areas, we were regarded with some suspicion by the local population, with long memories of the attempted uprising led by Che Guevara. Some locals had seen the Geobol logo of crossed hammers and mistakenly assumed it was some kind of communist symbol!

At the time, police and military personnel would man road blocks in remote areas, and one night we were on our way to Cochabamba when we came upon one such road block complete with a black metal gate across the carriageway. Our driver, Raymondo, did not attempt to stop but put his foot on the accelerator, crashed through the gate and hurtled off into the night pursued by a military Land Cruiser with soldiers waving guns out of the windows! We managed about five miles before we were forced off the road and hauled out of the vehicle at gunpoint! We were then taken back to the roadblock where the damaged gate was shown to us and an estimated repair cost of 1,000 pesos (about fifty US dollars) was suggested. We were told that should this not be forthcoming immediately, we would be held in detention for three weeks, and there would be no need on their part to inform anyone! Grudgingly we had to pay up by putting the folded money into the commander's top pocket, and we were free to go. Just as we got into the Land Rover a local came up to us and remarked that 'They were doing well tonight, as we were the third vehicle to be caught in the trap!' When we reached La Paz, we reported the incident to the British Embassy, and were told that they would be writing to the regional military asking for the local commander to provide an official receipt for the payment.

On another occasion, as we drove the Land Rover through the La Paz suburbs on a Sunday afternoon we were stopped at a police post and told we were breaking the law by driving a vehicle with a CD diplomatic number plate on a Sunday. We argued 'diplomatico' but that made the officer in charge shout something to another policeman who rushed out of a building with a screwdriver. He unscrewed the number plates and then told us it was a serious offence to drive a vehicle on the public road without number plates! At this point, one of our Bolivian counterparts stepped forward and asked the policeman if there was a telephone in the police building as he wished to make a call. 'To whom?' asked the policeman and Alphonso responded 'To my father, the chief legal advisor to the government, or maybe my uncle, the foreign minister, who will not be too happy to hear how foreigners are dealt with by the police.' Instant activity erupted, with the policeman screwing the number plates back on, smiles and saluting all round, and we were quickly on our way again!

A Suspicious-Minded Prime Minister
Bob Addison

The Solomons was a dream posting in many ways, especially for those not obliged to participate in arduous fieldwork. But it could be quite culturally challenging on occasion, as getting work done or services provided required patience and persistence, the main issue usually stemming from a lack of available materials or equipment to carry out the job.

Geological Survey Division headquarters, Honiara, Solomon Islands. (Photograph by B. Hackman.)

We had a few difficult personalities around the Geology Division. I was mentoring a young geologist earmarked for promotion to Director of Geology. Unfortunately another exceptionally clever guy felt he had been overlooked and started to become obstructive. He was given a high level of responsibility and treated with respect and consideration but never would carry out his duties consistently, and spent most days in the bars in town. We went through full civil service measures to get him back into line with verbal warnings and written warnings over many months, but in the end he rolled up to the ministry quite drunk and began molesting various female and male colleagues. Soon, under instruction and in full collaboration with the permanent secretary of the ministry, I had to throw the book at him. Needless to say his reactions were volcanic but then to cap it all I got a letter from him to the effect that he would sue me personally for abuse of powers and unfair dismissal.

The Prime Minister was almost as difficult. The Ministry of Natural Resources in the Solomons was host to a US Geological Survey seismic station which Solomons staff manned and from which they issued reports. As the equipment was old, it was arranged by the USGS to provide a modern system emplaced in a borehole drilled at the ministry compound. The New Zealand Geological Survey was commissioned to drill the borehole and install the seismometer. All of these arrangements had obviously been cleared at the highest level within the ministry.

Everything was going well until the Prime Minister got wind of the project just as the NZ team were completing the borehole. An immediate embargo was placed on the project, NZ staff and I were ordered out of the country and serious questions had to be answered as to the sensitivity of the equipment and its ability to pick up conversations and telecommunications in the prime minister's residence some 750 metres away from the site. Fortunately the minister and permanent secretary were able to explain its true purpose and capabilities and thereby pacify the PM. We were reprieved!

Paddling Your Own Canoe [1]
Poul Strange

The Solomon Islands government maintained a fleet of small boats to service their inter-island activity, and the Geological Survey was assigned a 'schooner' called the *Coongoola*, a seventy-foot sailing boat which had been built in 1949 and had once taken part in the Sydney to Hobart yacht race. It had seen better days, but provided us with transport to our current mapping area on Choiseul, a sea trip of two or three days at a speed of seven knots. This was not the luxury cruise you might hope for—sleeping in a stifling airless bunk smelling of diesel fumes with giant cockroaches scampering across you every few minutes. Occasionally, the crew hoisted the main sail and we flew along at ten knots. Today the renovated and updated *Coongoola* operates in Vanuatu, taking tourists on day trips round the islands.

Sometimes there was no shipping available for us and we had to make a treacherous seventy mile open sea journey from Choiseul to Gizo, capital of the Western Solomons, using a twenty-foot long fibre glass canoe, with a single 12 hp outboard motor, and a few paddles as back up! The four hour journeys were always started an hour or two before dawn to take advantage of the calmest sea conditions. The islanders would take a few coconuts as sustenance should we have an engine failure and drift at sea! At that time there was no search and rescue service in the Solomons and telecommunications were non-existent outside the main settlements. It was not unusual to hear tales of islanders floating at sea for days before landing on a far distant island.

---

1 IGS/BGS involvement in the Solomon Islands began in the 1960s and extended over a period of many years. This involved both the running of the Geological Survey (under OSAS arrangements: see Bob Addison's anecdote above) and the conduct of a more focused ODA Technical Cooperation project. Poul Strange was one of a handful of geologists sent out to survey the geology of the Choiseul and Shortland Islands between 1976 and 1979, which formed the first phase of a larger TC project covering the Western Solomon Islands.

The fibre glass canoes were our daily means of transport around the islands and along the coasts, which alternated between thick mangrove swamps and white sand beaches. Sometimes a large fish (presumably a shark) would go into a feeding frenzy around the spinning outboard motor propeller and bite the propeller, snapping the shear pin. I recall one day having to pull the motor up to change the shear pin on the propeller whilst a shark menacingly circled the canoe. Nevertheless, we could swim in the sea without worry when sharks were present. They didn't seem to concern the islanders who said there was plenty of fish for the sharks to feed on and therefore they were not interested in taking humans! It was commonly believed that most 'shark attacks' may in fact have been crocodile attacks.

On one of my early trips to Choiseul we camped by the mangroves on a muddy beach, and the islander assistants placed my tent (actually just a plastic fly sheet on an open tent frame) near the water and fifty metres away from the main camp, as they were concerned they would make a lot of noise and disturb me. I had a good night's sleep, but was woken in the morning by much animated shouting. My assistants were pointing at the muddy areas around my tent and identifying crocodile footprints and tail marks where a large croc had circled my tent and bed several times. Needless to say, we moved away from that site the same day.

A Sad Month in Quito [1]
Chris Evans

1 IGS undertook its first assignment in Ecuador in 1969–70, when Brian Kennerley (together with an Ecuadorian counterpart, Luis Almeida) carried out a photogeological mapping project in Loja Province and in the remote mountains of Llanganates. The success of this undertaking led to a more extensive geological mapping and mineral survey project, which ran from 1972 to 1980. Chris Evans, a member of the IGS team, recalls some tragic events that occurred half way through the project.

In 1976, I was one of a group of five IGS geologists in Quito, Ecuador. Brian Kennerley was our project leader, and in August of that year Brian had arranged to take his family on a motoring holiday in nearby Colombia.

As was Brian's way, he had organised everything meticulously, informing the Overseas Division of IGS in London and the British Embassy in Quito of his plans. Somewhere north of Cali, Colombia, an oncoming tractor overtook a bus and drove into the Kennerleys' car. Tragically, Brian was killed and the family injured, though none too seriously. Margaret, Brian's wife, and the children were taken to hospital in Cali and Norma, my wife, and Bill Henderson (another member of the IGS team) arranged to visit her. They were entertained in Cali by 'Wop' the local UK consul, a larger than life character who fed them mostly on gin and tonics. One of the upsetting aspects of the incident was the local practice of showing photographs of car crash victims in the local paper, and a photograph of Brian's body duly appeared in *El Comercio*.

Brian and his family were members of a local church and he was buried in a cemetery in the north of Quito overlooked by Pichincha volcano. Following his death there was a major issue, eventually resolved, in sorting out the family's pension arrangements, for Brian had formally informed his employers, The Natural Environment Research Council, that he was on holiday, so the incident could not be considered a death in service.

Just a week or two before Brian left for Colombia, a British army expedition of six arrived to climb Sangay, a remote 5,300-metre-high active volcano in southern Ecuador. I asked Brian if I could join the expedition but he insisted, thankfully as it turned out, that I should continue my mapping on the northwest coast. On reaching the lower slopes of the volcano the expedition were informed by a team of French volcanologists, led by Haroun Tazieff, that the volcano was active and dangerous, but they decided to continue. On 12 August, when they had reached the middle slopes of the volcano, it erupted, showering them with blocks and ash. Two members of the group were killed and three others seriously injured. One of the group, Nick Cooke, bravely stayed on the mountain to look after his injured friends and was subsequently awarded the George Medal.

Jeff Aucott, by then the leader of our team, together with staff from the embassy, were involved in bringing the group back to Quito where their kit was placed in our store and I had the task of auctioning off the items not worth returning to the UK. To this day I feel guilty that I bought immediately their tins of baked beans, which our two children had not eaten for a year. It had been a sad month for the remaining IGS team in Quito.

In 1978, Richard Snailham, a civilian on the Sangay expedition, published a book, *Sangay Survived: Story of the Ecuador Volcano Disaster*, in which Brian is described as having a lean and boyish look, and Jeff is mentioned for his post-accident assistance.

Cocktail Dress Optional
Fiona Darbyshire

My first encounter with the Overseas Division was in 1975. I had been working for the Institute of Geological Sciences for several years, initially at the Age Determination Unit in Oxford and then, rather bizarrely, in an old post office sorting depot in Young Street, off High Street Kensington. However, by 1975 we had been renamed the IGS Isotope Geology Unit and were housed at Gray's Inn Road. Jevan Berrangé came over to see if I could determine the age of some basaltic rocks he had collected in Vietnam. Faced with an apparently intrepid adventurer, with amazing tales of field work on Highway 10, I wasn't quite sure if I could survive such an experience. However, I did, so a couple of years later Jevan was back with more rocks to date, this time gem-bearing lavas from Cambodia and Thailand.

In the meantime Martin Brewer had joined the unit, principally to work on an Overseas Division project in Zambia and Malawi. We had been friends in Oxford where he was a Rhodes Scholar and, as he had collected a lot of rock samples in Africa and had an enormous amount of work to do in the laboratory, I was delegated to help him. One Friday at lunchtime Martin took me to the Gunmaker's, the pub behind the IGS Overseas Division office in Clerkenwell Road, and there I discovered that it wasn't only Jevan who had a collection of fascinating stories and a sort of grown-up Boy Scout's attitude to life: Arthur Stevens, Richard Johnson, John Baldock, Howard Bateson, Tony Reedman and many other Overseas hands could be found in the bar drinking a half pint or two to wash down the Gunmaker's lunchtime sandwiches which had extremely thick bread and a not inconsiderable amount of filling.

On one such occasion I was introduced to Keith Bloomfield who was shortly to go to Bolivia as head of a team of ten Overseas Division geologists committed to Proyecto Precámbrico, a project to map the eastern part of the country. On learning that I was a geochronologist he suggested that I might like to get involved in the project and even go into the field. My boss, Norman Snelling, clearly thought that this was a totally unsuitable idea but agreed to let me work on a small batch of pegmatitic mica samples that the team had sent back during the first year.

Eventually the powers that be decided that it was all right for me to go out to South America and in 1977 visas were organised and travel arrangements made. To my amusement the Overseas Development Administration (ODA) list of items that I would be permitted to purchase officially included a cocktail dress, but I thought it very unlikely that I, as a field geologist, should ever need one. I was told that it was best to avoid wearing bright coloured clothing when working in the field because they would attract insects. However, that was the only piece of practical advice I remember being offered, it just seemed to be assumed that I would know what to do and I certainly wasn't going to ask.

I arrived in Santa Cruz de la Sierra after a brief stopover in Rio de Janeiro. In retrospect that wasn't a great idea because about two days later I was extremely unwell and the local doctor decided that I had contracted dysentery and wanted me to go to hospital. Keith Bloomfield however wanted me on the plane which flew only once a week into the field area and persuaded the doctor and me that I would be fine. It wasn't a particularly pleasant flight and when I saw the hotel in San Ignacio, which was shockingly basic, I rather wondered what I had let myself in for, because I tend towards a preference for the other end of the spectrum in hotel grading. However, thanks to the kindness of colleagues, particularly Dick and Helen Annells, I survived and things got much better when we headed out into the bush. I had never really camped before, but much to my surprise I enjoyed sleeping in a hammock and found I preferred it to a tent. We spent some time in the area north of San Ignacio between Carmen de Ruiz and San Simón sampling the Velasco Alkaline Province. Then we made our way south to San José and finally east to the Rincón del Tigre complex between Santo Corazon and the Brazilian border collecting in all about fifty rock samples.

The field conditions in eastern Bolivia were often extremely difficult and I was very fortunate to have the good company of not only Dick and Helen Annells, but also Chris Fletcher, Peter Pitfield and Eugene O'Connor and their 'brigadas' whom we met along the way. Driving on terrible tracks resulting in inevitable punctures and delays, walking in line through the scrubby jungle which had been cut by the man at the front with a machete, and the interminable insects, are best forgotten. However, the amazingly colourful birds and butterflies, the beautiful Jesuit Mission church in San Rafael with terracotta and ochre painting on white walls and a terracotta tiled roof, the

Mennonite community in Esperanza where we bought cheese, and encounters with small groups of local children who found everything we did a source of amusement, are all memories to be treasured.

The journey back to Santa Cruz was by the train from Puerto Suárez near the Brazilian border via Roboré and San José, it was called *El Rápido* but went so slowly I would hate to have been on the less speedy version. Then followed several weeks of work in the GEOBOL (Geological Survey of Bolivia) laboratory crushing the rock samples in order to be able to take a more manageable sub sample of each back to England. Samples collected for geochronological studies need to be at least the size of a football in order to be considered representative of the whole rock, and very fresh, i.e. not weathered. So you need to process a lot of material and then clean the crushing equipment very carefully in between samples to prevent cross contamination. The very macho Bolivian geologists were not thrilled by this task and it took a lot of effort to persuade them that this was a vital step in the whole procedure and that not doing it properly could prejudice the chance of getting an accurate age for the rock sample.

Finally I flew home via São Paulo where I spent a couple of days visiting the laboratory of a famous Brazilian geochronologist. He had a very different approach to both sampling and treatment of the final data and I wondered what my colleagues at home would think of his methods. I was to find out when he came to give a lecture in the UK and one colleague asked why he had chosen to draw a line though some of the sample data points and not the others. His answer was that if he included all the samples he wouldn't get a realistic age. It is absolute heresy for a geochronologist to ignore data points, you may not end up with the age you hoped for but the data tells you something more about the history of that particular geological formation.

A year later I made a second trip to South America, though this time I went into the field with a Bolivian counterpart, Edmundo

Justiniano. There was a new paved road from San Ignacio to San José, though bizarrely we seemed to have more punctures. Also, bliss, there was a new hotel in San Ignacio. We headed west to Concepción which has another pretty Jesuit Mission church and on to San Javier where there were eight hours of torrential rain after none for the previous four months. After eight days of speaking only in Spanish, a language in which I am by no means fluent, it was a relief to meet up with Martin Litherland and his counterpart Juan Carlos. They had obtained fresh meat and Juan Carlos, who had been in England earlier in the year, had saved a bottle of Argentinean wine, so we enjoyed a feast that evening.

A few days later we drove to Peter Pitfield's camp where his Bolivian counterpart Edgar made a very florid welcome speech and presented me with a bunch of flowers. We were working north of Tunas by the Brazilian border in an area with some spectacular scenery. Apparently the land used to belong to Bolivia but the owner gave it in exchange for a white horse. At the Brazilian army post on the frontier we met the Prefecto for the whole of Santa Cruz State who had just flown up from Santa Cruz in his private plane. Edmundo was most impressed, though he nearly blundered by calling the accompanying general 'mayor'.

Quite a lot of smuggling went on across the border: motor engines and cars from Brazil and wood and petrol in the other direction. Petrol cost three pesos a litre in Santa Cruz, five in San Ignacio and eight in Asuncion which is close to the frontier. However, it was eleven pesos in Brazil, so it was very usual to pass trucks carrying huge drums heading for the border. Cars in Bolivia were three times the price of those in Brazil so it was a lucrative business smuggling them over the frontier and driving them during the night to Santa Cruz. But given the state of the road from Tunas to San Rafael it is a wonder that they arrived in one piece and were marketable.

I was surprised how often we were asked for medical advice, which I suppose is because we carry the title of doctor and the nearest medical one is often one to two hundred kilometres away. In Peter's area there was a nine year old girl with some sort of creeping paralysis. On the first day she had no feeling below her knees and by the next evening none below her waist. Her mother had six other children and her husband was away across the frontier, so it was impossible for her to make the two-day journey by camionetta to San José where there was a rather basic hospital, always supposing she could afford the drugs. Peter gave the girl some tetracycline which might help if it was just an infection, and as she went barefoot it could have been; it wouldn't do her harm anyway.

In 1980 Jevan Berrangé took over from Keith Bloomfield as head of the team mapping the northern zone of Proyecto Precámbrico. However, logistical difficulties in that region of trackless forest and swamp with no roads made it impossible to organise another sample collecting programme for me, so sadly I never went back to Bolivia. I subsequently made many other overseas trips, though not all under the auspices of the Overseas Division. Sleeping under the stars in the desert of northern Sudan certainly rivals sleeping in a hammock slung from two posts on an estancia forecourt. I even lived in a five star hotel while working in Hong Kong to the consternation of the reception staff who watched me go out in the morning looking quite presentable but return at the end of the day somewhat dishevelled and covered with rock dust. Even if there were many other people in the lobby, I never had to wait for my room key. However, nothing ever matched the exoticism and delight of that first visit to Bolivia. I count myself fortunate that the many good friends I made through working with the Overseas Division over the years remain so today.

Transports of Delight [1]
Barry Webb

There were two railway lines into and out of Santa Cruz, our base in Bolivia. I never used the one that went down to Paraguay and Argentina, but I have heard tales from those who did, of passengers being sent off into the jungle with machetes to restock the engine's wood supply when it ground to a halt miles from its destination.

The line that we used, eastwards to Brazil, was much more 'modern'. You had three trains to choose from and all were diesel powered. The fastest of these was the *Ferrobus*, which could get you to Brazil in a day. It was very aptly named being, indeed, a bus—an old US school bus mounted on iron train wheels. It was a strange vehicle to look at but the most efficient of the three at getting you to your destination.

El Tren

El Rápido, despite its name, was not particularly rapid. It did, however, have the expected appearance of a train with a normal engine and carriages. The cheapest and slowest of the three was *El Tren*. Although it pulled some passenger carriages it was, basically, a goods train and consequently very slow. It was quite possible, if you felt the need for exercise, to jump off it, jog alongside for a while and then get back on. Not only that, but it was also used for shunting duties at the various stations through which it passed. The net result was that you

---

1 The present and previous contributions provide lively and vivid accounts arising from the Eastern Bolivia Mineral Exploration Project. Proyecto Precámbrico, as it came to be called, was conducted over a ten-year period from 1976 to 1986 and was the largest and most ambitious undertaking by the IGS up to that time, involving the exploration of an area of Amazonian rainforest roughly the size of Great Britain. The terrain varied from remote and almost inaccessible jungle and swamp to mixed grassland, scrubland and deciduous forest, and included the almost legendary plateau of the Serranía Huanchaca—the inspiration for Conan Doyle's novel *The Lost World*.

couldn't guarantee to within a day or two when it would arrive at any particular destination.

The first time I encountered *El Tren* was at a small station between Santa Cruz and the next major town of San José. It was night and I was sitting on a log, a little way from the station, enjoying a beer and a cigarette. I gradually became aware of a rather disconcerting noise. There was a regular, somewhat drawn out roar accompanied by a lot of panting which was slowly getting louder. I jumped up and asked one of my Bolivian counterparts what on earth it might be. He didn't seem to be very sure but pointed to our right saying that he thought he could see something approaching. Yes, there was a yellowish glow intermittently visible between the trees. As the thing got nearer and the noise increased it was apparent that the roar and the yellow glow coincided. It soon became clear that it was a long tongue of flame being blasted forward from something still invisible. My God, it was a dragon! It couldn't be anything else. 'No', my counterpart laughed, 'It's *El Tren*' and so it was, although, in the dark, it was certainly the closest thing to a dragon that I have ever seen. It was very large and, being black, somewhat indefinite in shape. The firebox appeared to have been removed and the boiler was heated by blasting blazing diesel along the length of its under surface. The resulting roar and tongue of flame was worthy of any dragon.

By the time that I got to ride on *El Tren*, it had been given a slightly more modern engine with much less resemblance to a dragon. It was still, however, an experience. We had been working near the Brazilian border and, although we had driven there, the thought of driving back was far from appealing. Much better to put the Land Rover on a flat car and be pulled home by *El Tren*. We could travel back in the vehicle, on the flat car, or get seats in one of the carriages. We chose the latter but soon discovered that it was much too hot inside, even with the windows open, and the journey was going to take at least two days. Our driver, who occasionally went back to check the Land Rover on its flat car, said that it was cooler outside because the train's forward motion, although slow, did produce a bit of a breeze. We went out to see if this was the case. At the end of the carriage you were sheltered from the breeze but there was a ladder leading up onto the roof. Perhaps it would be better up there. I climbed up to see. It was like emerging into a separate reality. The train stretched ahead like a huge, curving snake and the slowly passing view of the flat semi desert and scrub with towering red cliffs off to the north was breathtaking. And

Ferrobus, a diesel-powered former school bus converted for railway use, Bolivia. (Photograph by B. C. Webb.)

there was a pleasant breeze. There were also a lot of people. Little groups sat here and there all along the carriage rooftops, chatting, drinking, playing cards or dice or just dozing in the sun. This was obviously the place to be. The carriages did sway slightly but with the train travelling so slowly it was not enough to throw one off balance. You could stroll along the whole length of the train stopping to chat here and there or share a beer. The views were stunning and the gentle breeze provided the ideal temperature. It might have been a slow journey but I count it as one of the best I've ever made.

Roads and Ruts

Much of our travel was by road. However, the jungle of eastern Bolivia was not your typical Amazon rain forest. It had a definite wet season when it became extensively flooded, so that travel by vehicle became impossible. As the wet season closed, the trees burst into flower, produced fruits and then shed their leaves in preparation for the dry times ahead. It didn't take long for the roads out of Santa Cruz to dry out and this was when we made our return to fieldwork. Unfortunately, the loggers could also get back to work and their large lorries, with chains fitted on their tyres, would invariably be the first vehicles on the move. The ruts they left in the roads were horrendous, well over knee deep.

For our first field season we were using Toyota Land Cruisers supplied by the Bolivians. Although these had much smaller wheels than the timber lorries, they had the same axle width. As a result, if the wheels on one side slipped into a rut, those on the other side dropped into its companion and you were suspended; the chassis grounded and the wheels spinning in the air, or water. With no winches, it was best to be in a team with two vehicles but that wasn't always possible. On your own, it was a matter of getting under the vehicle and chiselling out some of the central pillar of mud (iron hard if it was dry) and cutting down trees to pack under the wheels. Best, of course, not to fall in at all. If it was dry, you could attempt to straddle one rut but it only took one small damp patch and in you'd slide. If it was wet you'd just go at it as fast as possible and hope that when you did drop in, you'd toboggan to the far end. Sometimes you did and emerged to contemplate the next section. Sometimes you didn't. Sometimes you'd only manage a few hundred metres in an entire day.

The project Land Rovers, when they eventually arrived

A geologist's wife (Kate Webb) 'enjoying' the mud, eastern Bolivia (Photograph by B. C. Webb)

in Bolivia, were an improvement over the Toyotas, having a narrower axle width. If you dropped in one rut you didn't drop into the other and could still manage a modicum of forward power. The best things, however, were not the Land Rovers or their drum winches but the chain saws we carried in the back. Until we got those we were largely at the mercy of the jungle. I remember one spot where we were bogged down for over two days. Returning later, with chain saws, we cut a new road several hundred metres long around the obstacle. It took less than two hours! The jungle, which could trap you so completely if you were ill equipped, was, in reality, very fragile.

On Foot; Me and Other Animals

Moving around the forest or jungle on foot could provide some interesting moments as on the following memorable occasion whilst wending my way through the undergrowth.

I saw the snake as soon as I turned the corner. It was lying across the path. I couldn't see much of it; the path was only about half a metre wide and bordered by dense undergrowth. All the same, the beast was as thick as my thigh, so I guessed that there was a good deal of it on either side of the path. What to do? From its orange and yellow, roundish markings, and its girth, it must have been some sort of boa. They get up to around five metres in length and, although not poisonous, will happily attack and devour creatures much larger than me. It wasn't moving. Perhaps I could just step over it. Not really fancied, and anyway, that would mean Don Esquibel would come across it and blast the hell out of it with his .22. He was only behind me now because he'd stopped to shoot at some wretched creature he'd spied in a tree. While it was unlikely he'd hit it, he couldn't miss this poor snake. Maybe I should give it a kick; they're not supposed to attack humans—normally—but then perhaps not many humans kick them. Quandary!

The problem was solved a moment later by the arrival of Don Esquibel. Asked what we should do, he raised his rifle and 'Blam!' The next few moments were amazing. There appeared to be snake everywhere. Loops and coils swishing all around us and then . . . silence; just the path, the jungle and the two of us. Don Esquibel looked very satisfied. I realised that I might as well keep my thoughts to myself.

On another occasion I remember that my wife and I were sitting on the sofa listening to a record, probably sipping a Martini, when I thought I saw something scuttle under the cushion at the end. It seemed to have a lot of legs. We got off the sofa and I flicked the cushion onto the floor. A large orange centipede skittered off to safety beneath the sofa. It was the first of these that we had seen but we knew that they were venomous and could give you a very serious bite—not something you wanted lurking around the house. 'I'll get a bucket to catch it in', said my wife. 'Yes and a fork to poke it in with', I suggested. Once armed, we pulled back the sofa. The centipede, with nowhere else to go, started snaking up the wall. Holding the bucket below it, I tried to knock it off the wall with the fork. Horrors! Clinging to the wall with only its last few legs it rose up and snapped at me with huge black mandibles that appeared from under either side of its head. It was about seven inches long and the fork was clearly too short to deal with it safely. 'Get a broom', I squeaked. One was produced, the centipede knocked into the bucket and covered with the cushion. The whole lot was then flung out into the garden to be retrieved next morning, thankfully minus the centipede.

Food for Thought

At Open University summer schools there is often a quiz in which students have to guess which of the tutors had done some specified but seemingly unlikely act. Consequently, as a tutor at such schools you have to come up with something unusual that you have done. Overseas work could always be relied on to provide a suitable topic. One question to which I was the answer was, 'Which of the tutors ate his friend's guinea pig?' Not surprisingly, this always caused great consternation and, thankfully, I was not often the one they guessed had perpetrated this fiendish act. Roast guinea pig is, however, quite common market food in Bolivia. My children having kept an extremely ill-tempered example as a pet in the UK, I was quite happy to try one now that I had the chance. They are quite attractively served, being coated in a red chilli sauce and having their incisors hooked over the edge of the plate. I think that is what first put my friend Malcolm off. In fact, they turn out to be rather poor eating. There is very little flesh and, even with the chilli, it has little flavour. My friend decided that he didn't want his and so, since we had paid for them, I ate his as well. Not quite as fiendish an act as it appeared.

Navigation for Amateurs
Rob Evans

During the Bolivian Project Proyecto Precámbrico, a major igneous complex, Rincón del Tigre, was discovered in the jungle of eastern Bolivia, close to the border with Brazil. In 1978 a one-month geophysical survey was requested to help define the structure and mineralisation, and the survey was to be undertaken by myself. On my arrival at the project headquarters in Santa Cruz, the geology of the Rincón complex was explained over a few evening beers by one of the IGS geologists and I was provided with a preliminary geological map of the complex.

Next morning a small plane was waiting at the Santa Cruz airport, together with a Bolivian pilot and counterpart Bolivian geologist who was to accompany me for geophysical training. I climbed aboard and put the delicate geophysical instruments beside me. Soon after take-off from Santa Cruz and bound for Rincón, over three hundred miles to the east, it became apparent that the flight was going to be mainly over featureless jungle. Some two hours into the flight I heard the pilot and my counterpart discussing the location of Rincón, where, I now realised, they had never been before. To my considerable dismay, they asked me, 'Which way is it to Rincón?' At that moment I just wished I had paid more attention to the previous night's discussions!

It seemed I had no option but to use the preliminary geological map as a means of navigation. The jungle below looked remarkably impenetrable and featureless, but eventually, scanning the horizon in all directions, I saw a ridge far to the south-east. Was the pilot off-course and north of out intended flight path? There seemed no option other than to change direction towards the ridge, although aviation fuel was now very low, and there was no sign of any place to land safely.

Fortunately when the ridge was reached it was possible to identify it on the geological map, and the map and its topographical features were followed until the large water tower of the mission station airstrip at Rincón was seen. The pilot landed safely on the bumpy strip with the fuel gauge close to zero. Fortunately drums of aviation fuel for refuelling beside the airstrip had already been arranged. The pilot then took off and headed back to Santa Cruz once a date had been agreed with him for his return to Rincón in a month or so, when he would take me back to the project headquarters.

I took the instrumentation to the foot of the water tower to establish the base stations for geophysical work. I noticed that the water tower carried an inscription 'Bienvenidos a Rincón del Tigre, Cristo la Única Esperanza' which translated means 'Welcome to the Corner of the Tiger, Christ is the Only Hope.' After my perilous flight I was not going to dispute these words, neither with the mission priest nor the IGS geologist who had arrived to meet me.

One month later with the survey completed I was waiting on the mission airstrip for the return plane, but this time the pilot flew too far to the south, closer to the railway line from Brazil, and never found Rincón at all! I therefore had to make my way back with the delicate instruments on a bumpy overland journey to El Carmen railway station in order to catch the next train from Brazil overnight to Santa Cruz. Mission accomplished.

A Map and a Monkey
Richard Johnson

In early 1978 I spent a couple of months in India based in Bhopal from where a joint British–Indian team was assessing the groundwater potential of the Betwa Valley. The majority of the team undertaking the Betwa project were residential. My role as photogeologist was to make a reconnaissance geological map of the whole project area using air photographs supported by a limited amount of field checking. It had been arranged that I would stay with the Team Leader, Howard Versey, in the suburban house rented for him by the project. He was a Leeds graduate and the son of Dr H. C. Versey, a member of staff in the Geology Department at Leeds when I was an undergraduate. For the first week I stayed in a hotel, as Howard's house was being redecorated. The hotel was a former maharaja's guest house with marble floors throughout and a marble tiled bathroom. The only problem was that it took well over an hour from ordering to serving dinner. However, this difficulty was overcome by ordering a couple of hours in advance. I subsequently discovered that someone was sent to the market to buy the appropriate provisions after I had ordered!

Bhopal had outgrown its infrastructure and both the electricity and water supply were unreliable. Our house had a tank in the basement that filled when the water was on, and from which water was pumped to a further tank on the roof when electricity was available. In rocky places the mains water was laid above ground, and local women would take advantage of leaks in such spots to do their washing, which was then spread out on the rocks to dry. In general, electric wiring had an improvised look about it: thus an overhead power cable and telephone wire crossed at right angles over the street in front of the house. To prevent the two touching, a brick was tied to the lower at the crossing point!

There had been some delay in my departure from the UK as our host organisation had to obtain security clearance for a foreigner to look at the air photos. Permission was given on the basis that they would only be available to me in the presence of a counterpart and, in his absence, they were locked away in a steel cabinet to which I did not have a key. The Betwa area is in the middle of India away from any sensitive borders. As usual, when national security is believed to be at stake, common sense does not prevail.

Field excursions were made accompanied by my Indian counterpart to check the air photo interpretations. Preparation for such a trip meant dealing with Indian bureaucracy. Changing money at a bank involved visiting several desks in turn, in the nether regions of the building, in order to obtain the necessary document to present to the front of house cashier. Topping up the oil in an official vehicle involved the driver taking it to a government depot where the amount of oil to be purchased was determined and a requisition issued. This was taken to a private sector garage where the oil was added; the vehicle was then driven back to the depot, where a check was made to ensure that the correct amount of oil had been supplied. Assuming all the personnel concerned were in place, this process took half a day.

We stayed at government guest houses which provided simple, clean accommodation. A resident cook was given money to buy provisions from which to prepare our meal. I saw a pencilled list of what he had bought, with the price of each item. The spices were itemised by the number of leaves or seeds purchased!

Travelling through rural areas in India invited comparisons with Africa. Colourful Hindu shrines and temples were ubiquitous and walking through the bush one commonly came across the ruins of ancient structures of Hindu or Mogul origin with elaborate carved stonework reflecting the longer, more diverse cultural history of the country. The contrast between rich and poor appeared starker than in Africa. Villagers looked less well-dressed, housed and fed than their equivalent in central Africa. Labour was clearly cheap: I saw a new motorway embankment being constructed; the earthen material was being carried by a long line of sari-clad women with baskets on their heads.

Towards the end of my stay in Bhopal I had an outbreak of athlete's foot between my toes. My previous experience was that the best remedy for the condition was to expose the affected parts to the sun and air. Accordingly, on several Sunday mornings I sat on the front veranda of the house, reading a large book I had borrowed, with my feet in the sun and some white pebbles between my toes to improve ventilation. The Hindus next door noted this Sunday procedure and asked Howard Versey whether it was some Christian ritual!

I was never quite happy about the map that I produced for this project—my timetable did not allow for enough fieldwork to check the photo interpretation. The only local reaction to my work came when a monkey entered an open office window and urinated on the finished map!

On Wearing Two Hats
Richard Johnson

Politics and Diplomacy

In late 1978 I was seconded to Malawi as head of the Geological Survey Department where I subsequently served for two tours, with a period of home leave in between, finally returning to IGS in 1983.

Sometime before my arrival, the Malawi government had abolished the title of 'director' for its heads of departments and re-titled them 'chiefs' on the basis that ministers gave directions and civil servants carried them out. This caused some confusion internationally as 'director of Geological Survey' is a recognised post in government circles while 'chief geologist' is more ambiguous. Internally it was fine, in particular because junior staff, who would be uncomfortable in using my Christian name, simply addressed me as 'Chief'. I quite enjoyed sitting in the middle of Africa and being so styled. I should add that some visiting IGS staff also used this mode of address, but not so respectfully! Another change enacted at this time was that each 'permanent secretary' became a 'principal secretary' (conveniently maintaining the abbreviation PS) to remind them that they were anything but permanent.

As a seconded officer I was part of the Malawi Civil Service and for most of the time the PS to whom I was responsible was a Malawian. The Geological Survey was staffed entirely by Malawians except for Mike Crow (assistant chief, also seconded from IGS). Early in my second tour he was replaced by James Chatupa, who was clearly destined to take over from me. So at the end I was an ethnic minority of one in the chain of command!

The process of replacing expatriate geologists with those of Malawian origin had been achieved gradually following the country's independence from British rule in 1964. An interesting document, which I discovered amongst office files dating back to colonial times, was a minute issued by the Governor of Nyasaland shortly after the end of the Second World War. This said something on the following lines: 'Now that hostilities have ended it is being suggested, in some quarters, that the British Empire should be broken up and the colonies should be granted self-government. However misguided this might seem, the possibility should be borne in mind, and civil servants should attempt to create good relationships with those members of the local population they may come into contact with.' This far-sighted observation, which I suspect originated in London, was made many years before Harold Macmillan's 1960 'Wind of Change' speech.

The Geological Survey was one of a handful of government departments which still had its headquarters in the former colonial capital Zomba. All ministries and most departments had, in the 1970s, moved to the new capital Lilongwe, some 170 miles by road to the northwest. During my first two-year tour the Geological Survey came under the Ministry of Agriculture and Natural Resources and had as its minister, His Excellency the Life President Dr Hastings Kamuzu Banda or HE for short. Dr Banda combined his presidential duties with holding this portfolio. Later, Natural Resources was split off and had its own minister while the president continued to hold the Agriculture portfolio.

In Malawi 'the Government' meant the president, who could best be described as a benevolent dictator, though his benevolence only extended to those who supported him and carried out his wishes. The country was a one-party state. The candidates for election to parliament were chosen by him and, in any case, parliament only met once or twice a year for a couple of weeks at a time. Speeches made by parliamentarians were largely words in praise of his policies along with statements on how their constituents benefited from them. His rule could be compared with that of a mediaeval king where loyalty to the king was the supreme virtue amongst the barons: if they showed signs of becoming too powerful they were imprisoned, or worse.

Rather surprisingly I found that being an expatriate scientific civil servant, under the above-described system of government, a quite comfortable experience bearing in mind that the worst that could happen to me was to be sent back to London. There were two advantages of the system. Firstly, the president, as a former medical doctor, had a scientific background: he expected each PS to be fully informed on the scientific and technical matters which fell within his remit and to be able to explain them to him in language that he could understand. Consequently, they were obliged to seek advice on a regular basis from their departments. The scientific community had considerably more influence on government policy than in some countries. Secondly, major decisions were made by him alone—quickly—and were binding on the whole of the government machine. One did not have to wait for committees to sit or councils to meet.

Communication with the minister involved deploying a memo. These missives were always 'deployed' as if they were a platoon of infantry! Memo writing was something of an art: they had to be less than two pages long, free of abstruse technical jargon and written in good English. Due to HE's respect for the classics, long non-technical words of classical origin, or better still, Latin phrases were approved of. One could usually work in phrases such as a *sine qua non* or *inter alia*. In one memo that I drafted, I had written 'miniscule' instead of 'minuscule'. A deputy secretary rang me up and said that he could not find the aforementioned word in his dictionary and had I got it right? My mistake caused some hilarity as short skirts were disapproved of in Malawi. I suggested that he could replace it by 'minor' but he said, 'No, minuscule is the sort of word the president would like!'

Another memo that I drafted concerned a politically sensitive project for the development of a cement works in the north of the country. I had to explain that the viability of the project was dependant on the availability of rocks with a high calcium carbonate to magnesium carbonate ratio. The memo was referred back to our ministry from the office of the president with a request that the words calcium carbonate and magnesium carbonate be put in layman's language! I pointed out that, as a former medical doctor, the president would be familiar with these terms. The memo went forward as I had written it.

The Trouble with Consultants

The government of Malawi at this time had little interest in funding further geological mapping. Malawi was one of the few countries in the world with a complete set of modern geological maps thanks to the efforts of a dedicated series of British geologists in the closing years of colonial rule. However, the Ministry of Trade and Industry (MTI) wished to upgrade certain mineral based industries, which were then being undertaken on a small scale by traditional methods, including brick-making, lime burning and pottery. They also wished to begin the manufacture of glass bottles, in which they had little or no technical capabilities, and came to us for information on the raw materials. We had limited specific knowledge on industrial minerals but they had requested, through various aid agencies, a series of consultants. We found space in our office for the visitors and so their expertise was passed on to ourselves rather than to the MTI. Industrial mineral investigations thus became an important part of our field programme.

Because of the limited amount of specialised knowledge available in the country, the use of outside consultants, usually funded by aid agencies, was widespread throughout government. In my dealings with such consultants I was very much aware that although I was in the country as part of an aid package I now had to wear the hat of the host country. Such consultants were a mixed blessing. Firstly, because of the lengthy bureaucratic procedures involved in requesting and identifying a suitable consultant, the Terms of Reference (TOR) might not be appropriate by the time he arrived. Secondly, because they were necessarily drawn up by non-experts, the first thing that the visitor might point out were deficiencies in his TOR. With some agencies it was possible, at this late stage, to agree to modify them but with others the consultant had to stick to his brief to the letter, otherwise he would not get paid. A third difficulty was when a consultant had only one solution in mind and was travelling around the world looking for a problem which fitted it.

Consultants could be of any nationality. I saw a draft of a report by a UN expert who referred to the Geological Survey Department as having been headed by a series of notorious geologists! The expert was of French nationality—he had mistranslated the French 'notable'.

An example of the arrival of a one-solution consultant arose out of a request by the MTI for assistance in upgrading the efficiency of lime burning, the consultant again being based in our office. In Malawi lime burning was carried out on a very small scale. Individual lime burners fired a heap of limestone and wood fuel on a stone base and shovelled out the ensuing burnt lime. This was labour-intensive—not regarded as a bad thing in Malawi. The main concern was that it was very wasteful of fuel.

However, rather than attempting to up-grade the operations of the individual lime-burners the consultant proposed a single semi-industrial kiln which would replace all the artisanal activities. The lime-burners got wind of this and one morning a lorry load of them, dressed in their Sunday best, crowded into my office—it was standing room only—and delivered a polite but firm protest. As promised I passed their views to the MTI. I heard nothing more about the proposal.

The preference for labour intensive solutions mentioned above, though political in part, was based mainly on sound economics—labour was cheap. My journeys along the main road from Zomba to Lilongwe passed a point where a slowly moving landslip had developed on the slope overlooking one side of the road. A small group of men were permanently employed to use shovels and a couple of wheel barrows to remove the offending, quite soft, material before it encroached on the tarmac. They had to wheel it across the road and tip it down the bank on the other side. We were asked by the Ministry of Works (or was it Transport ?) to look at the problem together with one of their engineers. The study concluded that it was less costly to continue with the present arrangement than to embark on major remedial works, bearing in mind that the weathered rock which was the source of the slip would eventually be exhausted. When I visited Malawi in 2006 the slippage had indeed ceased but the site was marked by a large lay-by, developed on top of the many hundreds of tonnes of material which had been wheeled across the road.

My PS, who was originally chief veterinary officer, told me a story which encapsulated some of his reservations about consultants and in particular his preference for people, like me, who *did* things, rather than transients who merely advised on what others should do. It also illustrates the importance of drawing up proper terms of reference. Appropriately, the story concerns farm animals. A certain African country wished to improve its national cattle herd by importing a bull. The request for assistance went through the usual channels: the originating department, its parent ministry, the Ministry of Foreign Affairs, the local office of the UN Food and Agriculture Organisation (FAO) and, finally, into the FAO bureaucracy. After the appropriate committees had sat, the donation of the bull was approved, a suitable animal was identified and, at long last, shipped. It was received with acclamation by the beneficiary country and introduced to eligible cows and heifers. After a few months had passed there were no signs of any offspring being on the way. In response to a further request, sent through the above-mentioned channels, an FAO expert arrived to investigate the non-performance of the bull. The expert reprimanded the bull for his lack of activity. The bull said, 'I'm sorry, sir, but my terms of reference clearly state that I am here in an advisory, rather than an executive, capacity.'

Witchcraft

In spite of the fact that a high percentage of the population are regular church attenders, witchcraft and traditional healers were widely respected in Malawi. When one of my professional staff became a father for the first time, his mother-in-law wished to use traditional methods to improve the well-being of the baby. He told me that he had allowed her to tie to the baby good luck charms to keep evil spirits away but had insisted on a nil-by-mouth policy over traditional remedies. He later told me that he was unhappy that, when relatives were looking after the child in his absence, they gave her antibiotics for a common cold. He was trying to defend his child against potentially harmful traditional medicines on the one hand, and unnecessary modern ones on the other.

I did not normally have to deal with sick-notes, but one that was sent up to me was from a traditional healer, or witch-doctor, written in pencil on a scrap of paper. It said that one of the Accounts staff should move away from Zomba as the area had become unhealthy for him. My Malawian staff interpreted this as meaning that the accountant believed he was being bewitched by someone in the vicinity. I sent the note to the Accountant General with a covering minute saying that I had no objection to his being transferred providing he was immediately replaced. The transfer happened within days!

The most bizarre story relating to witchcraft occurred towards the end of my time in Malawi. We were told by our servants of a couple living in or near Blantyre where the wife had obtained a potion from a witch-doctor intended to increase her husband's affection for her. She was instructed to put it into the water in which her husband was bathing and then leave without turning back and looking at him. This, I was reliably informed, is a fairly standard story. However, she did look back, whereupon he turned into a snake with only his head unchanged. He was taken to the main hospital in Blantyre where he died, and his corpse was transferred to the National Museum and put on display. This tale spread like wildfire in Zomba and, I suspect, throughout the country. Even some of my professional staff were inclined to believe the story. To quote one of them: 'Something must have happened.' Note that this account was spread by word of mouth—nothing appeared in the media. This episode invites reflection on the reliability of hearsay evidence especially when it concerns 'miracles' or other supernatural phenomena.

A few years after I left Malawi, I attended a conference on African geology at St Andrews in Scotland. The conference dinner was modelled on a Burns Night festivity—the Haggis was piped in, addressed and stabbed; Tam o' Shanter was recited. One of the African delegates turned to me and said, 'Scottish missionaries come out to Africa and tell us that witchcraft is bad and should be abandoned; so what is all this?'

Rifles and Red Faces [1]
Russell Arthurton

Baluchistan is harsh country—a desert of bare rock, alluvial fans and saltpans, with sand dunes fed by windstorms from neighbouring Afghanistan. Yet it is home to a proud and hospitable people.

My sentry at Mashki Chah, a day's rough drive west of Quetta, was the *kadkhoda*—the village headman, with whom I could communicate in Farsi, the Persian language. He took it upon himself to guard my mud brick house through the night, squatting in his *pakolhat* and baggy brown *shalvar* trousers, rifle at the ready. Sitting cross-legged has never come easily to me, but it was *de rigueur* for our formal meals.

Breakfast consisted of *chapattis* with vegetable curry left over from the day before. My charming companions, mindful of my possible homesickness in that remote place, produced a jar of James Keiller's Dundee marmalade as a special treat. Evenings in our desert camps followed a strict and hallowed protocol. After dinner, sharp on eight o'clock, a bearer arrived carrying the transistor radio with 'Lilly Bolero' presaging the BBC news. After the news, the bearer reappeared, this time with the pack of cards for the evening's bridge. To my great embarrassment, I found myself an absolute beginner amongst grand masters.

Safeguarding vehicles' fuels supplies was a constant worry for the survey team. In the desert there was a ready market for any 'surplus' that our drivers seemed to have carefully estimated. Miscalculations were not unknown, stranded drivers insisting that consumption had mysteriously rocketed.

The little towns of Chagai District were served by a railway

---

1 Between 1977 and 1985, IGS undertook a range of short-term advisory visits to provide expertise and training to local counterparts in Pakistan. Russell Arthurton was sent for a two-month visit in 1978, and again in 1979, to assist the Geological Survey in field mapping in the Chagai District of Baluchistan.

link, constructed in 1917 between Quetta and the city of
Zahedan in southeastern Iran. It carried two or three trains a
week in each direction. The train trip must surely have been the
most comfortable means of crossing this rugged terrain, as the
road was dusty, rutted and corrugated. One section, recently
'engineered' at considerable expense, had been washed away by
flash flooding, its design no match for the deluges to which it was
periodically exposed.

One evening our team went to Dalbandin to meet the head
of the Geological Survey off the train from Quetta. He had come

Our hosts outside the IGS quarters at Maski Chah, Chagai District, Pakistan. The village
headman is second from the left. (Photograph by R. S Arthurton.)

to carry out a field inspection. We headed back to camp along
a winding dirt road as night was falling. Red tail lights showed
that our lead vehicle, which was carrying stores and equipment,
had stopped ahead of us. It had been ambushed by a unit of
the Chagai militia, assuming that our convoy was part of some
smuggling operation. Seven rifle rounds had been fired at the car,
fortunately missing the driver.

An interesting discussion followed in the glow of headlights, rifles now at rest. I picked up some of this—professional people in Pakistan speak an interwoven tongue of English and Urdu. The officer in charge of the militia unit, who had a rather low grade in the civil service scale, implored the head of the Survey, somewhere near the top of the scale, to save his skin by keeping the incident off the record. I never discovered the outcome.

Possession and Protection
Bob Addison

On reflection, I think the most remarkable feature of the East Kalimantan Coal Project in Indonesia (1978–81) was the phenomenal provision of material aid. Three English Drilling Corporation (EDCO) rigs, rods and bits, each capable of drilling five hundred metres into the Miocene coal-bearing strata, had been provided. The other remarkable aspect was the huge provision of counterpart staff from the Directorate of Mineral Resources, based at Bandung. EDCO provided two very experienced drillers to commission the rigs but the Indonesian geologists and drillers proved more than capable of handling the work once the commissioning had taken place.

The Indonesians built us a timber construction base camp from scratch, about twenty kilometres south of Samarinda, beside the Samarinda Balikpapan Highway. The lasting legacy is now a village, I'm told, called UKRI which still uses the project huts, though occupied mainly by 'professional girls'.

There were a few cultural eye-openers. We had a team of local support staff including cooks and wash girls as well as staff brought in from Bandung to earn some field allowance. One chap, the accounts clerk, obviously found it all too much as he fell under the spell of being 'possessed' on a couple of occasions. Luckily the cook was a Dukun (Medicine) lady from Sumatra and was able to extract him from his trance on the first occasion. On the second occasion he was discovered in the middle of the night, stark naked, trying to climb through the window of the screaming Julie, a wash girl from Flores. Once again the Dukun was able to restore the 'possessed' accountant to normality, and he was sent back to Bandung in disgrace. It is sad to report that he was later seen manning a *becak* (bike rickshaw) in Bandung, his accounting career having been brought to an untimely end.

Possession was quite widely discussed in Bandung. The common belief was that men would transform into wereboars when the moon was full. Black and white magic was also common practice among the house staff in Bandung too. Some teachers who were neighbours of myself and Jean and Barrie Page (Barrie was managing a separate IGS project in Sumatra) found chicken heads strung in the back of their pick-up and were told it was to protect them from motor accidents! A nice gesture. Towards the end of my time my mattress was scattered with white crystals as a means of guaranteeing my return after the end of the project.

Obviously such safeguards were a useful additional insurance policy. But the worst aspect of the work in Indonesia was the need to take frequent flights, operated by local air-carriers, between Balikpapan and Jakarta. There were too many air accidents for real peace of mind. On one trip I was sitting in the row next to the emergency exit and I noticed that the cover over the emergency handle had slipped out of place. I pointed this out to the air hostess who stuck it back with a piece of masking tape—as you would! Oddly enough the plane then seemed to descend. But the most chilling aspect was that as we came in to land in Balikpapan, the window/emergency door dropped inwards by about a centimetre. Obviously it had never really been secure at all—it had been held in place by the air pressure in the cabin. During the journey I had noticed a couple sitting opposite who appeared particularly unnerved by the whole incident. The gentleman was manager of the Hilton hotel in Balikpapan. To allay their fears they switched to another airline on their next trip out, and were both killed when the plane crashed.

Ancestral Voices
Nick Cameron

My Overseas Division career was mainly spent in Indonesia where I was a participant in the Integrated Geological Survey of Northern Sumatra project in which I was involved from 1976 to 1981. Possibly my memory of that time has faded, but I do not recollect too many untoward things happening. Indeed life in the field was pretty unremarkable with more dramatic events seemingly occurring in the daily lives of our wives back in Bandung. What problems we had arose from the lack of field work experience by our counterparts and, more especially, by the people they hired, since most Sumatrans had no need to venture far from their homes and did not really need Javanese wages.

My recollection is of life bumbling along without too much incident. Indeed I look back with considerable pleasure in the camaraderie and support everyone provided and regard the Sumatran field work as one of the best things I have done. Not for a moment did I feel unsafe, though this was not always the case for our fellow Indonesians as there was a deep fear of the supernatural. On one occasion a counterpart geologist was lost and we all went out looking for him as night fell. We spread out along different tracks calling to each other. Despite soon finding tiger tracks over his presumed footprints, the real worry was not whether he had been eaten, but whether some of the 'human' voices were in fact spirits calling them to their doom. Even I could sense what was going on as the calling voices became ever more frantic. Fortunately, there were no spirits about that night and everyone returned safely. The missing geologist was found the next morning, having slept in a hut quite unaware of the previous evening's drama. As to whether the *orang asli* (the original peoples of Sumatra) exist, and whether they would be friendly if met, we never found out. But they certainly caused alarm.

We also had problems when a counterpart geologist was bitten by a tiny ant and reacted strongly, coming up in a few moments in huge lumps and then quickly becoming delirious. This was

Field party at Pelang, ready to depart for a three-day traverse to Pameue, northern Sumatra. (Photograph by N. R. Cameron.)

a bit tricky given that we were so far from anywhere. And then it started raining. The remedy, which fortunately worked, was to set camp (never an easy task) and make him hot sugary tea. Thereafter, I always brought a supply of adrenaline for him, provided by the Hospital of Tropical Diseases. I wanted to ban him from the field, but they needed their field allowances. He survived without further incident.

There were also occasional encounters with venomous snakes, such as on my first day in the field when a cobra swam down a stream towards us and was quickly killed, only to find another snake inside it! I also once discovered a snake in my tent while listening to the Overseas BBC. What to do? Simple, I was told. Put a magnet next to it and it will go away. No such thing happened. Our tents were small and not easy to get out of, but on this occasion I managed to make a hasty exit, which was a lucky escape as we were in a very remote location.

Our Sumatran field crew were great fishermen and since the rivers in interior Aceh (the northernmost province of Sumatra) were full of fish, evening meals invariably consisted of fresh fried fish as good as in any fine restaurant, along with rice and young fern shoots (always a bit worrisome as we had to trust the gatherers knew what they were collecting). But our clothes the next day, as they were dried on the same fire, were always a bit fishy.

Finally there was the geology. Three finds were especially memorable. Once when hammering dull looking metasediments on the west side of Lake Toba, a whole load of what looked like cogs and gear wheels fell out. What were they? Had I found

Sampling concentrate for gold at Pameue, central Aceh, Sumatra. (Photograph by N. R. Cameron.)

a pre-human civilisation? Reality kicked in when I recognised that they were loose, disarticulated crinoid stems (sea lilies). They proved however to be a new find and could be tied to rocks of Permian age in Malaysia. The second event was hitting equally dull looking rocks, this time in a river bank in the rain as it was getting dark, and finding that they consisted of pure copper and lead sulphides, chalcopyrite, galena, etc. The last memorable discovery happened while in the company of IGS colleague, John Aspden. We rounded a corner in West Sumatra and realised, after seeing red cherts, that we had found the southern continuation of the Aceh ophiolite succession.

Sumatra geology was like that, since so many areas had never been visited before. Some of the work I was involved in has had lasting consequences in that gold mineralisation has subsequently been prospected, albeit in primary jungle. But this once remote area, which took us several days of walking to reach, is becoming more readily accessible as primary jungle falls victim to palm oil plantations.

THE 1980s: CHALLENGING TERRAINS

The Admirable Qualities
of an Overseas Division Geologist
Arthur E. Stephens

This is my last stint as editor of the *Overseas Newsletter*,[1] a publication which over the past fourteen years had the sole merit of a weight/lift ratio so precisely defined that if held in the left hand top corner between thumb and forefinger it can be floated accurately fifteen feet straight into the wastepaper basket.

Fifteen years as a unit head have provided ample time to observe the main characteristics of the gentlemen who serve overseas with Overseas Division. They are initiative, a stoic acceptance of the inevitable and an innate kindliness. All three were well exemplified in a report originally published in the newsletter some ten years ago and repeated here for the benefit and moral uplift of those who have joined the Division since then.

At that time one of our chaps was staying in a Vientiane

1 In January 1969 the first edition of a quarterly *Overseas Division Newsletter* appeared and was sent to all Division geologists serving overseas. The aim was to keep staff informed of developments both at home and abroad, and for the first fourteen years its editor was Arthur E. Stephens, the head of the Division's Photogeology Unit. In the last of the fifty-two editions he edited, he included the following anecdote, written in his characteristically self-effacing style.

hotel. He phoned down to the desk to ask for a pot of tea to be sent up to his room and then went for a swim in the pool. When he returned to his room he found that there had been a mix-up in the orders; there was no pot of tea but in its place and in his bed there was a personable and stark naked young woman. At this point our colleague amply demonstrated those characteristics of which we are all so proud. He showed initiative by not batting an eyelid, he stoically accepted the inevitable, and before doing so demonstrated his innate kindliness by giving a passing thought to the unfortunate chap elsewhere in the hotel who had received the pot of tea.

Overseas Division Newsletter
No. 52, April 1983

Tribal Tales
Roger Key

The Samburu–Marsabit Project (1980–86) involved the geological mapping of a large part of Kenya to the north of the equator as far as the Ethiopian border and between Lake Turkana in the west and the Somali border in the east. The IGS team comprised Brian Hackman as project leader, with Tim Charsley, Al Wilkinson and myself as geologists, John Ridgway as the geochemist and Gary Wood as cartographer. We were joined by counterparts from the Kenyan Geological Survey as we were also expected to provide training as part of the work programme.

An abiding memory of these seven years was the outstanding beauty of the landscape. We mapped the northern part of the great East African Rift Valley, with spectacular descents into the main valley and ascents of conical volcanic peaks. We traversed great river systems to the east of the Rift Valley and climbed the many summits of the Ndoto mountain range. Then there were the large shield volcanoes of northern Kenya including the Marsabit volcano with its forest cover and protected elephants; and Mount Kulal with one-thousand-metre-high narrow ravines on its eastern side, carved by the monsoon rains sweeping in from the Indian Ocean. The northern slopes of Mount Kenya straddled the southern edge of the mapping area. Three of us climbed to the lower summit of this mountain carrying our own gear and food. Altogether it was an absolute joy working on this project.

Airborne

The residential team, along with their families, was based in Nairobi, and field work took place during trips of up to six weeks in the field areas. Fieldwork commenced in 1980 in three areas close to Nairobi, which permitted access by road. However, it became apparent that helicopter support would be needed in order to complete the mapping of the northern map sheets within the time frame of the project. The British High Commission office in Nairobi had to be convinced that the extra expense this entailed was justified. To do this a trial helicopter flight was arranged from Nairobi into northern Kenya for senior High Commission staff and the Project Leader. To demonstrate the ability of a helicopter to land in all kinds of terrain the pilot landed his craft on top of a peak at the northern end of the Ndoto Mountains. Everyone disembarked and one of the High Commission men jumped out of the helicopter straight onto a snake which, fortunately, rapidly disappeared into the nearest undergrowth. The trip succeeded in convincing the High Commission that helicopter support was essential to the success of the project.

Air support started with a large, modern helicopter and an ex-British Army pilot who was a veteran of the recent Falkland Islands War. He could literally land the helicopter anywhere that had clearance for the rotor blades. The pilot stayed in our field camp, along with my wife and our youngest daughter, although he didn't really approve of families in the bush. We had drums of aviation fuel in the camp which were to be guarded by the camp cook. One day a small boy from the local village came into the camp leading an old man who appeared to be blind. It transpired that our cook had been siphoning off the aviation fuel and selling it as home-made alcohol to the village men. Our helicopter pilot was not impressed and that was the end of the cook.

For the final period of fieldwork there was not enough money to pay for the large helicopter, so a smaller helicopter was hired. This was a two-man machine that had crashed and been re-built by its young Swedish pilot. It was used in the mapping of the area along the Ethiopian border. At that time there was almost continuous fighting between the different tribes whose traditional tribal areas extended across the border. To combat this, the Kenya Army had posted troops along the border. On one occasion as we flew over an army camp a surface-to-air missile was fired at us and the pilot had to swerve to avoid the missile which slammed into a cliff face behind the helicopter. We made an emergency landing in the camp, only to be approached by an apologetic officer who told us one of his men had pressed the wrong button!

Local People

Fieldwork was mostly done from camps sited close to a village or town. Field assistants and camp labourers were recruited locally so that local communities would receive some immediate benefit from the project. Much of the southern part of the project was in the tribal lands of the Samburu people, who are fiercely independent and proud of their traditional lifestyle. They were wonderfully knowledgeable about the landscape and wildlife, and our traverses would be accompanied by my Samburu assistants singing their chant-like local songs. Wilfred Thesiger, the famous British explorer, was living in the local community (at Maralal) and he helped us to integrate with the Samburu people. We had local tribesmen as camp guards, more to keep out wildlife than thieves. One morning, we heard a lion roaring as it approached our camp. Everyone dived into their tents, apart from our Samburu guard who calmly sat by the camp fire holding his large spear. The lion walked right through the camp ignoring the guard and everything else. Afterwards we asked the guard why he was not afraid. He replied that he could tell from the lion's roar that he had just eaten a zebra and his tummy was full.

In the northern half of the project area, the local people (including the Samburu and Turkana people) retained with great pride their traditional nomadic lifestyles and customs. These people walked across northern Kenya with their livestock in search of the best grazing provided by seasonal rains. Isolated hand-dug wells were a common source of water. During one traverse in the Kaisut Desert I could hear a strong whistling sound and asked our local guides about this. They said that they usually avoided the area because of the sound. We approached its source and found that it was caused by air being expelled through fissures in basaltic lavas. It was clear that there must be an underground river that was forcing air out of the ground. Mount Kulal is a large shield volcano on the western side of the Kaisut Desert. The steep eastern side of the volcano has one-thousand-metre-deep ravines gouged by torrential rains brought in by trade winds that sweep across the generally flat desert landscape of northern Kenya from the Indian Ocean. Mount Kulal is the first large mountain met by these west-directed trade winds and is where most of the rainfall is concentrated. The rainwater percolates into the porous basaltic bedrock without flowing over the land as a surface river. In my report I mentioned that there was a potentially large source of underground water beneath the Kaisut Desert, but rather hoped that my observation might be overlooked as this could potentially change the nomadic lifestyle of the Turkana people who clearly did not want to abandon their traditional way of life.

There were dangers in mapping in the northern part of the area because of frequent clashes between local tribes, mostly over cattle rustling, and a general mistrust of outsiders, especially government officials. As our field vehicles had Nairobi number plates and Kenya government logos we were initially treated with suspicion when we met local people. In most cases, once we had explained what we were trying to do, we received the full support of local communities. However, I did break camp after only one night near a settlement on the eastern shore of

Dug-out canoe on the edge of Lake Turkana, Kenya, which was used to gain access to North Island. (Photograph by R. M. Key.)

Lake Turkana very close to the Ethiopian border. Six months previously, an American missionary had been murdered in the village and there was a distinctly bad atmosphere about the place which was unsettling.

Paddling Someone Else's Canoe

In order to get to North Island at the northern end of Lake Turkana, I had to hire a dug-out canoe from local fishermen as the helicopter was not allowed to fly over water. The canoe was very large which is a necessity as the lake is well known for sudden storms and large waves. Unfortunately, my canoe only had a 2 hp outboard motor which made for a very slow journey to the island, especially as it was not a calm day. After several hours we arrived at the island just as a fisherman was being dragged out of the water with a badly damaged leg sustained after being attacked by one of the lake's large crocodiles. On the return journey to the mainland the outboard stopped so we had to paddle the canoe most of the way. Though the geology of the island proved fascinating, I was glad to get back at the end of a very long day.

Fair Game

There were several national game parks in the project area. Each day we had to tell the senior game warden exactly where we were planning to work, and we had Kenyan government soldiers as armed guards. One day, we were traversing a dry river bed in the Samburu National Park when we were shot at by the park's wardens from the river bank. Shooting stopped when they spotted a white man (myself) in our party. We were told to lie in the sand as the wardens approached. We explained what we were doing and that we had told the senior warden about our work. Unfortunately the senior warden had gone into town without passing our message on to his staff. Meanwhile, some tourists, seeing us walking up the river and mistaking us for poachers, had informed the nearest wardens, who had tracked us down. Fortunately no-one had been shot in our party.

Observing the wildlife whilst mapping often provided the highlight of a day's work. There were frequent sightings of large herds of elephant, buffalo, various antelopes and the several large cats. In a well-known incident the eminent British geologist, Robert Shackleton, who mapped part of the project area in the 1940s, had been badly gored by a rhinoceros and had reported the constant menace of these animals during his mapping. We had been asked to look out for rhinoceros but we never saw a single one during the entire field campaign.

The Goat Incident
Tim Charsley

In 1984 the BGS Samburu–Marsabit project team, of which I was a part [see previous account by Roger Key], had reached the northward limit of the mapping area and I was working to complete the Laisamis 1:250,000 map sheet. On 27 July 1984, I set off north from Nairobi in my Land Rover with my family (Tricia and my sons, Jonathan aged eleven and Drew aged eight, along with our dog, Chips). I had a camp set up at Ngurunit close to an unoccupied UNESCO camp. We settled fairly quickly into camp routine, with me traversing from about 7 am to about 2 pm, after which it became too hot to work. Meanwhile, the boys did some school work, read, played and went for walks into the surrounding scrubby woodland. By 13 August we were in need of supplies, including fuel and food, so we all headed off in the Land Rover to Maralal, two hundred kilometres away.

We left camp at 7.30 am with me driving and a full load of three spare tyres, a drum for petrol, and two of our employed Samburu men, Ngilicho and Lolokuru, plus my sons in the back. The first incident occurred when I was trying to push a herd of goats to leave the road in a narrow cutting. They panicked, and one went down and under a wheel. Not a nice sound, but I made light of it with my half-asleep passengers who hadn't really twigged what had occurred. I didn't stop, as the rule was, if you think you've injured someone don't stop or you may be lynched, but report it to the nearest police post. So I thought I'd treat goats the same and report it in Maralal.

We made good progress until the top of the volcanic scarp at Marti where we got a puncture and I got badly scratched by thorns while changing the tyre. On reaching Maralal we found they had only three hundred litres of petrol, so we were allowed seventy-two litres and I said I'd get the rest next day after being assured that a petrol tanker would arrive in the afternoon. We managed to get a room at the Safari Lodge, but only with a bit of friendly persuasion. On our return to town and back we got two more punctures! The Avon tyres which came from England with the Land Rovers were absolutely useless for Kenya conditions. We eventually changed all the British Avons

Early morning view from camp at Ngurunit, northern Kenya. (Photograph by T. J. Charsley.)

on team Land Rovers for locally manufactured Firestones that had a higher Carbon content and so were more rigid and, as it proved, more thorn resistant. Of course, with all the punctures and the fuel problem I forgot all about the incident of the goats and made no report!

A few days later we were back in camp and I was writing up a report at the end of a morning traverse when two Assistant Policemen with kalashnikovs arrived, sweating profusely, having walked about fifteen kilometres from Illaut in the north.

They told Ngilicho that they were looking for a white Land Rover, and a white man with two white children—and there was a matter of five dead goats! Since the only other whites in the whole area were the missionaries at Arsim it was difficult to deny it was us. Our hearts all went bump. Was I being arrested? They said I'd have to go to the police station at Baragoi, but I said I'd go to Illaut, where they were based, to speak with the local chief. They agreed, so I suggested we went in the Land Rover and they got into the back. I took Ngilicho with me to translate. Once they were on board I said that, as they'd come a long way and we had transport, did they want to visit any relatives in the village? One of them said yes, he'd got an uncle here, so we drove to the village and he spent a few minutes with his uncle. I'd taken several packets of cigarettes and gave instructions to Ngilicho to offer the policemen cigarettes, one after the other to make sure they were calm and regarded the whole thing as something good rather than an unpleasant duty, since they'd had to walk so far in the heat. We also stopped at one or two places to distribute some money for famine relief from the chief.

At Illaut I met the chief, who was very jovial and friendly, and then the owner of the goats appeared with a pile of goatskins. I stood back to let everybody talk. It came down to a claim of nine hundred Kenya shillings (£47) which I thought a little much. I admitted to 'perhaps one goat', but then said to the chief that if I was to pay that much, 'Where is the goat meat? That should be mine too.' So I proposed 'say four hundred shillings', but sensing reluctance I said, 'Alright, five hundred shillings without the meat.' The chief got my drift, accepted the argument, and it was all settled amicably. I took out five hundred shillings in notes and was about to pass them to the goat owner when the chief snatched them from my hand! He then dismissed the man and invited me in for tea! At that point I admit that I did feel somewhat guilty. So then I went in to the chief's house for tea and *chapattis*, and he asked me to collect fifteen bags of maize tomorrow from Baragoi to which I agreed. We parted with handshakes all round, from the chief and his hangers on and the assistant policemen, but not with the poor owner of the goats who at this stage was outside the hut being ignored.

There was a relieved welcoming party when I arrived back in camp. They had remained moderately calm as Stephen Laon, my wise Masai driver, had told them not to worry as the *bwana* would know how to deal with the situation. I was left hoping that the incident was closed.

Aerial Adventures in Amazonia
Peter Pitfield

The Douglas C-47 Skytrain or Dakota (from the acronym DACoTA, for Douglas Aircraft Company Transport Aircraft) was developed as a military transport aircraft from the Douglas DC-3 airliner. The C-47 differed from the civilian DC-3 in numerous modifications that included being fitted with a cargo door and a strengthened floor. It was used extensively by the Allies during the Second World War and was vital to the success of many Second World War Allied campaigns in Japanese held territory, in particular at Guadalcanal and in the jungles of New Guinea and Burma (source: Wikipedia). It remained in front line service with various military operators through the 1950s. Thousands of other surplus C-47s were converted to civil airline use. It was to my great surprise that during the second phase of the IGS Bolivian Proyecto Precámbrico, between 1980 and 1982, the C-47 was still in service; and what is more it was the only commercial option available for transporting field teams, their equipment and supplies for the ten-week campaigns in the evergreen tropical forest of eastern Bolivia. This was my first introduction to TAURO, the local C-47 aircraft operator.

Forest Flights

During this three-year period I was working with IGS and GEOBOL (Bolivian Geological Survey) colleagues in the Beni Department, north of latitude 14° south and east of the River Itonomas. The area was located along the border with Brazil, which was marked by the Rio Itenéz (known in Brazil as the Rio Guaporé). Even this far up the Amazon basin, and only about four hundred kilometres from the watershed with the River Plate catchment, this river was already one to two hundred metres wide and its main tributaries anywhere between thirty and sixty metres wide. These perennial rivers were navigable for much of their length but riverboats other than small motorised launches and dugouts were scarce. The main population centres were Remanso in the east and Baures in the west.

The area was covered with dense evergreen forest (alternatively classified as submontane dense rainforest) interspersed with swamps and savannah-like floodplains which would be under several metres of water during the latter part of the wet season. A dry-season four-wheel drive dirt road connecting with the road network in the Department of Santa Cruz existed but in the early 1980s was in such an appalling state that it was deemed impassable. The only way to gain access to the mapping area from our office and residential base in the boom town of Santa Cruz de la Sierra (with a population of about a quarter of a million at that time but now over one and a half million) was by air.

Given the poorly developed road system in the lowlands of eastern Bolivia there was heavy reliance on air transport at that time and thus airstrips were plentiful. The uniformly flat lateritised peneplain, which covered a large part of the northern zone of the project area, meant that air strips could be easily constructed by felling a corridor through the forest or flattening the termite mounds on the alluvial grasslands. Thus most communities in the area had a grassed air strip of several hundred metres usable by Cessna aircraft for commercial or emergency use.

The C-47 required a standard runway length of eight hundred metres but when lightly laden could manage with as little as five to six hundred metres as long as a corridor was open for one hundred metres at both ends for a low angle take-off and landing. Unfortunately many of these strips were seldom used and secondary forest growth increased the approach angle.

Puerto Villazon—a Forgotten Naval River Base

Puerto Villazón, situated about four kilometres north of the village of Remanso on the bank of the River Itenéz, was at this time a naval base with a two-kilometre-long airstrip. The base was manned by a commandant and about a dozen demoralised and wretched ratings. This was a period in Bolivian history marked by inconclusive elections and a series of *coups d'état*, counter-coups, and caretaker governments. In 1980, General Luis García Meza Tejada carried out a ruthless and violent coup d'état that did not have popular support, and after a military rebellion forced him out in 1981, three other military governments in fourteen months struggled with Bolivia's growing problems, including hyperinflation. It was apparent that this isolated outpost, which was meant to be the bulwark against Brazilian expansionism, had been totally forgotten. They hadn't been paid or supplied in months and were reduced to subsistence farming, hunting, fishing and general scavenging. Despite the run-down condition of the base the airstrip was in fairly good condition and so was used for air-lifting the teams into the area, from where they would deploy up and down river. A smaller naval outpost further downstream was in a particularly sorry state with a small bat-infested dwelling and, when one of our project teams visited in 1982, no means of transport—their only canoe having drifted off down river after being inadequately secured.

Much of my work was conducted inland utilising existing trails, which at the start of the season were still under water. We usually travelled on horseback accompanied by additional pack animals for a couple of days until the terrain became too difficult and we were obliged to continue on foot with a team of trail blazing porters. The area was laced with numerous footpaths for natural rubber collection, an industry which started in the second half of the nineteenth century and reached its peak during the rubber boom of 1879–1912.

The rubber collection was organised around a system of patronage. A few local unscrupulous businessmen employed teams of labourers engaged in rubber collection for about seven months of the year. They operated a debt-bondage system which was tantamount to modern-day pawn slavery. They provided all the supplies for their workers at inflated prices and their employees would be obliged to work to pay off this debt but, of course, were never able to clear it. The debt was passed to their offspring and so the system was perpetuated. The patrons were all powerful and typically would father a large tribe of illegitimate children. For us to work in the area it was essential to maintain a good working relationship with them, however unpalatable this might be.

Wherever possible, local access into the densely forested areas was along the watercourses and therefore most of our operations would involve the use of aluminium boats or canoes. The boats were powered by 6 hp two-stroke outboard motors. For a ten-week field campaign one team would require two boats with all the accessories, tools and fuel as well as all the camp, field and kitchen equipment, non-perishable food stocks, short-wave radios, medical kits, firearms, fishing gear, alcohol and cigarettes (for bartering and bonuses) and personal effects. All this gear to support two geologists and a team of locally hired labourers, an indigenous native guide and a gang foreman would weigh around one tonne.

The C-47 aircraft had a designed payload capacity of 2.6 tonnes or twenty-eight troops. TAURO's aged aircraft had a permitted load capacity of 2.2 tonnes which enabled two teams to be taken in one round trip. The tie line distance from the city of Santa Cruz (Trompillo airport) to Puerto Villazón was approximately 475 kilometres, which at a cruise speed of around 250 kmph ordinarily took about two hours. The plane was manned by a pilot, co-pilot and maintenance engineer. The inclusion of an engineer was essential as the engines continually needed checks, running repairs and topping-up with oil. The aircraft clearly showed its age in that all the porthole windows of the cargo bay were crazed to the extent that it was impossible to see out of them. The only way to see the terrain was to venture into the rather cramped cockpit.

Dakota C-47 (TAURO) being loaded up at Puerto Villazon, eastern Bolivia. (Photograph by M. P. Hawkins.)

Back in the 1980s there was no GPS-assisted navigation; instead the plane was navigated by dead reckoning and visual recognition of ground features such as rivers, hill ranges and occasional cultural landmarks. Round trips to Puerto Villazón did not normally present a problem, as the crew were familiar with the route, but any destination unknown to them constituted a challenge. In these instances they were heavily reliant on navigation charts as well as guidance and information provided by the geologists on the condition of the landing strip. On one occasion the crew became disorientated and the plane strayed into Brazilian airspace near Pimenteiras in the State of Rondonia until they realized their error. It added twenty minutes to the journey which otherwise passed without incident. With the C-47, which had a range of 2,500 kilometres, there was ample capacity to search for the target area if the navigation was awry.

By contrast, with a Bell helicopter of that era, which was occasionally required for deployment to remote areas with no airstrips, the operational range was about four hundred kilometres and so there was little or no margin for error, especially over densely forested terrain. There was at least one incident during the project where a helicopter had to make an emergency landing in a gap in the forest canopy as it was about to run out of fuel, having failed to locate a rendezvous point. For such eventualities, project personnel flying over the rainforest were instructed to carry emergency survival equipment (machete, file for sharpening machete, penknife, compass, string, cigarette lighter, candle, fishing hooks and line, nail for use as a fish spear, small medical kit), and a rudimentary system of bonfire, flare and body/hand signals was established to enable basic communications with any search and rescue aircraft. Most helicopter operations required the establishment of fuel dumps and in some cases the TAURO C-47 aircraft was employed to transport the 200 litre drums of helicopter fuel to the nearest usable airstrip.

Serranía Huanchaca—the Lost World

One such operation required the helicopter airlift of a team with all their equipment, including aluminium boats, onto the four-hundred-metre-high plateau of Serranía Huanchaca. This plateau, which covers an area the size of Yorkshire, was made famous by the explorer Percy Fawcett in 1908, and four years later provided the inspiration for Conan Doyle's *The Lost World*. It is now part of a protected UNESCO World Heritage site, named the Noel Kempff Mercado National Park. The plateau had a short airstrip usable with a Cessna but of insufficient length for the C-47. A few years after the geological survey was completed this short airstrip was used by an illicit cocaine factory. Noel Kempff Mercado, a renowned Bolivian naturalist who had lectured our project team on venomous snakes and the treatment of snakebites, landed on Serranía Huanchaca with several other scientists during a field campaign in 1986. Upon discovery of the cocaine factory Kempff Mercado and most of the scientists were killed by the criminals. In 1988 the Huanchaca National Park was renamed the Noel Kempff Mercado National Park in his memory.

The helicopter airlift onto Serranía Huanchaca required the establishment of a fuel dump at the village of Florida by the Rio Paraguá, which in the 1980s still had a serviceable airstrip and coincidentally was the roadhead for four-wheel drive vehicles. With a load capacity sufficient only for the pilot, one or two passengers and equipment loaded in the skiffs (or tied to the skids), the Bell 47J helicopter had to make several trips to ferry the team, equipment and supplies. It was decided to airlift 1,400 litres of fuel (seven two-hundred-litre drums) to Florida, enough for both the deployment and later evacuation of the team from Huanchaca and to allow for wastage.

TAURO had not used the Florida airstrip previously and so an IGS geologist (with air photos in hand) accompanied the crew to assist with the navigation. Somehow they overshot the landing site and continued travelling north with little idea of their position. In a mounting state of uncertainty verging on panic they spotted an airstrip at the village of Piso Firme by the side of the Rio Paraguá, a piranha-infested tributary of the Rio Itenéz, and promptly landed without realizing, or having due regard for, the short length of the airstrip. If they had continued twenty-five kilometres further north they would have encountered the Puerto Villazón airstrip. The Piso Firme airstrip was only six hundred metres long with minimal clearance at each end, and there was no way that a fully loaded C-47 would be able to take off. The TAURO crew was obliged, therefore, to offload three drums of fuel to reduce the payload to no more than one tonne. With gritted teeth and at full throttle the crew barely managed to take to the air and clipped the trees as they gained height to clear the forest canopy. Fortunately no real damage was sustained and they were able to deliver their cargo—enough fuel to at least airlift the team onto Huanchaca. Additional fuel was brought in subsequently by four-wheel drive vehicle and trailer for the evacuation. I was then dispatched to Piso Firme by river launch, not to retrieve the fuel but to donate it to the local people—a welcome windfall of about twenty litres per family.

'Illicit' Trade

Up to three teams operated concurrently out of Puerto Villazón and so TAURO was kept quite busy during the field season (May–November). For at least one leg of the round trip the C-47 was empty or very lightly laden. As this was ostensibly a bilateral government financed operation the local patrons took it as their right to use any spare capacity for trade and in particular to bring in supplies. Actually throughout 1981–82, as the Bolivian economy went into freefall, the operational costs were financed solely by the UK Overseas Development Administration. Although much of the rubber and timber trade and procurement was done along and across the river with Brazil, the opportunity that the TAURO aircraft presented was too tempting. Amongst the more exotic and heinous consignments were animal skins and live birds.

On one return trip to Santa Cruz in the C-47, half a dozen blue and yellow macaws escaped from a poorly constructed crate and were flying around inside the plane. They made a beeline for the cockpit which looked like the best avenue of escape and a scene of chaos ensued with the crew frantically trying to contain them while still flying the plane. With the birds in flight there was no time to test that age-old conundrum as to whether the plane weighed less or not!

Things came to a head at the end of one particular campaign in 1982 when the C-47 was due to come to Puerto Villazón to collect my team. A consignment of provisions was delivered to the plane in Santa Cruz without any formal submission, notification or authorization. The UK manager in a fit of pique decided to stop all shipments of supplies requested by the 'patrons'. Their immediate response was to take me hostage. They also approached the commandant of the naval base to petition that the plane be impounded when it landed. I was detained in a rough-built wooden shack the walls of which were little more than an insecure palisade. I was permitted to use our Racal radio with its wind-up alternator to explain the situation and after some deliberation my manager relented and allowed the freight to be sent in exchange for our return.

A Country in Crisis

This second phase of Proyecto Precámbrico took place against a back-drop of acute political instability and insecurity. García Meza came to power in July 1980 in what was known as the 'Cocaine Coup'. Colonel Luis Arce-Gomez, a coup organizer and the cousin of cocaine kingpin Roberto Suarez, went into partnership with big narco-traffickers, including Cuban-American smugglers based in Miami. A co-conspirator Second World War Nazi war criminal, Klaus Barbie, recruited Argentine death-squads, ex-Nazis, young neo-Nazis from Europe and various sociopaths from around the globe. The victory put into power a right-wing military dictatorship indebted to the drug lords. Bolivia became South America's first narco-state.

Illicit cocaine refining factories sprang up in remote parts of the forested orient where we were working. Overflying the area these were easily spotted as they would cut an airstrip or rehabilitate abandoned airstrips for Cessna aircraft to come and go. These factories would produce free-base cocaine paste which would be smuggled by air to Colombia for further refining.

A curfew was in place during the first six months of García Meza's government. It was initially between the hours of 6 pm and 6 am but over time was gradually relaxed. In García Meza's immortal words 'Bolivia is perched on the edge of a precipice but we are about to take a step forward.' By late 1981, US-Bolivian relations had been stretched to breaking point. When Bolivia's corrupt military junta was finally overthrown and Barbie's identity became known, the French secret service secured Barbie's return to France to face a war-crimes trial in 1983.

The Falklands War in 1982 and Bolivia's political support for the Leopoldo Galtieri regime made our presence in Santa Cruz very uncomfortable. During the late seventies Santa Cruz was still flying the Argentine flag alongside the Bolivian flag and at the time of the Falklands/Malvinas conflict there were an estimated thirty thousand Argentines living in the city. All outward evidence of the British Mission was removed and we kept as low a profile as possible. Following death threats we had two policemen posted at the house for a while and I declined to visit my Argentine barber—the thought of him wielding a cut throat razor left too much to the imagination!

By the end of 1980, Bolivian access to private international capital markets had dried up, and from 1982 to 1985 inflation accelerated to dizzying hyperinflationary levels. The new Bolivian leaders naively thought that steering the country from a narcotics-ridden dictatorship to a fresh democracy would be sufficient to attract substantial aid from the Western nations. During the period 1982–83 the annual inflation rate ran at about 300 per cent. The black market parallel exchange rate was over double the official rate. One did not only have to choose the most appropriate day to exchange money but also the optimal time of day. Items were priced in US dollars and vendors would calculate the cost in pesos at the time of purchase. When it came to selling my car at the end of the tour I walked away

Design for t-shirt worn by staff working in Bolivia when, in 1984, IGS Overseas Division became BGS Overseas Division, BIGSOD. (Photograph by K. B. Bloomfield.)

with a sack of local currency, mostly in tightly packed bricks of notes that no one bothered to count anymore.

Economic disaster and criminality in Santa Cruz was capped by a catastrophic flood of the Rio Pirai in March 1983 in which an estimated one hundred people were drowned and a further nine hundred people registered missing. The 1982–83 El Niño event was one of the two most extreme in the twentieth century, causing severe flooding along the western seaboard of South America. Following heavy rains in the sub-Andean ranges a wall of water eighteen metres high emerged from the canyon at the Andean front about seventy kilometres upstream. By the time it reached Santa Cruz it was more like a debris flow several metres high. It caused the river to change course, destroyed the road bridge, obliterated the botanical gardens and devastated a broad swathe of low lying ground on the north side of the city.

Shining Stones
Don Aldiss

Since the early 1980s Botswana has been the world's largest producer of gem-quality diamonds. It seems inevitable, therefore, that individuals will attempt to trade illicitly-acquired mine output on their own behalf. As the unlicensed possession of uncut diamonds is illegal, it is almost as inevitable that some of these people subsequently get involved in discussions with the legal authorities concerning their possession of 'shining stones'. Such discussions generally hinge on the proper identification of the rough stones as diamond, so it is natural that, every so often, representatives of the Botswana CID turn up at the Geological Survey Department in Lobatse, seeking the professional opinion of a qualified geologist.

Positive identification of uncut diamonds is a reasonably straightforward business and, aside from the necessary paperwork that accompanies the process, I found it a pleasure to be able to handle and study these amazing little objects. To me, an uncut diamond with natural faces is far more attractive than the common brilliant cut stone. Sometimes the stones that arrived for examination were not so little. I once handled an uncut diamond slightly larger than the tip of my little finger. I later saw the same stone while I was at the witness stand, although it was very rare to be called to court. So the always unannounced Monday morning arrival of the CID would be followed by pleasant anticipation during the short stroll across the jacaranda-shaded courtyard to the mineral preparation laboratory where the examination would be conducted.

Inspection with a binocular microscope was usually enough to show the reality of the policemen's suspicions. After all, the local CID had fairly frequent opportunities to 'get their eye in' with genuine uncut diamonds taken from their suspects. Aside from the characteristic lustre, inspection of natural triangular crystal faces would generally reveal 'trigons': tiny facetted triangular pits in the crystal face whose apices point away from the apices in the face itself. To be completely sure, this was followed by immersion in heavy liquids—diamond floats in tetrabromethane but sinks in Clerici solution—and a scratch hardness test with a piece of synthetic corundum. For all of diamond's reputation for resilience, I generally found the results of the hardness test the most equivocal of the three diagnoses. All that then remained was the preparation of a short written statement for the court, and the CID would go contentedly on their way.

Sometimes, however, the 'shining stones' brought to us by the

CID were not diamonds at all. Zambia, which shares a very short border with the north of Botswana, is a leading producer of high quality emeralds. There is a corresponding black market trade in uncut stones, and also of apparently similar materials: I was told that few of the traffic lights in Lusaka retain any green glass! I had been warned of the possibility that suspected emeralds might be brought in for verification, and of the corresponding difficulty of certifying that this or that piece of beryl (possession of which would not be, of itself, illegal) is, in one's professional judgement, sufficiently clear and green to justify its classification as emerald.

Eventually, though, the day came when the CID appeared at the door bearing a glass jar full of green-coloured crystals. My heart sank. The jar was sealed top and bottom in a hard plastic casing helpfully moulded with the words 'Zambian emeralds'. Cut open, the jar turned out to contain seventy-six bright green crystals, mostly well-formed hexagonal prisms and evidently not just bits of green glass. Clearly, I was going to have to make up some kind of diagnostic procedure as I went along, while the CID waited at my shoulder for my authoritative statement. Equally clearly, if these objects really were emeralds, then they were going be worth a truly enormous sum of money. But while that observation might have provided grounds for suspicion, it was hardly submissable evidence.

Happily, the lab chief, Haroon Kara, was on hand to suggest that we try XRD analysis—that at least would confirm a crystal structure and might eliminate some possibilities. So a chip was cut from one of these potentially extremely valuable stones and taken away to the XRD room. Meanwhile, I thought that I might as well examine the stones under a binocular microscope—if only to satisfy the waiting policemen that testing was continuing to the GSD's usual high standard, as normal. One by one, I stared at these remarkably uniform, beautifully green, pellucid crystals, hoping for inspiration. Eventually, I noticed that one of them had a few very tiny shreds of dry grass stuck firmly to it. Indeed, the shreds appeared to be embedded in the green material forming the crystals. I called for a beaker of acetone and dropped the objects of suspicion into it. As if by magic, the acetone turned green and the crystals turned colourless, revealed to be common quartz wands (natural quartz prisms) that had been coated in paint, just as Haroon returned with the confirmatory XRD result.

So on this occasion, our reputation for gemmological expertise was preserved. The CID left disappointed, although they perhaps contemplated a charge of attempted deception or conspiracy to defraud, rather than merely one of 'possession'.

Verses from the Interior
Martin Litherland

Conan Doyle and I

From the Overseas Division of IGS (later BGS) geologists were posted all around the world. I was lucky enough to be sent to Bolivia, working for part of the time in Serranía Huanchaca, the *Lost World* of Conan Doyle's novel. Doyle had received descriptions of the region from its first European explorer, Colonel Percy Fawcett. Surrounded by Amazonian forest, this remote tableland, the size of Devon, straddles the border between Bolivia and Brazil and is bounded by steep cliffs. I was taken into the area by helicopter for two three-month trips, being probably the first to explore it since Fawcett himself.

The Lost World
(Written in camp on Serranía Huanchaca, 1981)

A civil servant though I be,
My life requires no fantasy.

Each year civilisation fades,
As with the chopping of the blades,
I reach again that fabled land,
Engraved by Conan Doyle, whose hand
Saw the pterodactyls fly
Against the *Lost World*'s painted sky.
Month after month I toil up here,
With faithful Indians for cheer,
With Percy Fawcett's spirit free,
Within whose company I see
The vista when the day is clear:
The forest of Bolivia.

Dangerous Encounters

In the forests of the *Lost World* the local fauna, lacking human contact, could become curious, as my encounter with a panther (which the locals call *tigre*) demonstrated. Also, my base-camp in the *Lost World* was pitched alongside a picturesque waterfall with a deep swimming pool, which had another inhabitant!

Encounter with an anaconda, Bolivia. (Photograph by M. Litherland.)

In the Forest of the Night
(With apologies to William Blake)

Tiger, Tiger burning bright
In the forest of the night,
Scorching eyes in torchlight's glare,
Curdled blood and needled hair.

Never smelled a man before,
Never known the need to roar,
In the *Lost World*'s sanctuary,
Violated territory.

Up the creek we follow her;
Droppings every day appear;
Light the fire, a place to stay,
Winding down another day.

Now with torches do we seek,
In the stillness of the creek,
Epicure's aristocrat:
Jungle feast of Branick's Rat.[1]

But she's waiting for the same:
Roars into the torches flame.
'Do not shoot,' I whisper first,
'Wounded tiger is the worst.'

Sleeping bag I have today;
Slung my hammock far away;
No mosquito net required:
Nice and cosy, warm and tired.

1 A tasty, giant rat, like a huge, hopping rabbit.

Night is cooled by polar air;[1]
Boys have only clothes they wear;
Sling their hammocks by the fire:
Nice and warm when they retire.

Woke up by her mighty roar;
Round the forest she does paw.
Circling round the camp by night;
Scenting blood, provoking fright.

What am I supposed to do?
Play Lord Roxton[2] born anew?
Grip the shotgun! Do not speak!
Do not let them think you're weak!

After half an hour of this,
In a numbed paralysis:
Loose the hammock from the tree:
Courting death is not for me.

Sling it up beside the fire,
Add more fuel, and then retire.
Boys just mutter drowsy deep,
Tiger roars me off to sleep.

1 Cool air from the south, known as a surazo.
2 A character in the *Lost World* novel.

Snake Story

What shall we make of the great snake story?
    Is it a geologist's tale?
Is it embellished for personal glory?
    Let us then follow its trail.

As evidence he has preserved its skin,
    Some seven metres long;
And there too is a photograph
    Of this great snake's swansong.

He says it was pulled from a very large pool
    Beneath a waterfall;
On a river which drains the *Lost World*'s plateau
    Of Doyle, Fawcett and all.

After longish traverses the team used to rest
    In the base-camp's relative cool;
While the boys would wash in the shallows above,
    He would swim for a while in the pool.

'Let's all swim together down here in the pool,'
    He would often be heard to cry:
'No gracias doctor, estamos bien,'
    Was invariably their timid reply.

If a great anaconda came hungry and fast
    As it silently searched for a meal,
Would he see it at once and then swim for his life?
    How then would our geologist feel?

Were he taken by jaws and wrapped in the coils
    To struggle and fight for his breath,

Would the gun go off, bang! and kill the great beast?
    So escaping a most fearful death.

Being squeezed to a pulp and swallowed alive
    Is a thought that wakes one up at night—
Best blank out the thought and start counting sheep,
    Until the grey morning's light.

Culture Clash

It was a feast day in a small village in the eastern Bolivia forest. One of the children's games involved burying a live duck in the soil until only its head was showing. A child (in this case a girl) was blindfolded and given a stick. She beat the ground with the stick and amid shouts which can be translated as 'warmer' and 'colder'—eventually she clubbed the duck to death!

Village Games

Girls wobbling, bobbling up for the apples.
    Boys scrambling, clambering the greasy pole.
Frolicking feast day in jungle village.
    Laughing, shouting children out of control.

Other games are playing all around us.
    Some boys asking for a Land Rover ride.
Now what's going on with so much shouting?
    Oh no! This is not for a lecture slide!

A blindfolded girl with a great big stick,
    And a live duck buried up to its chin.
The girl gets closer, the shouts gets louder.
    Cannot hear the death squawk over the din.

Enjoy your games, girls! Enjoy your childhood!
Enjoy the crunching of the duckling's head;
For your life will be as short and painful:
Seven kids and toothless, and then you're dead!

The Matthew and Hunter Affair
Sandy Macfarlane

The New Hebrides Condominium (since 1980 the independent Republic of Vanuatu), where I served on secondment from IGS from 1974 to 1984, was created in 1905 by two major colonial powers of the time—Great Britain and France—out of reluctance. Reluctance to take individual responsibility for these South Pacific islands on the one hand, and reluctance to bequeath sole possession of them to a rival on the other.

Suffice to say this grand experiment of joint administration was doomed to end in tears. With political aspirations for self-government taking root in the 1970s, an Anglophone Melanesian majority was elected to Parliament prior to full independence—promoted enthusiastically by the UK, anxious to be gone, but much less so by France, still with other 'possessions' in the Pacific, such as the nickel-rich New Caledonia in particular. In a last desperate act of defiance a Francophone-sponsored opposition group on Santo (the largest island in the chain) declared self-rule. This attempt at secession failed, put down by the military intervention (the so-called Coconut War) of a joint British-French-PNG Field Force, before the Vanuatu flag was finally raised at the end of June 1980.

Not surprisingly, diplomatic exchanges between France and newly-independent Vanuatu were in the early years decidedly frosty; and it was in an atmosphere of mutual distrust that a Vanuatu government expeditionary mission to the islands of Matthew and Hunter was undertaken in March 1983. The principal objective of this 'administrative visit' was to strengthen the Vanuatu case to UNCLOS for ownership of these two islands against the counter-claim of the neighbouring territory of New Caledonia (i.e. the sacred soil of France).

An excellent account of the mission was given at the time in the local press (*Tam Tam Special Issue*, March 1983) whereas a somewhat more 'tongue-in-cheek' piece appeared in the French international magazine *Paris Match* (April issue, 1983) entitled 'Bataille pour un Rocher'. The latter article includes a double-page pictorial spread of the South Pacific Ocean from the prow of the expedition's vessel, MV *Euphrosyne*, with Hunter Island emerging on the far distant horizon. The photographer (in fact me) was not acknowledged. In Vanuatu the thirtieth anniversary of this event was apparently celebrated (9 March 2013) in grand style with a parade and presidential salute outside parliament, and with a speech by the deputy prime minister, Ham Lini, lauding us, the intrepid voyagers, as 'brave heroes'.

To begin with, you may well ask what right had I to be part of the Vanuatu government's expeditionary mission in March 1983 to lay claim to the islands of Matthew and Hunter. After all, I was on secondment to Vanuatu at the time from the Institute of Geological Sciences, and therefore, in all but name, a UK civil servant. Well, firstly, as director of the Geology, Mines and Rural Water Supplies Department, I was officially an employee of the Vanuatu government and in the terms of my ODA contract, subject to instruction from the Minister of Lands. The UK government therefore had no call on my loyalty in Vanuatu matters.

Secondly, within the context of the Law of the Sea, Vanuatu is defined as an archipelago and as such the submarine geology could have an important bearing on defining the limits of its territorial waters. So as an earth sciences adviser to government I was in a position to present a geological argument in support of the political and historic case for including Matthew and Hunter within Vanuatu.

Very briefly, the geological argument for Matthew and Hunter's inclusion is this: the Vanuatu landmass is a narrow chain of Tertiary to Holocene (*ca.* twenty-five million years to present) volcanic islands and extends some seven hundred kilometres from the Torres group in the north to Aneityum in the south and onwards to Matthew and Hunter. Together with the Santa Cruz group in Solomon Islands, Vanuatu lies within the New Hebrides Arc which bounds the western margin of the Pacific Plate at its juncture with the subducting Australia-India Plate. In other words the islands of Matthew and Hunter are a natural physiographic extension of the Vanuatu archipelago. They are also age-wise and in terms of their petrology and geochemistry identical to the most recent cycle of active volcanism from centres on the islands of Vanua Lava, Aoba, Ambrym, Lopevi and Tanna.

Back then to the events of March 1983. Looking back, it seems now to have been a terrific adventure, a tale from the *Boys' Own Paper*, a story to tell my grandchildren—a mixture of high drama and low farce. Allowing for selective memory this is my version of events:

Monday 7 March. To avoid any unwelcome attention (from British, Australian, or French diplomatic eyes) I did not board the government vessel MV *Euphrosyne* in Vila with the other members of the mission, led by Joe Joseph, Secretary of Tafea Local Council. Instead, I flew later to Aneityum, ostensibly to look at rural water supply projects with my head of RWS Section, Captain Rod Bridges of the Australian Corps of Engineers. There I boarded the *Euphrosyne*, skippered by Leith Nasak, and we set sail for points south on the evening tide.

Tuesday 8 March. In the morning a gentle rolling swell propelled us southwards across the vast and empty South Pacific Ocean. Then in the afternoon huge rafts of fresh pumice floating on a yellow-tinged sea crossed our bows. Possibly we were sailing through the 'area of discoloured water' marked on the Admiralty charts and witnessing effluent discharged from a submarine volcano nearby. Alternatively, the pumice had drifted westwards from Tonga some one thousand kilometres to the east, the product of a major volcanic eruption reported there in previous weeks. Similar material from earlier Tongan eruptions now litters many of the beaches around Vanuatu's islands.

Wednesday 9 March. I remember waking at daybreak and seeing Macji Bohenska, the chief navigator, standing on the foredeck with a hand-held gyroscope pointed towards a wide and forbidding skyline. My God, I thought, how are we going to find tiny islands like Matthew and Hunter (think Edinburgh's Arthur's Seat for size), in this fashion? But a couple of hours later there she was, Hunter Island as it turned out (was that the plan I wonder), a

pinprick on the horizon. And as we got closer we could see smoke billowing from the island's western flank—to my trained geologist's eye an obvious indication of volcanic activity. Wrong, as I was later to learn from a reliable source: the French Navy had recently been targeting the island for gunnery practice and had set the hillside vegetation alight.

We scrambled ashore: a plaque placed by the French in 1975 claiming sovereignty of

Hoisting the Vanuatu flag on Hunter Island, 9 March 1983. (Photograph by A. Macfarlane.)

the island was quickly torn from its mooring. The Vanuatu flag was hoisted, the national anthem sung, and a custom ceremony performed at the site by chiefs from the Tafea Local Council. Hunter Island was theirs! Meanwhile Bob Makin, director of Radio Vanuatu, was busy franking envelopes with Vanuatu stamps at the temporary but official 'Post Office' established for that purpose (must have some value now, these letters). At the same time I set about collecting rock samples for analysis— they should still be in Vila if they can be located following the incineration of the Geology and Mines Department a few years ago. Then back on board the *Euphrosyne* and north-westwards bound for Matthew Island that evening.

Thursday 10 March. A beautiful sunrise as we approached Matthew from the southeast. Then on the western horizon a ship appeared from the direction of New Caledonia. It could be no other than a French naval vessel—a minesweeper, the *Dunkerquoise*, as it turned out. As both vessels approached Matthew from opposite directions we temporarily lost sight of the *Dunkerquoise* as the *Euphrosyne's* course took us behind the island in search of a suitable landing point on its southern flank. Then abruptly the *Dunkerquoise* came into view again on near-collision course. Plan A, to land on Matthew, was quickly abandoned. Plan B, to head back to Vila at maximum knots, hastily put into action. And as the two vessels passed, with just a few metres between them, my recollection is that the *Dunkerquoise* was packed with military (marines or SAS perhaps) armed to the teeth and itching, or so it seemed, to get on board the *Euphrosyne* for a bit of action.

It did occur to me then that we might be in some trouble. However, the *Dunkerquoise* remained close to our stern and together with a low-flying French military plane shepherded us back into Vanuatu waters before heading off back to New Caledonia. I was later to hear that we were a star item on the Noumea TV News that evening. Some ORSTOM friends, geoscientists also, recognized me and in anticipation of my arrest (thankfully not to happen) were preparing to visit me in Noumea jail bearing suitable gifts of food and drink.

The MV *Euphrosyne* eventually arrived back in Vila early evening on Saturday 12 March with all hands safe on board. And in this I have nothing but praise for the seamanship of Captain Leith Nasak and his crew for the way they handled the vessel in what were difficult circumstances that could have had a less than happy ending. Credit is also due the French Navy which displayed a show of force but declined to carry it through.

Life was a wee bit dull for a while after that. The British and Australian High Commissioners were pretty po-faced about it all when I met them at a cocktail party a day or so later. I never did get to hear the French Ambassador's take on the Matthew and Hunter Affair.

Postscript. Discerning readers of the International Press will have noted in the *Vanuatu Daily Post* of Thursday 9 January 2014, the banner headline 'Another Matthew/Hunter Hero Honoured'. Accompanying the article is a photo of the former director of Geology, Mines and Rural Water Supplies (i.e. me) being presented with a medal at State House in Port Vila by the acting president of Vanuatu for my 'scientific role in the first post-Independence official visit to Matthew and Leika (Hunter) islands'. The same award was made to the other members of the expedition on 9 March 2013, the thirtieth anniversary of the voyage. Vanuatu's rightful claim to Matthew and Hunter is still being vigorously pursued with the United Nations and a successful outcome is anticipated despite counter-claims from the French government. But for the moment at least the *Bataille pour un Rocher* continues!

Stealing the Rain
Mike Hawkins

Field work in the high Andes of southern Peru in the 1980s was a challenge for the three-man BGS team mapping between Lake Titicaca and the city of Arequipa. Much of the project area was at an altitude of well over four thousand metres and in some areas the night-time temperatures were so low that even the battery acid in the project Land Rovers would start to freeze.

The lifetime of the project (1983–86) also coincided with a severe drought in southern Peru, triggered by the replacement of the cold Humboldt ocean current, which usually extends along the length of the Peruvian coastline, by the warmer El Niño current from the north. The local population, largely dependent on subsistence farming, was seriously affected by the lack of rainfall, so a more easily identifiable explanation for the change in climate may have seemed appealing to some. In one area a belief that the drought was caused by foreigners who had installed rain-removing instruments on the tops of hills had taken hold and some villagers even claimed to have seen these instruments and to have witnessed their ability to make rain-bearing clouds disappear.

This was also a time of greatly heightened tensions in rural Peru with a brutal war being fought elsewhere in the country between Maoist guerrillas of the Shining Path movement and government forces, with the local population often caught in the middle, so perhaps it was not so surprising that the arrival of a group of geologists intent on climbing the local hills was met by a few of the locals with some suspicion and hostility.

We had already been chased off a couple of hills when, returning one day to our base in a local village, my Peruvian counterpart, driver and myself found our road blocked by a barricade of wheelbarrows. A large group of villagers armed with pick-axes and rocks then surrounded our Land Rover and started to search it for 'rain-removing instruments'. For a while the atmosphere was tense and there was even agitated talk of overturning the vehicle. One rather over-excited youth leapt onto the Land Rover bonnet and declared that the jerry cans which we had on the roof must contain some of the stolen rain but his enthusiasm was soon dented when he wrenched open one can to find that it contained nothing more than diesel fuel.

I was just starting to wonder if the scintillometer which we had in the back of the Land Rover would be considered one of the magical instruments when a local teacher came running across the fields having seen the situation developing from afar. With his help we were able to defuse a tricky situation and convince the locals that our intentions were benign. Eventually, and with some considerable relief, handshakes were exchanged and we were allowed to continue on our way.

I never did discover where this strange belief had come from or what apparatus might originally have been misinterpreted as having rain-removing powers. Fortunately we were received with much kind hospitality in other parts of the project area and, in any case, a year or two later the rains returned and normal harvests resumed.

Friends or Foes?
John Powell

Not all Right Jack!

Between 1984 and 1996 IGS/BGS provided technical support to the Natural Resources Authority of Jordan in geological mapping and geothermal studies. Prior to our own Land Rovers arriving at the start of the project, we relied on Jordanian Survey (NRA) vehicles. On a traverse across the rocky *hamada* desert east of Al Hasa, in a battered Land Rover, we got a puncture in the back wheel about fifteen kilometres from base camp. 'Let's change the wheel', I said to the driver.

'No jack', he replied, and proceeded to loosen the wheel nuts on the punctured back wheel, then drove back and forth at speed across the mud-flat until the wheel spun off the axle and grounded the vehicle on the rear axle. With my geological hammer we spent the next three hours in searing heat digging out a semi-circular pit in the mud-flat sediments below the rear axle so we could attach the spare wheel. We then had to dig out a gradual slope up which he could drive the vehicle. Eventually we succeeded in driving out of the pit, and I insisted we return to base camp. Off we went, but the driver said he knew a short cut across the sabkha. However, recent rain had softened the mud below a thin surface crust, so that with me shouting at him to stop, we sank deeper and deeper into the mud up to both axles. Exasperated, I left the driver and walked the last five kilometres back to base camp vowing never to use him again. I heard later that he waited for the mud to dry out in the sun and rocked the Land Rover out of the mudflat. Needless to say he was sacked by the NRA shortly after for dangerous driving!

Shots Across the Bow

In 1985 we carried out fieldwork along the Jordanian shore of the Dead Sea (440 metres below sea-level) using a small inflatable dinghy which was launched from our Land Rover on the northern shore after first contacting the army check point who would forward our permissions to the lookout post further south. As we sailed southwards, close to the shore, we were passing the last military lookout post, when suddenly bullets came singing past our ears from a machine-gun on the shore. Waving and shouting furiously we headed towards the shoreline only to be told by the lookout that he thought we were Israelis trying to invade across the Dead Sea—our presence had not been sent down the line from the first army post! We were very nervous as we sailed back later that day past the same lookout post!

Special Brew

During 1986 the British Army paid a visit to Amman. One of the secretaries at the Embassy put on a Thursday night party to which they and my BGS colleague, Bill McCourt, were invited. It was a fairly raucous affair, and after a few beers Bill returned to his Land Rover, earlier loaded with crates of beer. (It was regular practice for Technical Cooperation officers to visit the Embassy Commissary on a Thursday—end of the working week—to stock up on duty-free beer). but now full of soldiers who were drinking his beer. In the dark, unaware of who they were, Bill remonstrated with a few choice expletives, but to his surprise he was unceremoniously pinned against a wall as they explained who they were and that even a stocky Cumbrian was not going to cause them any sweat. Anyway, they departed thanking Bill for his 'round', which Bill regarded as a lucky escape!

Carrying out geological mapping in southern Jordan in 1987 with Jordanian counterparts, it was usual to leave the field camp at 6 am, while the air temperature was cool, and then stop around 8 am for a breakfast of bread, hummus and cucumbers with sweet black tea cooked over a brushwood fire. As we ate among the dunes, a machine-gun Jeep arrived, and the soldiers told us we were illegally in Saudi Arabia—we protested that our crude base map showed that we were in Jordan (this was before GPS). The Saudi army patrol arrested us, suspecting that we were smuggling goods across the border, and escorted us in my Land Rover to a nearby border fort. Here, we were impounded despite our remonstrations that we had been in Jordan. We were politely served tea while they sent for a senior officer from a nearby fort. Unknown to all, I had a six-pack of lager in my wooden 'emergencies box' (my emergencies box contained corned beef, sardines, onions, tabasco sauce, Ryvita, bread and water, plus some Land Rover spare parts!), so I sat there nervously praying for three hours that the Saudis would not search the Land Rover (alcohol is legal for foreigners in Jordan, but severely punished in Saudi Arabia). Eventually, the Major arrived at the fort, and whilst insisting that we had been in Saudi territory accepted our explanation, and we were released. The alcohol was never found, but needless to say, the 'Powell Patrol' incident was discussed at the weekly Embassy briefing!

The Wild Man of Wadi Hasa

Wadi Hasa is a deeply incised wadi draining into the Dead Sea, along which I needed to log geological sections in 1987. This was in the days of lone fieldwork, and as I walked upstream, I saw a figure dart among the boulders. A man suddenly confronted me, naked from the waist up, with long, bedraggled hair (unusual in the Middle East) and no hands. He looked like the hairy guy emerging from the undergrowth at the beginning of the *Monty Python* TV series. As I said my usual greetings in Arabic, he darted off only to reappear from behind another boulder shouting at me while swinging a spade around his head, which he contrived to do by swivelling the 'D' of the spade handle on his arm stumps. I hurried on very quickly, but to be honest I think the poor man (obviously an outcast) was more scared of me encroaching on his patch, than me of him. My young children always asked me to tell this story when they wanted to hear a scary tale!

The Great Outdoors
Chris Johnson

Most of us who follow a career in geology do so because of our love for the great outdoors and the opportunities that fieldwork gives us to engage with it. My overseas destinations were a bit more exotic than the moorlands of the Northumberland Trough (my main field area during my initial years with IGS/BGS), though it must be noted that, on an unusually hot day's fieldwork near the Kielder Forest, I saw more snakes (adders) in one day than I ever saw whilst working in other parts of the world.

For my first field season abroad, in 1984, I was really thrown in at the deep end. A trip into the mountains of northern Sumatra was planned in order to follow up some of the geochemical anomalies found during an earlier project (1975–83). Additionally, John Bowles and Bret Beddoe-Stephens wanted to do some work on the alluvial gold that was known to occur in the River Baso area. John Bowles wisely ducked out of being involved in the fieldwork, leaving three expatriates: myself, Frank Coulson (project leader) and Bret Beddoe-Stephens, to do the work. The nine Indonesian counterparts, who had been well trained in regional geological and geochemical mapping during the earlier project, led the field logistics. We spent a total of forty-four nights under canvas; and for all that time, save for the first two days, we were out of contact with the rest of the world. The labourer carrying the short-wave radio managed to stow it upside down, spilling out all the battery acid, and we thus lost our only means of communication with the outside world. The Los Angeles Olympics started and finished whilst we were away and totally passed us by.

At the most extreme point we were three days walk from the nearest settlement. A supply train was set up using numerous labourers, bringing in rice and taking back samples. There was a sack of potatoes which never quite caught up with us before they went rotten. We lived off nothing but rice twice a day supplemented by the occasional fresh-water fish and some tree leaves. A tortoise was caught and eaten but didn't go far amongst the twenty or so people at the base camp. The only game we ever saw on the ground was wild boar, and being a Muslim area there was no tradition of hunting them. This was just as well because they were said to be riddled with worms.

I had a small metal box containing all of my personal possessions, most prized of which was a can of Guinness and a bar of fruit-and-nut chocolate. Never has a bar of fruit-and-nut been made by me to last so long—I rationed myself to one small square every other day. The Guinness went in celebration of surviving one month in the jungle. Clothes became worn and ragged, and walking boots disintegrated. Eventually I was just left with essentials, most prized of which was a towel, a sarong and a pair of cheap rubber flip-flops. Apart from the clothes one had on, as exemplified by what the labourers carried, this was all that was needed.

Our main access into the mountains usually meant walking up river valleys. Our topographical maps were poor and there was no GPS to help us locate ourselves. We had to rely on low resolution black and white air photos and would count joining river tributaries to ensure we took the correct route. The walk up the river valleys could take several days; routes could be blocked by waterfalls, deep gorges or, in areas of logging, natural log jams. This usually meant a long diversion to bypass these obstacles, though on occasions we did climb up the waterfalls or swim the deep gorges. Sometimes, when we were confident we knew the river channel well, a journey of three days walk up-river would be finished by a half-day return journey using our airbeds to raft down-river. This was exhilarating and great fun, especially in the fast flowing sections. Our Indonesian colleagues always declined such an adventure, which was not surprising as most of them could not swim.

Floating down the river on an airbed is associated with one of my more memorable encounters. Frank Coulson and myself were returning down river on our beds after a week or so out in the bush. We were both looking very ragged and worn, and I had a big bushy unkempt beard. As the river entered the coastal area settlements became more frequent. At the first such settlement, nonchalantly laid out on our airbeds, we drifted past a young woman, completely naked, who was washing at the edge of the river. The look on her face was one of total disbelief—it's not every day a couple of white men drift past in such a fashion. A legend was born, second only to Mr Ooha's famous bridge.

Mr Ooha was one of the Indonesian drivers who doubled up during fieldwork as a pocket action man. He was a very small guy, always kitted out in army jungle fatigues, and never stopped moving. Towards the end of our epic Kreung Baso expedition we had a long walk back through the mountains to meet with the vehicles at the agreed rendezvous. This had been fixed before the expedition started, which was just as well since we had no working radio from day two. We'd been in the bush for nearly seven weeks and there was tremendous momentum behind us in the long march home. However, the night before we were due to arrive we made the mistake of pitching camp on the wrong side of a large river. We camped on the soft sand of a large meander in the river rather than crossing it and pitching tents on the very rocky opposite bank. During the night there was a tremendous thunderstorm that never actually hit us but clearly affected much of the upper river catchment. The river rose during the night, flooded out the tents and forced us to spend much of the night huddled together on higher ground listening to the sound of a raging river.

By next morning it was clear that the river, difficult to cross by foot in normal flow, was now impassable and we were within a day's walk of our final destination. We were obliged to spend several days stranded on the wrong side of the river. Our Indonesian counterparts kept themselves busy during the day devising ways of crossing the river. Mr Ooha first led the construction of a massive raft, watched all day with amusement by ourselves and the local labourers. Unfortunately, it was made with hardwood and rapidly sank during river trials.

Next came the bridge. We were woken early in the morning by the sound of giant trees falling to the ground. Mr Ooha had decided to build a bridge and was clearing a fair bit of jungle in the process. A crude walkway was constructed across the fairly shallow part of the river meander, but there was no well thought out method of spanning the deep raging river channel. Mr Ooha's bridge was doomed to failure and must have remained for many years after as a curious folly and a bridge to nowhere. When actually asked, the labourers built a splendid wooden raft in a couple of hours, capable of carrying four people and equipment. The method of crossing the fast flowing river channel was to launch the raft about five hundred metres upstream, then paddle like mad to get across the river so as to be in a good position to throw a rope to the brave labourer who had already swum the river and was waiting on the opposite bank. Knowing that there was a big waterfall one kilometre downstream added to the excitement. It took a few hours to get everyone and everything across the river in this way, and the effort certainly beat any management course team-building exercise.

After the Kreung Baso expedition we learnt not to involve ourselves in such remote field areas and much of our future fieldwork in Indonesia was centred around travelling along tracks and minor roads in our Land Rovers. That in itself had its associated problems. We had the brand new 110 model Land Rovers provided by the ODA. They had fantastic V8 engines and electric winches on the front, used on many occasions to pull us out of a river or remove a fallen tree. However, being the first of a new model we found many design flaws: fuel pumps inside the petrol tank, sliding windows that you could not open or not shut, and plastic door handles that were never up to regular jungle use.

It was during my second year of fieldwork in Indonesia that I had my first and most serious Land Rover breakdown. I was visiting a sampling team based in a rather remote part of northern Sumatra accessible by rough forestry tracks—the sort I used to refer to as 'brown trouser' drives. We had a large stone shoot-up from the front tyre which shattered the front disc brake. By the following morning we also had no clutch as the driver had never been told about use of the clutch housing drain plug when crossing rivers. We couldn't contemplate using the Land Rover with no front brakes and no clutch in an area of 'brown trouser' drives. So we were pretty much stranded. Fortunately, on this occasion, we did have a working short-wave radio. But given that this model of Land Rover was not available in Indonesia, there were consequently no spare parts available. By a stroke of luck the Camel Land Rover Rally had just taken place in Kalimantan and we were able to obtain necessary parts from one of the participating teams. The new disk brake was freighted to Medan and I had the great adventure of getting there, travelling for several days by foot, canoe and bus during the fasting month of Ramadan.

I think the moments I remember most about fieldwork in Sumatra are the evenings spent in jungle clearings, drinking Sumatran coffee, looking up at the wondrous night sky with the Milky Way vividly distinct in the absence of polluting light, and watching frequent meteors blazing across the huge horizon. It was always one of my greatest regrets that I was a scientist with a very specific specialism and not a natural scientist like the explorers of old. I often wonder how many undiscovered species of plants and insects passed me by unrecorded.

Put Me Down for the Snake Wrestling
Barrie Page

From 1975 to 1980 I led the initial phase of a project to carry out a geological survey of northern Sumatra, an area about the size of the UK. Six geologists from IGS formed the core team with numerous other geoscientists on short term assignments. The

Indonesian Directorate of Mineral Resources (DMR) provided counterpart scientists.

The team did a pretty good job and partly as a consequence of this I returned to Indonesia in 1985 as chief consultant to the DMR to implement an upgrading programme using an Asian Development Bank loan of around fifty-seven million US dollars.

So, there I was in 1985, sitting in my office and thinking about spending lots of money, when Eddie, the office administrator, waltzed in and said, 'It's our sports day in three weeks, what shall I put you down for?'

'What's left on offer?' I enquired, ever eager to appear cooperative. Eddie said there was climbing a vertical ten metre greased bamboo pole to release a cache of wrapped presents at the top—and snake wrestling! I had in fact planned to be a mere spectator at the sports, but since the greasy pole seemed a bit messy, I said to Eddie, as a throw-away, somewhat ironic, line 'OK, put me down for the snake wrestling,' and off he went.

Now Eddie had a perfect command of English, and, indeed Australian. He had worked in a bar in Bali and knew that cocktail and 'cocktile' referred to the same class of drink. However, one word it appeared did not feature in his vocabulary, and that word was *irony*.

And so it came to pass some three weeks later I was sitting in my office, still trying to spend the money, when Eddie appeared and said, 'You are on in fifteen minutes.'

I politely enquired, 'On what?' He said that I was number three entrant in the snake wrestling competition and he was first.

I had of course forgotten completely about the Sports Day and you could say I was somewhat surprised to hear I was about to wrestle with a very large python, and me in my best tropical suit. But, unlike my prospective opponent, there was no way I could wriggle out of this one. Eddie went off to prepare for his bout and I followed.

On the way to the arena I met the director of the DMR, Salman Padmanagara. He was the son of a Bupati—a Javanese Regent—and therefore from a very top notch Javanese family. A quietly spoken man—in fact the higher up the Javanese social ladder you were, the quieter you spoke. I always had to advise foreign visitors to sit as close to Salman as was politely possible otherwise they would not hear a thing.

Salman was always accompanied by several assistants, perhaps courtiers might be a more accurate word. During the course of a meeting—again 'audience' is probably more accurate—if Salman agreed that something should be done he would raise a finger, or perhaps an eyebrow, and an assistant would quietly detach himself from the entourage and Salman's will would be done. A master-class in control.

Salman was actually a really nice man and revered by his staff. Indeed, his organisation made trickle-down economics work. If there was any, shall we say, spare money available, the benefits did not remain solely at the top, every employee got something: for those at the lower end of the establishment this might be shoes or shirts for his or her family. He was the father figure of his organisation and consequently his Sports Day was a very popular and well-attended event.

So, Salman said to me, 'There are two pythons out there. One ate two chickens for breakfast, so choose the one with two lumps in it. It will be a bit slower.' A bit slower doing what, I wondered? Squeezing? Biting? Running away? Forgot—no chance of the last one of course.

Salman gave me a quick briefing. A circular area with a diameter of about twenty metres is watered, the ground outside remaining dry. The snake tries to remain on the wet area. It takes six or seven men to get the python out of a very large chest of water and the snake is put on the ground. The task of the contestant is simple, put the snake back in the chest of water.

I was told that the snakes belonged to the army and the

soldiers had brought them for the contest. Now we all know that an army marches on its stomach but these guys take it literally.

I arrived at the arena. There was a huge crowd. There was also a first aid tent, and Eddie, the first contestant, was already in it . . . and bleeding. He had done the preliminaries well enough, which requires one to pull the snake by the tail until it gets fed up and lies still. You then nip up to the head end, grab it by the neck, lift it and carry it to the chest.

It seems Eddie had been a little slow in grabbing the snake's neck, the snake had edged forward, Eddie's grip was too low down and the snake was able to turn and sink his teeth into Eddie's upper arm. The blood was impressive, Eddie was losing quite a lot of it rapidly, and I was losing interest at about the same rate.

Of course pythons are not venomous, but their dental hygiene leaves much to be desired and infection is just about inevitable. Just then there was a commotion behind as the second contestant was carried into the first aid tent. Same problem as Eddie, but he had been bitten on the thigh. The thought entered my mind that these pythons' mouths must be quite large to get such a big bite on both sides of a your thigh. I had better have some sort of battle plan.

I decided I needed to get a feel of what the snake was like, so I volunteered to help the men lift the snake out of the chest. The chest was full of writhing coils and there was no way I was going to be able to discern two lumps of ex-chickens anywhere in that unhappy mass of mixed reptiles. A snake head appeared and with one of the men helping with a sort of snake tongs I was able to get hold of the python's neck and others of the entertainment team grabbed the rest. There was a lot of the rest, about fifteen feet, with a girth thicker than a speed skater's thigh. I later discovered the snake was about as heavy as I was, which I suppose was going to make it a fair contest.

We took the snake to the centre of the arena. With a regrettable show of bravado I turned the python's head toward me, looked him straight in the eyes and announced, 'Now, I want a good clean fight—when I say 'Break', uncoil—and may the best snake win!'

The snake then looked me straight in the eyes and opened its mouth. I shall never forget this: the gape was wide enough to swallow my head and the interior of the mouth was a ghastly ghostly greyish white. But, too late to increase the insurance on my underwear, I was committed.

I started the routine of tail pulling, of which, by now, the snake was thoroughly disenchanted. But . . . it lay still. I crept up to its head. Fear was on my side and I plunged my right hand down onto its neck as fast as a snake's strike and so hard my fingers dug into the ground. I was not going to make the same mistake as Eddie. It was a struggle to pick up the rest of the snake but I managed to get it back to the chest, home and dry (well, for the snake it was home and wet) and I think we were both pleased with the result.

Many months later, as I was about to complete my work in Indonesia and return to the UK, I was walking in front of the DMR's main building with Salman. Coming towards us were two men who worked for the DMR, albeit in fairly lowly capacities. They looked at us as they passed and one said something to the other.

I asked Salman what had been said. He replied that one had asked the other what I did here. Now, having been pretty successful in my projects for the DMR in Indonesia, I thought the answer might have been something complimentary about my scientific contribution. So I asked Salman what the reply had been. Salman said that the man had replied, in a rather matter-of-fact way, 'Oh, him—he's the snake wrestler'! [1]

---

1 *Chris Johnson (see previous account) was also present at this python wrestling event and concludes that Barrie 'did more for British-Indonesian relations in those few moments than any number of visits by senior directors.'*

A Crocodile Story
John and Liane Baldock

Our last holiday weekend at the end of our second tour in Zimbabwe, in 1986, was spent camping on the banks of the Zambezi before our return home to England. We had just arrived after a longish drive from Harare and were having a late lunchtime sandwich and cold beer in this utterly peaceful and secluded campsite, with plentiful wildlife and stunning birds. We heard a distant commotion and splashing as a canoeing party upstream had a cooling dip off a sandbank near the opposite bank. A few minutes later we heard yells, screams and cries for help. The party must then have spotted our vehicle, which brought them rushing over—we thought, initially, looking for more supplies or beer.

But no—in the bottom of the canoe was a father with no arm and his son with a huge bite out of his shoulder. The boy had just got out of his depth and had been grabbed by a croc, so the father had stuck his arm in its jaws and managed to release his son—so all the croc got was one arm.

What to do? How to help? I decided I had to abandon our camp and take the two most seriously injured as quickly as possible to the National Park office, where there should have been first aid supplies. That drive took us nearly an hour and a lot of blood was lost on the way despite a tourniquet having been applied. Finally at the Park office there was saline but no drip needles to be found anywhere! However, there was a doctor on vacation from Botswana, who calmly looked around and selected a hollow whistling thorn that could be used as the drip needle! Once patched up and stabilised the father and son were flown out to Harare where they remained in hospital for two to three weeks due to infection.

Meanwhile back at our campsite tranquillity was still not restored—there were other minor injuries and the remainder of the group had to take their three canoes downstream to their allotted campsite, as they were not permitted to stay where we were! So off they went in the gathering twilight through hippo pods and unseen crocs, eventually reaching camp at 10 pm.

We heard, not surprisingly, that none of the party ever wanted to canoe the Zambezi again. However, the Zambezi Valley remains one of our favourite places on the planet and we were lucky enough to return in 2001 for the total eclipse—a magical and wonderfully dramatic event from that location.

Mountains and Memories
Martin Litherland

Having worked previously in Bolivia (see earlier verses), I found myself in the late 1980s working once again in South America, this time in Ecuador.

The Great Andean Adventure
(Traverse from Antisana Volcano to Cosanga, Ecuador, December 1988)

The greatest moments of one's life,
    You count them on one hand.
A high volcano was our start,
    Then down through unknown land.
Battling Cosanga's raging stream:
    A fortnight's journey spanned.
Frosty tents: the roof of the world,
    Down to tropical climes.
Miguel, Manuel as company
    Panting those airless climbs.
Laughing the river, to and fro:
    Those were the greatest times.
Exciting were those rocks we found,

Where they should not have lain.
A great nappe complex filled the hills,
    Due to a pushed terrane.
Serpentinites and skarnfields too
    Were secrets to unchain.
The joys of finding so much new:
    The scientific dream.
The exhilaration of the view,
    The working as a team.
Then, past the point of no return,
    Those struggles with the stream.
So those two weeks in Ecuador
    Fulfilled my life I know.
All came together on that trip
    As if in clockwork slow.
Sometimes I feel a sense of calm:
    A satisfaction's glow.

Local Hero

In the field overseas, a geologist will give his right hand for a man who is a good field assistant, driver, sergeant-major, trusty friend and a rock in times of adversity. So here is Manuelito who ticked all these boxes.

Manuelito
(A tribute to Manuel Celleri, field assistant, driver and friend)

¿Dónde estás, Manuelito? ¿Dónde estás? [1]
    You are sober through and through:
Man for a crisis, a family man,
    No macho poses for you.

---

1 * *¿Dónde estás?* ('Donday estas') = Where are you?

¿Dónde estás, Manuelito? ¿Dónde estás?
    You're built like an ox, we know.
But your knowledge and humour are enough
    When the weather starts to blow.

¿Dónde estás, Manuelito? ¿Dónde estás?
    Are you still eager to roam?
Like the times we shared when you pulled me scared
    Out of the Cascabel's foam.

¿Dónde estás, Manuelito? ¿Dónde estás?
    Do you remember those nights?
Your cursory glance in the jungle bar
    Would keep me out of the fights.

¿Dónde estás, Manuelito? ¿Dónde estás?
    Always a good man and true.
Breaking your back with the radio's bulk,
    Uphill from Rio Condue.

¿Dónde estás, Manuelito? ¿Dónde estás?
    In your eyes there is a gleam!
Hunting for rocks with your fourteen pound sledge,
    Panning for gold in the stream.

¿Dónde estás, Manuelito? ¿Dónde estás?
On our last trip we will seek,
Just me and you, the treasure of heaven[1]
In its Llanganates peak.

1 Atahualpa's treasure, (see poem opposite).

The Treasure Hunters

In Ecuador, tradition has it that the Llanganates Mountain is the site of the buried treasure of Atahualpa, the last Inca king. Many have sought the treasure and some have died in the attempt. I didn't expect to meet treasure hunters in this remote part of the Andes.

Atahualpa's Treasure

Llanganates, the mountains of the mind,
Where cold mists and rain leave you undefined,
You're straddled by Cerro Hermosa's sweep,
Atahualpa's treasure is yours to keep.

Ruminahui, loyal lieutenant he,
When advised of Pizarro's treachery,
Manoeuvred his gold-laden llama train
To this twisted, ice-worn, rocky terrain.

Valverde was first to the treasure site
In a cave or a lake? Which one is right?
Wrote his *derrotero* before he died:
It's always been an ambiguous guide.

After three days of walking, cold and wet,
We reach two mighty tents in silhouette!
Standing outside: 'Have you a drink for me?'
'Vee see you soon, Vee are having our tea.'

Bankers from Stockholm with tons of supplies.
So the next morning I sent out my spies:
Charting the lake with sonar equipment:
Trying to find Ruminahui's shipment.

We climbed Hermoso; we mapped all the rocks
We noticed the potholes that drained the lochs.
We followed the black marbles all around,
In which potholes and caves were underground.

Our final morning, approaching the Swedes:
'We know what you're doing! Hope it succeeds!
But surveying the lake may be in vain.
When our map's published, you should come again!'

Pit Stops
Pete Hobbs

I spent some time in the late 1980s in West Java (Indonesia) collecting geotechnical samples of tropical red clay from hand dug trial pits as part of an overseas research project. This work was shared with my BGS colleagues, Martin Culshaw and Kevin Northmore, and was invariably carried out in searing heat. Of course most of the hard physical work was done by a local crew who were used to digging water wells down to ten metres and whose fitness was frankly staggering. However, I pitched in as much as I could but in doing so lost a prodigious amount of fluid. The pits were dug on an *ad hoc* basis, often situated by the roadside, and generated great local attention, mostly from

Deep pitting for geotechnical sampling of tropical red clay in Java. (Photograph by P. R. N. Hobbs)

children. Usually our pits were dug with pick axes and spades to a depth of five metres and the spoil removed by bucket and rope. Needless to say no 'shoring' was felt necessary—fortunately tropical red clay soils are (somewhat counter intuitively) free-draining and self-supporting.

On a first day out in blistering heat, oppressive humidity and the occasional torrential downpour, it became clear that we needed a shelter. So the crew purchased a tarpaulin and some bamboo and with their machete constructed a shelter which could be built or stripped in two minutes flat and travelled around with us on the Land Rover roof for the rest of the sampling trip. Lunch usually consisted of maize roasted over a camp fire with some mangos, coconut milk and various odd looking roots collected en route. Usually the pits were filled in before moving on but occasionally we would leave one open overnight with appropriate safety precautions (bamboo fence). The next morning the termites would have started building a new home in its walls and there might be the odd rat that had fallen in and had to be removed before work could resume. Hornets were of the massive variety and distinctly unwelcome in a deep pit.

One of the strangest places we pitched up at was on the lower slopes of a volcano where an entire village was dedicated to the manufacture and sale of garden gnomes (maybe a hangover from the Dutch occupation). We also dug one pit on the football pitch of an army camp.

At the end of each day I had to pay the crew in low denomination bank notes. As I could only visit a bank at weekends this meant carrying a huge wad of notes in my back pocket, making me feel a bit like 'Lord Muck', and by the end of each working day I looked pretty mucky too. As the pay rate was so good (comparatively) I regularly had to turn away prospective workers who had heard about the project and were keen to demonstrate their digging prowess.

The same project also involved a visit to Kenya which was quite different to Java but our welcome from the local people was equally warm. The poorest of families would offer us food, drink and hospitality. The project provided me with an immensely enjoyable and rewarding experience.

THE 1990S: A COMPETITIVE WORLD

A notable feature of this decade in regard to BGS's international activities was the reduction in residential UK aid-funded work in the geosciences sector, and the consequent need for BGS to bid competitively for projects funded by international development agencies such as the World Bank and the European Commission. ODA/DFID continued however to fund an impressive programme of smaller technical cooperation projects under its Knowledge and Research (KAR) programme, which ran from 1989 to 2005.

You Must be Joking! Tales from an Administrator
Marion Squires

Attending to the requirements of staff on overseas postings included packaging equipment for mobilisation and forwarding items from family and colleagues at home. In our role as International Division administration team we had to complete the necessary customs documentation, and some staff were clearly unaware that we were required to open all packages that were to be sent overseas. The contents of such packages were not always what we anticipated! Some examples of note were:

- A package of 'field equipment' that included forty-eight jars of Ovaltine;

- A package of 'field equipment' that included one thousand condoms (for one person) but no Ovaltine;
- An 'emergency package' from a wife that included a feather duvet, pillow and a cuddly toy—nature of emergency unspecified.

The administration team were always hearing tales of hardship and lack of comfort, but sympathy was much reduced after a visit to two overseas project locations when the team saw the size of the houses provided, the swimming pools and number of servants. On that trip, however, there was an appreciation of some of the difficulties, such as being offered a coffee and then handed a tin of sugar in which the contents were seen to be moving, only to be told 'don't worry, they will die when they hit the hot water, and you are just getting more protein.'

It was a little frustrating for the office-based staff in Keyworth to administer travel claims from exotic parts of the world, and after a while we decided that we would not process any more claims unless we were brought back a small gift. After a few pieces of rock were received we expressed our thanks but explained that we had something more personal in mind, whereupon small wooden animals started to appear. At this stage we decided to be more specific—we wanted some 'duty free'. After that we began getting bottles of gin, vodka and whisky, all of which was gratefully received. And because we are very generous people we decided to share our spoils with all office-based staff. This saw the emergence of the overseas drinks cupboard, to be opened on special occasions, usually Friday afternoons. Even the director of the day was known to phone me and ask 'Marion, is the cupboard open?' The process wound down when returning staff started to bring back bottles containing bizarre additional ingredients such as lizards, snakes, scorpions and bits of vegetation.

Expect the Unexpected
Martin Smith

The Snake and the Maiden

Setting up a geological survey camp in the bush, especially when you know you will be there for several months, is an art form that requires experience and practice. There are a number of dos and don'ts, and here is a tale of one of the don'ts.

The BGS Phase II Geothermal Project (1988–92) involved the survey of a number of central volcanoes in the Kenyan Rift using helicopter support with flights from tented base camps. A suitable campsite location was therefore paramount in order to provide sufficient space for take-off and landing together with storage for fuel, equipment and tents to accommodate up to ten scientists, cooks, guides, engineers and counterparts.

Previously, the British colonial regime in Kenya had governed via a series of District Commissioners (DCOs) who when 'on tour' had an eye for selecting choice campsite locations in terms of shade, view and appropriate distance from the activities in the local village. One such site near the village of Nginyang was offered to the BGS project and viewed as ideal—extensive shade near river (dried-up), pleasant views and a suitable landing space nearby.

In setting up camp, the kitchen tent and dining and working areas take pride of place as it is here that all the important decisions are taken and must therefore have the best view. Secondly, the latrine (long drop) must be located suitably distant. The remainder of the tents are scattered around, with each person choosing a suitable spot. In this case Peter Dunkley, the project leader, perhaps seeking some relative privacy, chose a spot set back from the inner circle that had formed around the dining tent.

Our cook Joseph was an elderly gentleman from the Luo tribe in Uganda and a great character. Getting on in years he prevailed

upon his 'muzungus' to hire a local from the village to assist him
in his camp duties which included sweeping out the tents whilst
everyone was out at work. This was agreed and a young Pokot girl
was hired from the nearby village. After several days of relative
routine we returned from a day's reconnaissance to be told that
the young girl, upon entering Pete's tent to clean, had run out
terrified screaming 'Nyoka! Nyoka!—Swahili for snake! snake!
Others nearby, grabbed their pangas (machetes) and rushed to
investigate but found nothing. As it was the dry season and we
had seen snakes around we thought no more about it and Pete
slept soundly in his bed at night.

Next day, we returned to be told the same thing had
happened again with the girl rushing out screaming 'Nyoka!
Nyoka', claiming that she had stood on a snake. But again
when others immediately searched the tent nothing was found.
Being superstitious the Kenyans began to wonder if there was
something bad about the 'Bwana Kubwa's' (big bosses') tent and
the village girl refused to enter again on her own. Later that
night, being the last one to turn in, as I sat quietly finishing my
beer, a cobra (genus *Naja*) glided into the arc of light of the gas
lamp by my feet heading towards a nearby bucket of water. I sat
frozen to the spot, fascinated until it disappeared. Clearly there
were thirsty snakes in the camp!

Cobras very rarely attack people unprovoked, but when
disturbed, they will use their fangs to deliver a fatal bite containing
a strongly neurotoxic venom, which attacks the nervous system
causing paralysis. In Africa, animal noises dominate the night
time, but that night every rustle and slithering sound kept me on
edge and I thought twice about getting up in the night to answer
a call of nature! But why Pete's tent?

So on the third day a group of Kenyans suitably armed with
pangas and sticks lined up behind the girl as she entered Pete's
tent. At the first scream they rushed in—nothing. But then one
saw a fold in the groundsheet move and disappear. They dashed

outside and thus when we returned from a day's geology we were greeted with the sight of a large dead cobra hanging from the washing line.

The next day there were two, and the day after three! At which point, after some discussion regarding why Pete's tent should be the focus of such serpentine attention, it was decided to move it. What did we find? He had pitched his tent over an old infilled long drop toilet subsequently favoured as home for a nest of cobras with the entrance right under his groundsheet!

Cobras are known to be very secretive and often manage to live near houses for years without being seen, but in this case the condensation under the groundsheet of Pete's tent was attracting them out during the day. Obviously no-one was going to sleep easy that night now that we knew that a nest of cobras was patrolling the campsite—and my nine month old daughter was arriving next week! But with several hundred gallons of aviation Jet-A1 on site it did not take long for a final solution to be found.

At the next campsite we took more care in assessing the layout of previous occupants' facilities.

Killer Bees

Much has been written about the ferocity of the African bee (*Apis mellifera scutellata*). However the sting of the Africanised Honey Bee is no more potent than that of any other variety of honey bee. But according to Wikipedia what makes Africanised honey bees more dangerous is that they are more easily provoked, quick to swarm, and from their ground based cavities, they send out three to four times as many workers in response to a threat, and pursue their victims for greater distances. An Africanised bee colony can remain agitated longer and may attack up to a quarter of a mile away from the hive.

When swarming they can bring down a large animal with the huge number of repetitive stings, so they demand to be treated with respect. When a swarm approaches, the standard response is everyone stops and hits the ground. The golden rule is avoid aggravation at all cost.

One of the volcanoes that we were surveying during the BGS Geothermal Exploration Project in Kenya was Silali, a large volcanic caldera flanked by extensive lava flows of basalt cut by numerous faults and fractures. Satellite imagery and over-flights in our helicopter indicated the presence of water and vegetation in some of these fractures which would have to be investigated.

Martin Smith (right) with colleagues, Silali caldera, Kenya. (Photograph by A. J. Reedman.)

Operating practice was for the helicopter to drop off the survey team and then take off and wait at a prominent high spot until radio confirmation for a pick up. On the morning that we investigated one particular fracture it was typical rift weather, windless with temperatures in the mid to low thirties. I was dropped off with my local field assistant David to walk a short distance over the basalt flows to the fracture that we were to investigate. Wearing short-sleeved shirt and shorts and carrying a rucksack with sampling gear and limited water supplies, for it was only to be a brief visit, we scrambled up and then down into the fissure. About two and a half metres wide and four to five metres deep, the fissure was steep sided with sand at the bottom. Whilst sampling and recording water temperatures (cold) I noticed a few bees buzzing around. But it was not until we started climbing back out that I observed a small cleft in the side of the fissure wall from which bees were starting to stream above my head. David shouted we must go, *now*! and with a rising sense of panic we reached the surface as the bees started to swarm. Throwing rucksacks to the side we ran like mad-men for our lives across the rough black lava. Then, as the first bees alighted on us we threw ourselves to the ground.

As I lay there more and more bees alighted until I was completely covered from head to foot—in my ears, nose, up my shorts, and the noise was deafening. Chest heaving and sweat pouring off me I knew this was serious. Once the stinging starts it releases a chemical that encourages others to attack, but help in the form of the rucksack with the walkie-talkie and water was now a hundred metres behind me. With my face pressed to the ground I could just make out David lying deathly still a few metres away similarly covered in swarming bees.

Mercifully, the stinging never started. Whilst waiting for the bees to lift off I was treated to the spectacle of a line of ants marching past my nose—was I going to suffer a ground attack as well? After what seemed an age the last bee finally left my prone body and with only a few scouts left in the air David and I discussed tactics. Get up and run until out of range was the only option. Up, run and listen for the swarm approaching, hit the deck and don't move. We endured this for a total of four sessions before being able to stand up unmolested having finally reached the threat limit of the hive. It is distinctly unnerving to run at full speed unable to look back knowing that a black swarm of bees is about to descend on you and that you must hit the ground in good time to avoid being attacked. Miraculously, I only suffered about a dozen stings in total but now felt dizzy and exhausted with the heat and stress of being close to serious injury. Our only means of survival—our rucksacks—were now several hundreds of metres away, close to the nest, and we would have to retrieve them.

Time seemed to pass in slow motion as we waited for all the bees to finally return to the hive, but eventually we were able to walk and then finally crawl back to within a short distance of the rucksacks. Bee scouts were around with some resting on the rucksacks, so we would have to be very quick this time. David sprang to his feet throwing stones and yelling as he ran in off down slope. The bees swarmed furiously and set off in pursuit leaving me in relative calm to grab the rucksacks and run up slope in the opposite direction. I don't know if I could have endured a second flight from the bees but David survived and by the time we were finally reunited we were sweaty, exhausted and battled-scarred with red sting blotches and torn skin from the rough lava. A short sampling trip for a few bottles of cold water had turned into a four hour epic.

A Grand Day Out

During the BGS Geothermal Exploration project in Kenya we completed a mapping and sampling programme on a number of the central volcanoes in the Kenyan Rift north of Lake Baringo. Typically, after a month in our tented camp in this isolated area, everyone looked forward to a trip to the nearby town to purchase fresh meat, fruit and vegetables, repair clothes and vehicles and hopefully phone home. Euphemistically called 'a day-off', on one such occasion it provided some unexpected challenges.

On this particular occasion the team reassembled in the late afternoon after a day's successful shopping, paid off the *askari* and set off in two heavily laden Land Rovers back to camp. Nakuru, located in the centre of the Kenyan rift and with a population of around three hundred thousand, is a key market and trading town. In the late 1980s it had gained a reputation for vehicle scams. For example, coming back to your Land Rover to find brake fluid on the ground by the tyre and a helpful African hanging around who just happened to know a very good garage or *fundi* (workman, usually a relative) who could repair the supposed leaking brake pipe. It was therefore common practice to hire an *askari* or guard to watch over the vehicles whilst one was shopping.

The road from Nakuru back to our camp at Nginyang was part tarmac for five to six miles and dead straight, and then a dirt track. Driving along at 50–60 mph on the flat tarmac I was sitting in the front of the lead vehicle when suddenly it lurched violently to the left and the air was filled with a terrible screeching and grinding noise. Kangogo, the driver, did an amazing job keeping the vehicle in a straight line until it stopped. A burst tyre I thought as we jumped out but to our surprise I found that the wheel had come completely off and had disappeared! The brake shoes had gouged a furrow in the soft hot tarmac but surprisingly little real damage was caused. Was this another Nakuru scam?

We quickly straightened out the bent metal and fitted a spare tyre, having, amazingly, located enough of the wheel nuts back down the road to enable us to limp back to camp. But before we could leave there was the question of the lost wheel to resolve! We fanned out to look for it, but it was clearly not in the immediate vicinity. Running alongside the tarmac road was the old dirt road and as I walked along it several hundred metres beyond the Land Rover I could hear a low groaning in the bush. I then came upon a local Kenyan lying on his back in the middle of the track clutching his groin and with our Land Rover wheel beside him. Clearly he had been walking home minding his own business when he was struck from behind by our wheel travelling at speed—ouch!

Now the problems started. Clearly, the Kenyan was injured and we would have to take him to a hospital. As soon as he arrived the 'lawyers' would hear about this and descend on him promising huge payouts from the *muzungus* (us) for his injuries. We would have to report the incident to the local police and the British High Commission as a matter of urgency. My colleague, Peter Dunkley, re-arranged his Land Rover so that the victim could remain horizontal and set off for a local hospital about two hours drive away. My task was to find a local police station and make it official.

After about an hour of searching and as darkness fell we located a police post—no more than a hut with a radio and a flagpole in the bush. As we arrived a large tropical storm descended and to a background of flashing lightning bolts and torrential rain we entered the hut to find the incumbent three police officers blind drunk on local *chang'aa*. They dimly realised that we were presenting them with an opportunity to break the daily monotony of being stuck in the middle of nowhere, but also the possibility of some extra *chai*, but were incapable of rational thought, far less remembering the protocols. So I had to fill in the accident book as they bundled Kangogo, my driver, into a cell, stripping him of his shoes and ID until they sobered up and decided what to do next. Fortunately, they did not impound the Land Rover and I was able to drive back to camp.

It took another three days to get Kangogo out of the cell and the British High Commission lawyer on the case by which time the local grapevine had gone into overdrive and the victim was being encouraged to sue the British to make him and his family rich for life! It turned out his injuries did not compromise his manhood and future family options. But we duly spent another day in the police compound at Nakuru providing statements and cash inducements to have the Land Rover released before it could be impounded for a lengthy period. This time we carefully checked all vehicles before leaving!

What began as a 'grand day out' had turned into a farce which cost the project three days of down time and endless negotiation with officialdom. So when in Africa, always expect the unexpected.

Starting with a Bang
Bill Barclay

In 1993 a consortium comprising BGS and mining consultants McKay & Schnellmann won a three-year World Bank contract for institutional strengthening at the Zambian Ministry of Mines and Minerals Development—this in competition with Italian consultants who were already in place at the Geological Survey Department on an EC-funded contract. One of the BGS components of the contract was to edit and print twenty Geological Survey maps and accompanying reports, part of a large unpublished backlog that had accumulated since the early 1970s. So successful was the project that the ministry's permanent secretary persuaded the World Bank to award BGS a second three-year contract on single tender in 1997. The main component of this project was to map an area of northwest Zambia on the border with the Democratic Republic of Congo.

In the meantime, in 1996, BGS had won a two-year EC-funded contract to continue work on clearing the Zambian Survey's geological map backlog and edit and print another twenty maps and reports—this again in competition with the same Italian consultants. In the event, the contract was so over-financed that there was enough money to provide two contract extensions, so that by 2000 the entire backlog of about sixty geological maps and forty-five reports was cleared.

The BGS team of Sandy Macfarlane (regional geologist, Africa), Peter Mosley (to be the World Bank project manager), Bill Barclay (BGS project manager in Zambia) and Mary Hurley (BGS head of administration) travelled to Lusaka to negotiate the World Bank contract in April 1997. The permanent secretary's PA led us along the corridors of the ministry, where we entered a dimly lit conference room and awaited the arrival of the Zambian delegation. The permanent secretary immediately noted the lack of light in the room and asked for a fluorescent tube to be installed in a strip light above the conference table. An electrician was summoned but announced that the light wasn't working. 'Of course it's not working!' said the PS, 'go and fetch a tube!' Muttering to himself, the electrician went off, returned with a tube and clambered onto the conference table. As he inserted the tube into the fitting, there was a brilliant blue flash and a loud bang. 'Told you it wasn't working!' he said and made a hasty exit.

And so the negotiations began in a typically African way, and the contract was eventually signed and Peter Mosley flew to Lusaka to start the work later that year.

Tanked Up
Paul Turner

The 1993–95 World Bank funded project at the Zambian Geological Survey Department (GSD) included the daunting task of preparing twenty geological maps to be litho printed in the UK. These maps were to be prepared in the drawing office at Lusaka, where the staff and facilities were ill-prepared for the task. We would be employing the cartographic and reprographic techniques of the day: thus cartographers would be using scribe coat for the lines and stick-on lettering for the type and symbols. Combinations of percentage screens would be required for the colour separations, which meant that the working system would require a fully equipped dark room with a constant water supply for the operation of the photographic processing machine imported from Europe.

At the start of the project the water supply at the Survey was totally inadequate. The mains supply in that part of Lusaka was erratic and whenever the Survey's storage tank was filled it leaked so badly that the site was often without water within an hour. Consequently the main Survey toilets were a location of last resort for project staff! The GSD had no money to repair the tank, so the World Bank project staff decided that it would be better to pay for the design and installation of a new water supply system that could be used exclusively for the Drawing Office. The chief cartographer, Joseph Bwalya, was a Beatles fanatic and a very practical man. Having designed and built his own house, he relished the challenge of designing and ordering all the equipment necessary for working with the BGS senior cartographer, Christopher Murray. Within a relatively short time (by Zambian standards) the equipment was delivered and began to be installed.

Firstly, a large square-sided tank was placed on the ground and connected to the mains supply. This tank would be filled whenever the mains supply to the Survey was working. It was to be connected to a cylindrical tank about three metres in diameter and one and a half metres high that would sit on top of a five metre high tower erected next to the Drawing Office. Water could be pumped to the upper tank from the lower tank, and this would supply water at the pressure required to run the photographic processing machine.

On the day the cylindrical tank was delivered we gathered outside to see how it was going to be lifted to the top of the tower. But where was the crane? There was no crane. Instead, a team of about a dozen men appeared, led by a fearsome foreman. They leaned two pieces of wood the thickness of telegraph poles up against the side of the tower and rolled the tank into place against them. Four men clambered to the top of the tower holding ropes that were looped around the tank. As the men on the tower began to pull the tank upwards those on the ground used long poles to push the tank and maintain its position centrally on the two supports. At times the tank would appear to slide to one side or the other, and the watching crowd would move back thinking it was about to fall, but the foreman bellowed orders and the men on the ground quickly prodded it back into place as it continued its slow ascent. As the tank came level with the top of the tower we realised that it would overlap the edges of the square topped platform. We held our breath—surely the men at the top would be pushed off the platform as the tank reached its final resting place? The tank tipped onto the platform with a bang just leaving space for two of the men to stand on the platform's back two corners while the other two quickly climbed over the edge to escape being pushed off. Clearly they had done this before and all knew the drill. The tank was pulled and prodded into its final resting place and we all breathed a sigh of relief as the team climbed back to the ground and the foreman returned his men and equipment to the back of their truck and drove off.

Without any Health and Safety Assessment being undertaken we had our tanks in place and in the next few days the final plumbing work was completed allowing us to successfully test the system.

As a bonus the water tank was linked to the Drawing Office toilet, which thenceforward became a popular attraction in the GSD. The toilet was refurbished with a new seat but we quickly became fed up with the number of times that splashes were left on the seat after use by male staff. When staff were questioned about this we discovered that few of those who had a toilet at home were provided with a plastic seat, and for them the ceramic rim of the bowl was considered to be the seat. These people thought the plastic seat was merely a protective cover and therefore left it down when urinating so the rim 'seat' would not get wet. This cultural anomaly was soon pointed out and the practice was stopped.

The film processor was delivered and plumbed into the water system, and worked perfectly. The wooden crate that the processor had arrived in was an object of desire for several GSD staff. Because of his skills in plumbing and woodwork, which had helped us to refit the dark room, the Survey's handyman was allowed first pick of the wood. A few days later we went to see him in his workshop expecting him to be making a cabinet or something similar, but instead found him making a child-sized coffin from the lid of the crate. Almost every week during our time at the GSD a funeral collection would be made for a staff member who had lost one of their family, either to malaria or what they called 'this disease'—the AIDs epidemic which was then spreading rapidly.

The next weekend I helped Tyson Tembo, one of our cartographers, take some of the wood to his home in the high density suburbs—high density being the Zambian term for what is known elsewhere as a township. I also took with me my daughter Helen who was just over eighteen months old. This tiny *muzungu* with her straight blond hair was a source of wonder to the township children. When we got home an hour later she had to go straight into the bath to remove the finger and hand prints that had left red dust all over her face and hair.

We completed the twenty maps within the scheduled two years. Bill Barclay, the project leader, searched through every drawer in the library and contacted every ex-GSD geologist he could find in order to locate original material. Bill's success in finding even more original data led to a second contract, with some sixty maps being eventually completed.

Elements of Health
Fiona Fordyce

Working as a geochemist at the British Geological Survey I had several opportunities to work on overseas projects concerned with the study of the distribution of various chemical elements (arsenic, iodine, selenium and zinc) in the environment and their effects on either human or animal health. These projects, which were funded by the UK Department for International Development (DFID) and implemented by BGS International

Division, not only allowed me to travel to various remote parts of the developing world, which I might otherwise never have visited, but also to work on projects contributing to the welfare of poor local communities.

Cattle Country

My first overseas trip for BGS, in 1993, was to north-eastern Zimbabwe to study zinc deficiency in cattle in relation to the zinc contents of local soil and forage. The project was managed by my BGS colleague Don Appleton, and I will always be grateful to him for the opportunity to work on this and subsequent DFID projects, which have not only been career defining but have provided some of the highlights of my life.

I flew out to Zimbabwe with another BGS colleague, John Ridgway, who stayed for the first week and helped me to establish links with our veterinary counterparts in the Veterinary Ministry and University of Zimbabwe. Our contacts at the Ministry of Mines included Peter Pitfield and Diarmad Campbell, who were engaged on another BGS project related to gold exploration.

The area where I was to work, near Mount Darwin in NE Zimbabwe close to the Mozambique border, was very remote, and I set off with a field assistant, Richard Mbofana, in a Land Rover from the Ministry of Mines. We were able to stay in the local Tsetse Control Veterinary Station in the first field area. My job was to collect soil and vegetation samples from a predetermined set of villages that were predicted to be in either low or high zinc areas, whilst the vets were collecting blood samples from the cattle grazing in these villages. We had to work independently as the vets needed to get the blood samples back to refrigerate at the end of each day. Therefore, Richard and I would set off at about 4.30 am to get to our field locations in order to carry out the sampling whilst it was still cool. I'll never forget the magic of driving through the African dawn—the colours and hues as the sun came up were just spectacular. We were the only vehicle on the brick-red dirt roads apart from the odd heavily listing, overloaded, fume-belching bus.

Each village was incredibly clean, tidy and ordered with swept earth around the rondavels. However, the people didn't possess very much and all had to walk some distance to collect water. In one village a woman asked me to help her sick son and I had to explain, with difficulty, that I wasn't a doctor. Her son had been to see the witch doctor and had huge lesions on his legs as a result of the treatment. He was in the army and had come home sick. Sadly, he was the first person I saw with AIDS.

One day, we'd completed sampling a village and returned to the Land Rover only to find that it wouldn't start. Having had no Land Rover maintenance training, I couldn't see where the problem lay as the lights were still working and there was nothing obviously wrong. This was before the days of mobile or satellite phones and we had no radio. With no means of communication, we were stuck! We were told there was a telephone in the post office in the nearest town. We duly walked the twelve miles to get there and asked if they had a telephone. 'Yes,' said the man in charge very proudly lifting it onto the desk. The trouble was that the cable didn't go anywhere and it hadn't been connected for three years! Finally we were able to radio from the local police station, and in due course the vets came to our assistance! The problem turned out to be a faulty battery connection, enough to power the lights but not to turn over the motor—I lived and learned!

On another day we'd been driving for hours along what was basically a bouldery river bed in order to reach a village. Having arrived at this remote place we were greeted by a man dressed immaculately in black trousers, patent leather shoes, white shirt and black tie. He was the local school teacher and asked if we would mind giving him a lift back to the main road, which we did gladly. We had so much kit in the back that I couldn't really see very much behind me but was very surprised at the other end when not just he, but two woman, three kids and a flock of chickens made their way out of the Land Rover!

There wasn't any accommodation in the final field area, so I was kindly invited to stay at Richard's home. His wife killed a chicken in honour of his return. Many of his family came round in the evening and as had happened in a lot of the villages, children came up to touch my skin as no-one below the age of twenty-five had seen a white person in that area. I asked Richard how many brothers and sisters he had: 'Acht Fiona I don't know—my father has four wives—I have so many brothers and sisters' he said! The first questions I was always asked in every village were: was I married and how many children did I have. Since the answers were no and none I went from being something of a celebrity to being a very poor person in the space of a few seconds!

In between field areas I had to go back to Harare to drop off samples. It was always a rush to try and get back before it got dark as we'd been advised not to drive at night in order to avoid all the animals, people, carts, cars, bikes, lorries and buses using the roads without lights! I will never forget the smell when driving through the orange groves north of Harare at dusk—it was the most fantastic fragrance as the earth slowly cooled down.

In Harare I had a Zimbabwean friend from university and luckily was able to stay with her—much nicer and more convenient for sorting out samples than being in a hotel. It was interesting being able to experience both aspects of Zimbabwean society. After five and a half weeks hard graft in the field area and then sorting out and shipping the samples, I took a couple of days leave at the end of the trip to visit Victoria Falls. I did a flight in a small plane above the falls which was truly awesome—a much overused word but in this case justified. By some twist of fate I happened to visit Niagara Falls six months later and found them rather disappointing in comparison!

Our study demonstrated that there were indeed links between the zinc status of soil, forage and cattle and that zinc deficiency was a problem in that area of Zimbabwe.

Arsenic and Exotic Food

In 1994 I worked with fellow environmental geochemist Martin Williams on a DFID project that included an assessment of arsenic contamination of soil and stream water and shallow groundwater in an area of tin mining in central Thailand. Here, tragically, arsenic was causing skin cancer in the local population. Other than the study itself, which demonstrated that the local soils and the foodstuffs grown on them, as well as the local water, were a source of arsenic, what sticks in my mind was the food. I really struggled to face the traditional Thai breakfast of rice porridge with a raw egg and spring onions every day! Apart from that, however, the food was excellent and I enjoyed eating stir fried flying ants, garlic grubs and frog amongst other things. I also remember being in ramshackle wooden hut houses in quite remote villages that had large TV screens and all the locals knew the names of UK football teams. When they heard I was from Scotland they were even shouting out teams like Motherwell! It was very weird to be half way round the world in the middle of nowhere and to find your culture exported even there!

Travels with a Jam Jar

The year 1995 found me working in China and once again I must express my gratitude to Don Appleton for the opportunity to work on the DFID-funded project 'Prediction and Remediation of Human Selenium Imbalances'. This proved to be an incredible experience from start to finish. The project was looking at three field areas: Don led one, Chris Johnson the other, and I was in the middle area in Hubei Province, central-southern China. In my field area in Enshi District we were investigating the selenium status of the local environment—soils, water and crop samples—

and comparing that to the selenium status of the local population as measured in hair samples. The purpose of this exercise was to establish a link between a selenium deficiency-related heart disease, called Keshan Disease, on the one hand, and selenium toxicity or selenosis, which causes hair and nail loss and nervous disorders, on the other.

Having flown out for twelve hours overnight to Beijing, I arrived late morning at the Institute of Rock and Mineral Analysis (IRMA) and was taken to see our counterpart Prof Li Jiaxi, a fantastic person, and was introduced to my co-workers, Dr Ge Xiaoli and Prof Zhang Guangdi. Xiaoli was a young geochemist with excellent English and we got on very well and are still good friends. Prof Li Jiaxi explained that to save money on the project she had arranged for us to travel to Hubei Province by train rather than fly and that to save even more money we were travelling hard bunk (second class) not soft bunk (first class) on the train. I had already been on the go for over twenty-four hours when we arrived at the dwarfing architecture of Beijing central station at midnight to board the train.

The ensuing journey was an unforgettable experience. In each section, open to the corridor, there were six bunks that folded down into seats during the day. What immediately struck me was the immaculate dress of the train attendants: very smart uniforms with caps, brass buttons and white gloves, in total contrast to the toilet facilities. These basically consisted of holes in the floor of the train; it looked like someone had pushed their foot through the floorboards to create them! All of life was on the train: families, produce, chickens, household goods, all manner of worldly possessions, and rising serenely above it all, classical music piped permanently over the airwaves. The attendants came by regularly with hot water and tea and I quickly procured a jam jar with lid as a tea mug—everyone else had one! We travelled through mile upon mile of flat agricultural land with peasants (their words not mine) in traditional hats and arrived at the

Yangste River train terminus at midnight the following day. We were met by local drivers, transferred to minibuses and driven like crazy through the night on twisty mountain dirt roads, arriving at Enshi late morning the next day. By this point I'd been awake for well over forty-eight hours and had to go straight into a meeting with all the top local officials to set up the project.

The hotel in Enshi had en-suite rooms but although basins and toilets were present the plumbing didn't actually work—many world travellers will recognise this situation. We had excellent collaboration with IRMA and with the Department of Public Health local officials. It was an amazing experience travelling to remote villages, some of which could only be reached on foot. The villagers had never seen a Westerner before and in each one we were welcomed like celebrities with banquets laid on for lunch in many cases. I ate most things including boar's stomach, which was like a shoe-sole, but I remember at one banquet as guest of honour it was my role to start the meal by eating the eyeball of the baked fish that was the centre piece on the table. I'm afraid to say I declined and passed the honour on. Speaking to one of our local counterparts he told me that he had a degree in agriculture and broadcasting. This seemed like an odd combination to me until I realised that even the most remote villages had a public address system. Every morning at 9 am the national anthem was played and Beijing shouted out the news to every remote corner of China. It was also impressive that each village had electricity for at least some hours of the day and a school. We were often working in the schools, which had interesting open plan toilet facilities and on more than one occasion poor Xiaoli had to stand at the door fending off crowds of school girls all wanting to rush into the loo with me.

Two key hobbies/passions in China are karaoke and ballroom dancing. Everywhere we went we'd be working with officials in suits who were very serious but would then suddenly turn into Frank Sinatra in the evening! All our counterparts had really good voices, singing Chinese ballads along to laser disk karaoke machines. The only western song on these machines was Auld Lang Syne. I can't sing for toffee, but had to give numerous embarrassing renditions throughout the trip.

When I'd first arrived at Enshi the start-of-project meal was held in the number one banquet suit in the government restaurant. When we returned to Enshi I was no longer the number one guest, we'd been demoted to the number two banquet suite because the Province Governor was in town. We had our meal in the usual karaoke suite and then were taken downstairs to a vast ballroom with all the other guests. Much to my mortification the Province Governor asked me to dance—just the two of us on the huge dance floor with everyone else watching—a foxtrot. Being Scottish I'd been brought up on Scottish country dancing, not ballroom dancing, so I didn't know my foxtrot from my elbow. He very graciously said at the end—'so you are not very familiar with ballroom dancing'—after I'd stepped all over his feet! At the end of the trip I sent a message back to BGS saying that if I was to do similar projects in the future, I needed to go on training courses in hairdressing (we'd been collecting hair samples) and ballroom dancing!

It was a real privilege and pleasure to work with our counterparts in China, they became friends and we did very good work together to enhance the understanding of selenium geochemistry and health internationally. It was an experience I will never forget.

In 2000 I was fortunate enough to work with IRMA again in connection with Chris Johnson's DFID-funded iodine project in China (Environmental Controls in Iodine Deficiency Disorders). I flew out there with our UK medical counterpart Dr Alex Stewart. It was another amazing experience working in the Turpan depression and Taklimakan Desert in villages where IDD had been reported. We were again assessing the iodine status of soil, crops and drinking water against that of the local population. This is where China meets the Muslim world on the old silk route and it was fascinating to experience the merger of cultures with the local Uyghur people.

Even in the short space of five years, Beijing had changed dramatically. No more dominated by bicycles as it had been in 1995 but now choked with cars, McDonalds and IKEA—the West's 'gift' to Chinese culture!

Children waiting to be weighed, Xinjiang Province, China. (Photograph by F. M. Fordyce.)

Water sampling in the Wushi-Kuqa area of Xinjiang Province, China. (Photograph shows Fiona Fordyce, taken on BGS camera, photographer unrecorded.)

Smelling a Rat
Dennis Hackett

As a 'humble administrator' with visits confined primarily to Swindon and Edinburgh, I would view the foreign travel of staff from the International Division with some envy. But my opportunity to contribute to such activities arrived in 1995 when I was asked to join BGS geologists Sandy Macfarlane and Alf Whittaker in negotiating the World Bank funded Petroleum Exploration and Development Technical Assistance Project in Papua New Guinea. I felt rather a fraud as all the work on the bid had been carried out by the International Division's administration team, but as I was the NERC/BGS authorised signatory for contracts and the World Bank insisted that a contract be signed on the spot at the conclusion of successful negotiations, I found myself on the flight to Port Moresby. An added bonus for me was that the negotiations in Papua New Guinea allowed me to visit my parents in South Australia—at my own expense, of course!

And so it was that the three of us were standing in the arrivals shed at Port Moresby airport, looking very forlorn at the non-appearance of our luggage. I recall Alf and I feeling quite agitated whilst Sandy took the matter in his stride and using his diplomatic skills ensured that our 'lost' luggage would reach us within two days. The next thirty-six hours were spent by the poolside, as the people we were due to meet were not ready to see us, for reasons unknown to us. I recall thinking as I sipped a drink in my grubby state, 'this is the way to live, just as I imagined overseas work to be!'

On our return to Port Moresby airport to collect our luggage, we were directed to a dark storeroom, which emitted a disgusting smell. Our suitcases, once located, were seen to be damp and I remarked to Sandy and Alf that that rainwater must have penetrated the storeroom to which Sandy responded in a matter of fact tone, 'that's not rainwater, it's rats piss.' This did not deter Alf from sitting in the minibus on the return journey to the hotel hugging his suitcase as if it were a lost child.

As a footnote, a contract was agreed and signed, which initiated some fifteen years of BGS involvement in Papua New Guinea, encompassing eight separate projects.

Days of Note
Laurance Donnelly

Mother's Day, 1996

In 1996 I was on the island of Montserrat, a British Overseas Territory in the Caribbean, as part of a team responsible for monitoring the ongoing eruption of the Soufriere Hills Volcano. Sunday 12 May was Mother's Day on the island. The local people were busy gathering whatever flowers they could find that had not been damaged by ash from the eruption. I arrived early at the volcano observatory to begin work when suddenly an enormous ash cloud appeared near the summit of the volcano, which the prevailing easterly wind caused to drift in the general direction of the observatory. Soon, Sunday morning was transformed from beautiful and bright sunshine to blackness, as the sun's rays were totally blocked by the ash cloud.

As an officer on duty at the observatory, I had a fundamental question in my mind. Was the ash cloud arising from a hot pyroclastic flow travelling along the Tar River to the west from the volcano, or was this a surge cloud ahead of a pyroclastic flow? In other words, was the observatory in the path of a potentially devastating flow of hot ash? We had no way of knowing. The chief scientist asked for a volunteer to make for the helicopter, waiting several hundred metres from the observatory. The pilot was already at the helicopter and ready to fly to the summit of the volcano. I was at that moment taking refuge behind a reinforced concrete column in the observatory and decided to volunteer. Outside the observatory all was blackness with visibility reduced to zero. Hot ash and rain burned through my clothes, and thick, hot ash began to accumulate everywhere. With eyes already streaming from the effect of acidic gases, I managed to fix on my gas mask and helmet. I then located the roadside kerb with my right foot and in complete darkness followed the kerb line several hundreds of metres north until I came out of the ash cloud. The helicopter with rotary blades running was a welcome sight and after a few minutes we were ready to go.

Pyroclastic flows from eruption of Soufrière Hills volcano, July 1997, Montserrat; viewed from north. (Photograph by S. C. Loughlin.)

On the flight to the summit of the volcano I managed to ask the pilot to collect the observatory photographer and videographer, as they were located near St John's to the north of the island. I was now ready to observe, whilst my two colleagues could film and photograph the volcanic activity. On the approach to the summit of the volcano a small delta consisting of recently deposited volcanic debris was still incandescent and generating spectacular water explosions. This was clearly the result of a pyroclastic flow, which had generated the early morning ash cloud. The summit of the volcano was now shrouded in ash and cloud. In an instant we were hit by a sudden heat flux, which was felt inside the helicopter. The skilled pilot was able to track the pyroclastic flow along the Tar River Valley from where it then entered the sea, and on a cushion of compressed gasses and air was propelled across the surface of the Atlantic Ocean, expanding and accelerating in deathly silence. For the first time since the 1902 eruption of

Fountain-collapse pyroclastic flows and surges sweeping down the northern and northwestern flanks of Soufrière Hills volcano, October 1997, Montserrat. (Photograph by G. E. Norton.)

Mont Pelée on the nearby island of Martinique, which killed thirty thousand people, a pyroclastic flow had been observed to enter this ocean, and for the first time it had been recorded on film. It was a spectacular geological event, and soon the images were being transmitted around the world!

Welcome Friday

Fridays often brought me a welcome break from the almost daily routine of being covered in volcanic ash, often unavoidable during work on the flanks of the volcano. It was on Friday afternoons that I had the opportunity to speak and interact with the local residents, including the elderly and women and children of all ages. Many of the residents had been displaced following the evacuation of the capital town Plymouth and all were becoming increasingly concerned about the ongoing volcanic activity and associated geological hazards, which included pyroclastic flows, *lahars* (mudflows), seismic shocks, landslides and ash falls. Some were confused by the sudden influx of geologists, volcanologists and journalists from the UK and other countries.

Each Friday I would visit a different village and sit in the local evacuation camp. Often this comprised a tent or stone building (church or community hall). It was made known locally that I was available and willing to meet and talk with the residents. At first many were wary, but soon began to feel relaxed and confident. Face-to-face they had the opportunity to ask a geologist simple questions, to become better informed about the volcanic eruption or to lay to rest some of their main concerns. I found this was an excellent and effective way to communicate geoscientific and geohazards information to people who had little or no previous understanding of geology.

In 2005, having moved on from the BGS, and some nine years after my original posting to Montserrat, I visited the island again to design and implement a ground investigation for the construction of a bridge in the Belham Valley, which had been infilled by *lahar* deposits, and to investigate a landslide at the Montserrat Volcano Observatory. Many of the residents recalled the time we had spent almost a decade earlier, talking and discussing geology and the volcano. Most of the young children were now teenagers or young adults.

The positive feedback they provided, and the memories they shared, demonstrated the value of those earlier meetings and the subsequent communication programmes undertaken by staff of the Observatory with the local residents of Montserrat. Effective face to face communication, starting from the bottom upwards, has proved to be critically important during the management of the ongoing volcanic crisis on the island.

Going with the Flow
Chris Johnson

I've been a reasonably good distance runner most of my life. This I have done mainly for recreation and occasionally competition, but whilst working in Morocco (1999–2003) it was a skill I was very glad to have.

During a weekend off from our DFID iodine-related research project in the Atlas Mountains, I went with a work colleague to visit one of the large gorges in the Anti Atlas. It was a big tourist attraction, so we parked our hire car in a conveniently located car park at the bottom of the gorge. After four kilometres walking up the gorge we were passed by a Frenchman coming down on a mountain bike splattered with mud. He passed us with a lot of arm waving and shouting something about 'inondations'. That was a puzzle as there was no water to be seen in the dry river bed of the gorge. After another kilometre we were passed by a very muddy Jeep full of French tourists all urging us to turn back to avoid the 'inondations'. Well, they didn't stop to offer us a lift, so it couldn't have been that important. Just as we arrived at a restaurant in the middle of nowhere, owned by an elderly English lady living with a young Moroccan man, something resembling hot chocolate started to trickle down the erstwhile dry stream bed. After about five minutes this had turned into a faster moving torrent of very muddy water. High up in the gorge's catchment area there must have been a very substantial torrential downpour.

It suddenly registered that we had left our hire car at the bottom of the gorge in the car park occupying the dry river bed. Leaving my colleague at the restaurant I decided that I would have to outrun the flash flood to rescue the car. What a race that was! And what an incentive to win! The pathway crossed the river of mud in many places so the run involved quite a number of tricky crossings. It was like wading through treacle. I raced as I'd never raced before and caught the front of the flood about eight hundred metres before the car park. I must have been quite a sight running into the car park covered from head to toe in mud. I jumped into the car and moved it to higher ground just in the nick of time. I then returned up the gorge to join my colleague, a return journey that involved quite a tricky route along the wall of the steep-sided gorge as most of the pathway was now under water.

I'd beaten the flash flood and avoided having our hire car washed away. We declined the offer of a floor to sleep on at the restaurant, instead choosing to spend the night sleeping under the stars at the top of the gorge.

A CHAPTER CLOSES, 2000–2011

During this period DFID's interest in funding geoscience-related projects suffered a further decline. At the same time, health and safety concerns about working in challenging overseas situations, combined with high overhead chargeout rates, made it difficult for BGS to bid competitively in the world market place. This situation would lead inevitably (in 2011) to the dismantling of International Division as a distinct entity.

A Sort of Peace
David Greenbaum

Looking back, I recall that it was my colleagues Ian Penn and Mike Petterson who, in 2002, first blazed the BGS trail to Afghanistan. This was not long after Kabul had been liberated; the city was in tatters and was a forbidding and daunting place to visit, so all credit to them for braving it. At that time, I was BGS International's Regional Manager for the Middle East and South Pacific but had no formal involvement in Ian and Mike's venture. Indeed, it was a completely unofficial initiative as I recall. Even so, I was fascinated to hear their grim accounts of the city and see the photographs of bomb blasted buildings. I recall Mike's account of staying in one of the many 'guesthouses' that had sprung up in Kabul. His visit was in the depths of winter when temperatures drop to minus 20 °C. He related how the heating in the bedrooms was provided by diesel-fuelled, drip-feed stoves. No health and safety assessment there! In fact, Mike's stove somehow exploded one night and he was lucky to escape—and not to burn the place down in the process!

Mike and Ian reported back on the Afghans' desperate need for assistance. All that remained of the old Afghan Geological Survey (AGS) building was a concrete shell—pock-marked by

War-damaged building in Kabul, still partly occupied by homes and businesses, Afghanistan. (Photograph by R. P. McIntosh.)

bullet and shell holes but fundamentally solid. It had been built by the Russians in the 1980s and was intended to last. Located near the Kabul River it was on the front line during the fighting of the 1990s. It had taken much bombardment during the conflict: no windows or doors remained and all the wiring and everything else of value had been stripped out.

Despite this, and the total lack of resources or funding, the Afghan geologists turned up each day and sat drinking green tea. To their everlasting credit they had risked their lives to remove and keep safe the archive of old geological maps and Russian mineral exploration survey data, knowing full well how important it would be for the future. These documents they had buried or stored in their homes.

The US Geological Survey was already interested in getting involved as were we in BGS, but for us it was to be a long battle, both with the BGS Board—who were primarily concerned about the safety of staff—and with DFID, who now had other priorities than minerals and mining. It was only after a direct request from President Hamid Karzai to Tony Blair for assistance from 'the BGS' that the FCO called us to the table. The meeting I attended in London caught me somewhat unprepared. I explained what BGS could do and had expected some further technical discussion but in response I was simply asked how much it would cost. I hesitated, not wanting to rule us out of contention (our overtures to DFID had been roundly rejected up to this point), but then plumbed for what I felt was a modest figure in the low millions of pounds—nevertheless a large sum in terms of BGS projects hitherto! Their immediate response was 'Well, that shouldn't break the bank'. Too late, I realised I should have asked for a lot, lot more!

The project needed a fair bit of planning (as well as the Board's sanction) and I made several visits to Kabul over the next year or so to get it started. With only a single contact person in Kabul—a local 'fix-it' named Mr Shams, who Mike Petterson had found—I began the hunt for local staff (office manager, drivers, cook, security and so on) and for a house suitable for the project team. I was lucky to have been recommended to Zia, a well-educated and bright young Afghan, and I appointed him to be office manager. Large houses with compounds were scarce and the demand from westerners was high, so rents were exorbitant. After much searching, I managed to secure a six-bedroomed house in the Shar-i-naw district for a mere $84,000 per annum!

This was comparatively cheap and I even negotiated prepayment of only the first year's rent: usually the landlord demanded three years rent in advance. I held the staff interviews in a small room at the Assa 2 guesthouse on a very wet and windy day. Zia had lined up a bunch of unlikely looking candidates for the various positions and brought them in one by one. Speaking some English was of course essential, but beyond that it was very much instinct on my part. Making selections was not a pleasant task as all were hungry for paid employment and anxious to please. For all I knew I might have been hiring ex-Taliban to guard us!

Interviewing for the position of cook was especially difficult. How do you tell if someone can cook by just asking? I did not even have the luxury of a kitchen to try them out. One obviously good candidate (with hotel and restaurant references) wanted a lot more than I could offer, so in the end I chose someone else who seemed OK on the face of it. In fact, he turned out to be quite hopeless, despite the tireless efforts by members of the BGS team to teach him (especially Mike Watts, I recall, who even created a photo menu of the various dishes—just like a Chinese restaurant). So meal time in the BGS house was always an 'experience'. I particularly remember trying, usually without success, to cut through his pizza bases! Even so, and for reasons I never quite understood, the project team accepted this state of affairs, and it was not until one of my supervisory visits well into the project that I decided enough was enough. I dismissed him with a month's salary and recruited a proper chef. Thereafter, meal time was something to look forward to with real anticipation. It was only sometime later that Zia confessed the 'cook' had actually never been a cook. He was in fact a driver but since by the time of his interview all the driving jobs had gone he went for whatever position was on offer.

Afghanistan had its share of dangers, but these were not always the obvious ones. One incident early on in the project (27 September 2003) stays with me. Mike Petterson and I had been on a short exploratory visit to Kabul and were departing for Dubai on one of the four identical Airbuses that the Indian government had donated to Afghanistan's national airline, Ariana. That fact alone should have alerted us, and the knowledge that the UN did not allow their staff to fly Ariana should also have been a warning, but in reality we had little choice. On the face of it the aircraft looked sound enough but inside the seats were grubby and there was a distinct odour of age and sweat. It was far from being new and one could only hope and trust it was airworthy. As the plane accelerated down the runway I remember feeling a slight shudder and twisting motion but thought little of it and then we were airborne.

As is usual, the plane began circling the Kabul basin to gain the necessary height to clear the mountains, but when after half an hour I noticed we were still circling Kabul, I knew there was something wrong. Soon the captain came on the intercom and announced that there was a 'small problem with the undercarriage' and said they were trying to deal with it. For a long while we heard nothing more. Mike and I tried to remain calm but we were both fully aware that problems involving the undercarriage tended to be anything but 'small'. We spent the time considering our situation and wondering. As time went on and we continued to circle, we reasoned that the crew had not managed to resolve the 'small problem' and were now burning off fuel in preparation for a return to Kabul.

An hour and a half into the flight the captain came back on and confirmed this in a matter-of-fact voice. But the lack of any real information was worrying. To their credit, most of the passengers remained quite calm. Many were Afghans and I suppose to them it was just one more event in a series of life-threatening situations that they had learned to live with. Finally, as we approached the airport we were told to adopt the brace position. There was none of the usual pillows or blankets on board so I just cushioned my head in my jacket and hoped for the best. Finally, the plane touched down and remained for what seemed a long time on the rear landing wheels, only dropping down onto the nose wheel once we had lost most of our speed. As soon as this happened the plane slewed off the tarmac and almost immediately came to a standstill on the sand. The engines were immediately cut and everything went quiet. After a few moments the captain came on the loudspeaker sounding very relieved and admitted that the problem had been a lot more serious than he had told us: the nose wheel assembly had apparently twisted during take-off and could not be retracted. It appeared he had slowed the plane to minimal airspeed for landing keeping the fuselage at a steep angle and the nose up until the very last moment.

Despite the sorry condition of the plane, we had evidently been in very experienced and capable hands. The captain, when he emerged from the flight deck, turned out to be a very distinguished looking middle aged Afghan man with just enough grey hair to give him an aura of quiet confidence. Unfortunately, I never learned his name. Word had it that Ariana pilots during the war had to deal with all manner of situations, including missiles being fired at them, so probably this was a relatively minor incident to him! We later learned that we had had yet another lucky escape of which we were not even aware: apparently, the sandy areas off the runway had still not been cleared of landmines at that time so even after getting the plane safely down we could easily have been blown to pieces!

We emerged from the plane to a melee of fire engines, military vehicles and the UN, and were swiftly transported to the terminal in buses. It was still only mid-afternoon and despite our 'close encounter' everyone was anxious to get away from Kabul, so it was with some relief that we learned we would be leaving on one of the other Airbuses. But then all announcements ceased and the afternoon wore on. Because at that time the runway had no landing lights, flights were not permitted to depart after dark since they would not be able to re-land if there was problem.

Despite this, it was not until after dusk that the flight was finally called and we were all made to run across the tarmac and up the steps. Sitting in the same seat allocations on an identical Airbus (its registration differed by only one letter from the previous flight!) was a true déjà vu experience and rather unnerving. The same passengers were around you, the same crew, and the same smell of the aircraft. We were also conscious that were there any repeat incident, landing back in Kabul would not be an option. But finally we were off. No more emergencies and we got to Dubai somewhat late but only a little the worse for wear. From this point on in the project, we secured permission to fly all staff in and out of Kabul on the United Nations Humanitarian Air Services (UNHAS) flights from Dubai!

Kabul was always full of interest and excitement. One of our immediate tasks at the outset of the project was to renovate a small part of the geological survey building to provide a functional work area. So, from being geologists we suddenly became construction managers trying to organise a host of Afghan contractors and dealing with issues about which we knew little. I think we did a good job on the whole given our very limited finances and experience, and in a few short weeks managed to refit a number of offices, install windows and doors, furnish and heat them, provide generator power, set up a computer system, and start work on the geological database. But even amid the serious business of rebuilding the Survey, there were moments of humour.

There was, for example, the matter of the Survey's toilets. The only 'facilities' at the time were open-air pit latrines with hessian sacking for doors. You had to be brave—or really desperate—to approach them, let alone use them. Toilets and water were of course a priority. We knew there was an old sewer system leading away from the building and our idea was to get this back into use. I recall one sunny day standing outside the AGS with Zia, watching as a large tanker siphoned the accumulated sewage out from a massive septic tank. I reflected that what we were looking at represented the total output of the Afghan Geological Survey for the last twenty years! It was cruel humour but had Zia falling about with laughter. Mention of it afterwards never failed to get him giggling. Even so, we never did manage to completely sort out the toilets and it was not until the US project spent $6 million dollars renovating the entire building that the problems were finally solved. But even then toilets remained a preoccupation with the Afghans, and hours were spent at the weekly UNOPS meetings talking about such things as urinals, proximity of male and female toilets, size of cubicles, and the colour of the walls!

Throughout the project, Kabul remained a cash society with no facility for bank or credit cards, so having the necessary cash to cover all eventualities was important. Not only did we have to have US dollars for day to day expenses, we also needed to pay staff, cover larger purchases, and retain sufficient for emergencies. Our project was low in the pecking order in Kabul and held little sway with the authorities. My view was that in the event of a serious emergency, having a stash of cash could make all the difference. So I commonly held $25,000 or more in the house safe! There were real risks in this strategy but on balance I felt it provided the means of getting our staff out if it proved necessary. Visiting the bank was in itself an interesting experience. Standard Chartered was surrounded by a chicane of razor wire, and armed guards ascertained who you were before admitting you. Inside the compound you were scanned and body searched before being allowed into the bank itself. Each of the tills had a cash drawer filled wall to wall with dollars, mostly $100 bills, and refreshed by deliveries from the vault as 'supplies' dwindled. Just as in the movies, people would open up and fill attaché cases with $100 bills which were counted out by the teller using a money counting machine. My withdrawals of usually five or ten thousand dollars were, by comparison, small beer. But the main problem with cash was keeping detailed accounts of every expense however small plus receipts, and counting the notes on a regular basis to make sure it balanced. It was, of course, down to the team leader to make good if there was any loss. Even a one dollar discrepancy could mean counting it all over again. I have memories of piles of bank notes stuck with yellow post-its spread across my bed! I often longed for one of the bank's counting machines!

The BGS project was never well financed and we were forever under threat of closure for one reason or another. I recall the Afghan Minister of Mines coming to London halfway through the project and being told by the powers that be that the project was to be terminated. Once again, it took President Karzai's intervention to stop this happening. For BGS, staff safety was the main worry, and although we had guards at the house, they were not armed and our security relied mainly on keeping a low profile. In reality, we hoped our project was just too small and insignificant to be noticed—and it seemed to work! Our main protection involved staying alert and being constantly aware of our surroundings. Our ultimate security, if time allowed, would have been the British Embassy compound: we just hoped they would let us in if it came to it (but we could never be sure!). We did have a 'bolt-hole' in the basement of the project house stocked with emergency supplies plus a safe holding a large stash of emergency USD.

Fortunately, we never had to resort to extreme measures. The closest I came was the incident on 29 May 2006 when a US military vehicle accidentally collided with some civilians in Kabul. The troops handled the aftermath badly and it ended in riots and looting across the city. At the time, the BGS team was working in the AGS offices alongside Juliana Stoyanova from Adam Smith International (ASI). In contrast to BGS, ASI had round-the-clock professional security and she was immediately contacted by radio and provided with an armed escort to take her back to the well-protected 'Elephant House'. We were delighted

and very grateful when she offered to 'rescue' us too! We spent
the rest of the day sunning ourselves on the roof of their very
elegant and well-stocked house supping beers and listening to
gunfire across Kabul! Indeed, it was with some reluctance that
we finally returned to our own, much more basic and almost
'dry' house towards evening when all had quietened down!

Although the AGS itself was dysfunctional, one shining
star was the pre-school nursery housed in a low-rise building
alongside the war-ravaged main block. Somehow, this block
had survived, or efforts had been made to refurbish it, so that

Geological Survey pre-school nursery, Kabul, Afghanistan; the fancy dress items were donated
by BGS staff. (Photograph by R. P. McIntosh.)

the young children of the staff could be looked after. The ladies
who ran the crèche were very caring and it was a charming
scene, despite the facilities being basic. The children were
delightful and although they had little in the way of toys or
stimulation, it was evident that they were not short on love.
This was clearly an opportunity for intervention. Back home,
a call for toys and clothing on the BGS intranet, accompanied

by some photographs of the children, brought an immediate response. Soon we were inundated with no-longer-needed children's items, and a crate of donations was packed up and sent off to Kabul. I well remember the handover ceremony at the nursery, the gratitude of the ladies, and the excitement of the children—who had never seen so many toys. This provided a most rewarding experience and, unlike geology, one that brought immediate, tangible benefits.

A large number of BGS staff spent time in Kabul over the life of the project. Some were initially hesitant but almost all were keen to return after the first visit. It was that sort of place. Life in Kabul was never dull, and even though one had to stay alert to danger, we managed to get to some of Kabul's excellent restaurants, walk the back streets, climb the monuments, and visit the Friday markets or Chicken Street looking for antiques, rugs or mineral specimens. I even recall meeting the real 'Bookseller of Kabul'. Working with the Afghan Geological Survey and the ministry was always interesting, even if challenging, but I believe we made a difference. In fact, of all the difficulties we faced, the main bone of contention for us was the much better funded, parallel US Geological Survey mission in the AGS! I quickly came to realise what was meant by 'two nations divided by a common language'! Though our objectives were similar, our approach and attitude could not have been more different.

Postscript. After retiring from the BGS in 2006, I found to my surprise that I really missed Kabul, so much so that when the World Bank invited me to return and establish a new Project Management Unit within the ministry, I accepted and returned for a further nine months. I left Afghanistan for the last time in 2007.

Going the Hard Way [1]
Colin Waters

Short Circuit

There are two routes that can be taken across Mauritania eastward towards Mali. The recognised, southerly one is the Route d'Espoir, a partly metalled road from Nouakchott, the capital city, to the small town of Néma, the last habitation some two hundred kilometres short of the border with Mali. The alternative route, which we were to attempt as part of my two month field season in January to March 2002, was the northern one via the old Foreign Legion outpost of Tichit. More regularly travelled by camel trains, we had been told that in the previous year the Paris–Dakar Rally had followed this route and found it tough going, even with support teams. So here was a challenge if ever there was one.

The first nine days of the field season, starting on 5 February, initially involved mapping around Atar and returning to the creature comforts of a hotel in the evening. Atar is quite a large town, well stocked with provisions. It even had an international airport, though arrivals appeared to consist of a weekly direct flight from France: offloading tourists who would be immediately whisked off into the desert for a Beau Geste experience.

From 15 February we started a seven-day circuit of the Atar and El Gleitat region, with its own adventures to tell. The rocky desert to the southeast of Atar, though apparently desolate, seemed to be home to many small villages and nomad camps and did not feel too remote. Seeing grass huts shaped like igloos

---

1 Between 2001 and 2004 BGS undertook a geological survey of about 500,000 km^2 of southern Mauritania as part of a World Bank assisted Projet de Renforcement Institutionnel du Secteur Minier (PRISM). The project included the training of counterpart geologists from the Mauritanian Department of Mines and Geology (DMG).

dotted amongst date palms along dry *wadi* courses, such as I saw at Terjit, seemed like a journey back in time.

The route we planned to take was rumoured to be accessible by vehicle, though nobody was sure. It provided a perfect opportunity to establish a good camaraderie within the field team and learn from our mistakes before trying the grand traverse. The team comprised Takiyou Ammi, the driver of a Toyota Land Cruiser Station Wagon, which was also my vehicle, and Aba Ould Mohamed, driver of a Toyota Hilux, the camp cook Oumar Gassama, and the Mauritanian (DMG) geologist Diakhité Mamadou.

My BGS colleague, Roger Key, with his extensive field experience in Africa, immediately recognised in Takiyou someone who could be depended upon and suggested he should be my driver for the campaign. He was not wrong. Takiyou was very strong but equally gentle. He was profoundly deaf and found communicating difficult but was an excellent sand-driver and worked ferociously when it came to setting up camp. Aba was much younger, had much less experience and all the bravado of youth, and being a relative of the PRISM director led to some advantages for him. He had a tendency to race too fast, often getting stuck in sand dunes, and generated complaints from Takiyou that he would burn the clutch driving like that—a prophetic statement as it turned out. Ultimately, after a bit of confrontation, Aba realised that this was an opportunity to learn much from someone with great experience and he became a good team player.

We had found Oumar by driving around the market area of Nouakchott looking for someone who could cook. As the party had to be all male and men don't tend to cook in Mauritania, this was not easy. In the end Oumar was my cook on all my expeditions and did a wonderful job providing food with the limited resources available, not much in the way of choice of ingredients and, as the ultimate compliment, giving nobody food poisoning. It was only at the end of our time together when he explained that his trick to stop us being ill was to wash the meat in bleach! On days when we had a fixed camp he also washed some of my clothes, presumably using the same bleach. I would return to find underpants and socks rolled up neatly on my camp bed. At times Oumar would also act as my hammer carrier, decorating it with a tasteful pink ribbon. Diakhité, a young geologist, was initially quiet but I soon realised he had a wicked sense of humour and we became good friends, accepting that all conversations were in French, a second language for all of the team, but in which I was hardly fluent.

For the start of the seven-day circuit we were constrained to drive along a narrow straight gorge (the Oujeft corridor) extending south-eastwards about fifty kilometres as a deep cleft in the Adrar Plateau. A memorable overnight stop was at the sizeable but very remote village of Taungad. Dominated by small one-room adobe houses, this was more developed than many villages. As is typical of the hospitality of the locals, we were given use of a house for the night. The owners seemed happy to sleep outside and the least we could do was share our meal. With no electricity the village was pitch black by the time we were cooking by campfire, save for the myriad of other campfires outside all of the other buildings and the haunting sound of drums being played from various quarters of the village. The house was too small to accommodate all of us, so we pitched the cook's tent and I slept there for the night. At some point during the night I was awoken by a noise. As I strained to adjust my eyes to the dark, I realised that what at first sight appeared to be a gremlin, turned out to be a fennec fox with huge bat-like ears, perched inches from my face. I'm not sure which of us was more shocked, but the fox abandoned his snuffling through the camp supplies and dashed around the tent shrieking in a desperate attempt to find the exit.

The next village further down the gorge, Oujeft, represented living very much on the edge. It comprised one main street, which at one end was a hive of activity with people congregating outside their houses, watching the strange sight of our team arriving. The other end of the street was abandoned because large active sand dunes were rolling down the street swallowing up houses as they went. The next day we would encounter our first significant belt of sand dunes which would have to be crossed in order to reach Far'aoun.

This part of the campaign involved having to establish a new camp each night. We used two of the local *khaima* tents for camp. The *khaimas* were bulky and very heavy but relatively easy to put up, with a central pole and lots of sand heaped around the bottom of the tent to hold it in position. The fabric was porous to the finer fraction of windblown sand, so each morning one would wake covered by a coating of sand, which would get everywhere. On waking, my first experience of the day was the grinding of teeth on silica. If the winds got too strong the tents would easily blow down, and the trick was to collapse them and cover them in sand before they blew away, then spend the night trying to sleep in the lee of the Toyotas. Despite stories of the extreme cold at night in the Sahara, it was never unpleasantly cold, but often very windy.

Universally a problem, scorpions appeared to appreciate the warmth and shelter provided by the tents. There was a morning dance routine, akin to a Mauritanian version of the tarantella, on lifting the mats to find a scorpion or two somewhat annoyed at being disturbed. Food comprised rice and meat, the latter sun-dried on thorn bushes by Oumar whenever we stopped to look at geological localities. This form of *biltong* became tastier with time.

In order to complete the loop, there was a short traverse across sand desert to the metalled road that leads to Nouakchott. The last few miles were hampered by the only serious sandstorm I experienced in the desert. This was the sort of storm where visibility was down to a few metres. It was unnerving to find an old 2CV van half buried by sand, and I was left worrying that the same fate might befall ourselves. But the worst of the storm dissipated in an hour or two and we were relieved to be heading back to the big city.

The highlight of the three-day break in Nouakchott was the luxury of a wash/shower. During the traverses we had to carry all our water supplies in the back of the vehicles and it meant that when in the field we could only afford a wipe down with a wet face cloth. Safely back in the project accommodation, I could at last savour a cold beer/G&T or two, courtesy of a long-time resident and ex-BGS colleague, Al Wilkinson.

Le Grand Traverse

We departed Nouakchott on 27 February carrying out the full-day drive to Atar. Arriving at nightfall, the local Gendarmes were waiting to turn us all the way back to Nouakchott on the instructions of Samory Ould Soueïdatt (Le Directeur PRISM). We managed to get permission to stay the night in Atar so that I could find out what the problem was the following morning. It transpired that I had departed with the original team, but Mr Samory also wanted an extra geologist, Mohamed Abdellahi Ould Bouamatou (from Société d'Etudes Minières, Pétrolières et Industrielles), to be included. This presented us with a great logistical problem in that we were trying to achieve the crossing carrying all of our fuel and water supplies, with the need to leave space to collect hundreds of field samples. The addition of an extra person, with their equipment and food and water needs could jeopardise the whole trip. But, in order to prevent my expulsion from the country, I had to send a driver to Nouakchott to pick up the geologist and return the same day. This enforced delay allowed us to find the final member of the team, local guide Sid'Ahmed O. Megueya.

There was also the matter of a couple of days of field inspection by Frik Hartzer from the South African Council of Geoscience, and my counterpart Jack Rogers from BRGM, currently working further to the north. It was only when they opened up the back of their spanking new Station Wagon, showed me their fridge and offered me a cold coke that I realised how basic our existence was in the field. This was probably the only time in the field I had drunk anything colder than body temperature. At times, when we came across nomad camps, we were able to supplement our diet with some curdled camel's milk kept in goatskins. Surprisingly refreshing, but it couldn't stop my day dreaming for another cold coke!

On 2 March, we left Frik and Jack behind, and commenced our four-hundred-kilometre-vehicle-traverse on a track (or *piste* in local terminology, but nothing to do with ski slopes) from Atar to Tidjikja. The traverse followed at the level of the upper part of the Plateau d'Oujeft Group, with isolated sinuous ridges of quartzite of the Njakane-Abteilli Group representing so-called megacordons, and interpreted as the inverted topographical expression of Late Ordovician glacial meltwater channels. Exposures were limited, with extensive weathering on the Tagant plateau limiting the need to stop often *en route*. A notable stop was the Aouelloul meteorite impact crater, first identified in 1950. A clear elevated rim surrounding a sandy basin, there was no doubt this was a crater, but it was not sufficiently spectacular to much delay our journey southwards.

We arrived at Tidjikja at lunchtime on 6 March. Tidjikja is a small town where the last provisions, petrol station and water supplies were available. We spent a couple of hours buying provisions, repairing punctures and meeting the Wali, to seek permission to head eastwards across the desert.

The next stage, from Tidjikja to Tichit, was about 250 kilometres. We were able to travel fast in the afternoon without the need to stop as exposure was poor. After a further half a day driving on the monotonous sandstone plateau east of Tidjikja, the piste descended one of the few routes down the cliffs (Falaise du Hodh) into the Aouker Depression. The view southwards from these cliffs into an apparently endless sea of huge sand dunes was somewhat intimidating—this really felt like the Sahara. Our route, not marked as we had expected by a clear piste, relied upon following the narrow gap between the sand dunes and the cliffs. Following earlier tracks was somewhat dangerous as one would suddenly pull up realising that an active sand dune now buried the previous route. Here we started to become accustomed to the procedures of extracting vehicles from the sand. One such delay meant that we didn't arrive into Tichit until late afternoon.

We drove straight into the compound of the old Foreign Legion fort. We were allowed to pitch tents for the evening and given the luxury of using the shower—it was hardly a power shower, but any opportunity to remove the fine sand fraction from ones hair was always appreciated. We were told that we had just missed two British compatriots who had stayed in the fort the previous evening on their planned crossing of the Sahara by camel. This put our expedition into perspective. Though on subsequent days we looked out for them they were not to be found.

East of Tichit, the track rises from the Cambro-Ordovician succession of the scarp slope onto the escarpment of Siluro-Devonian sandstones and mudstones of the Aratane Group. With water supplies overly stretched by the enforced additional team member we needed to fill up our drums with rather saline well water at the last well before crossing the twenty kilometres stretch of dunes. The one or two camel herders at the well would be the last people we would see for more than two days. It was so remote that we came across a couple of white antelope, possible the very rare addax, and I had to stop the driver's natural instincts to chase after them.

In this area the sandstones were weathered into extraordinary arches and towers, many with petroglyphs. The most striking of

Sandstone arches at Makhroughat, Mauritania; this one resembles an elephant. (Photograph by C. N. Waters.)

Examples of petroglyphs at Makhroughat, Mauritania. (Photograph by C. N. Waters.)

these is at Makhroughat, a small mesa in which the sandstone had been sculpted into weird shapes and where we camped the night. As well as rocks in the shape of a camel and elephant, the most spectacular aspect was the presence of a large triple arch with broad views across the sand desert and a cooling breeze. This must have been a favourite camping stop for many years as the walls of the arches were covered in Arabic and older graffiti and petroglyphs. Walking around the cliff faces it was easy to find overhangs beneath which people must have sheltered long ago. It was possible to see that they had been working flint arrow heads in the distinctive green and orange chert found in the local Cambrian succession, leaving fragments of patterned pottery and broken ostrich eggs (probably used as water storage jars) and pestle and mortars.

We were aware of the security problem in the Néma area, notably smuggling and general banditry associated with the Tuareg tribesmen, because of proximity to the Mali border. Carjacking was the favourite activity, commonly involving attacks on campsites at night. The bandits would use the lights in tents to guide them and drive through the tents, killing or maiming the occupants and stealing their vehicles. On the positive side, immediately post the 2001 terrorist attacks in the USA, public opinion appeared to be still pro-Western and at this time pre-dated any clear terrorist threat in the region. We had decided, where possible, to stay overnight in villages, but here at Makhroughat we were at least two days drive from the next village of Oulata. That evening, as we sat around the camp fire, it was a worry to hear several distant gun shots. From here on we felt the need to be extra vigilant.

The crux of the expedition was whether we would be able to cross the twenty kilometres wide dune belt east of Aratane. With deflated tyres and regular use of sand ladders to negotiate the dunes and with our guide Sid'Ahmed running ahead to determine the safest route we crossed the dune belt in half a day on 11 March. At this point we felt, really for the first time, that we would accomplish the traverse and realised that going back was no longer an option as supplies would only last for the drive to Néma.

And so it was, that having crossed the hardest part of the traverse and feeling in high spirits, the Hilux suffered a complete failure of the clutch. At this point we knew we were out of range of the medevac facility we had arranged back in Nouakchott. It was suggested that we should leave the Hilux with a driver and one geologist and get rescue by driving the 140 kilometres or so to Oulata. However, my preference, met with a degree of incredulity, was to keep the team together and try and tow the Hilux. I made the satellite phone call back to the project house in Nouakchott to let them know the situation and see what could be done about acquiring a new gearbox. To make the situation more of a challenge, I was told that my flight out of Mauritania had been brought forward to the early morning of 15 March. At that point, Nouakchott seemed a very long way away to me.

For the remainder of that and the following day we towed the Hilux some 250 kilometres to Néma on a rough piste over regolith and sand with some active sand dunes. Progress was slow as we knew we could not afford to stall the Station Wagon in sand, so the guide and drivers would climb the highest dunes and meticulously plan out a maze-like route through the sand. Meanwhile project leader, Peter Pitfield, was busily searching for what turned out to be the only Hilux gearbox available in Mauritania at the time. He handed it over to a taxi driver and asked him to undertake the day or so drive using the 'easy' Route d'Espoir to meet up with us on the assumption we would get to Néma.

Just before we arrived in Néma, our last hurdle was having our passage blocked by a train of hundreds of camels, with several mounted by Tuareg nomads, each in dark blue headscarf, billowing *bou-bou* (the traditional gown) and obligatory rifle. Given their ferocious reputation we sat tight, unable to photograph this spectacular sight. They were heading for the route we had just taken, perhaps ultimately heading for Algeria.

By some miracle, within thirty minutes of us arriving in Néma, the taxi turned up with our spare part. Asking around, we managed to find a mechanic who did the full instalment of the gearbox outside his house on the sandy road, throwing in a couple of mud flaps which we'd lost on route, for the grand total of £8. After the Hilux clutch was repaired and the Wali at Néma had been visited to let him know of our safe passage, the remainder of 13 March and the following day were spent driving from Néma to Nouakchott, arriving back at nightfall on 14 March. There was no time to say thanks to the crew and dwell on the adventure. The next morning I was off to Casablanca, then on to Rabat to start working on my presentation, based on the field season's work, to the Nineteenth Colloquium of African Geology at El Jadida.

A Life-Changing Experience
Wilfried Bauer

First Impressions

When I was interviewed for a vacant senior geologist position at the British Geological Survey in October 2004, the final question put to me was, 'Are you prepared to work in Madagascar?'

My answer was simple, 'Yes, of course.' I had been working in several parts of southern Africa over the previous year, and thus the prospect of being engaged as a field geologist in a hot tropical country was nothing new to me. After the interview, I tried to recall what I knew about Madagascar:

- a large island in the Indian Ocean, off the east coast of Africa;

- a former French colony;
- noted for its lemurs—primitive primates which are unique to this island.

That was all. Not very much, I had to admit.

Once my appointment was confirmed I decided to learn something about the country in which I was expected to undertake my first assignment. This was, however, easier said than done. Except for some basic economic figures in statistical yearbooks and on the internet, Madagascar seemed to be of concern only to naturalists interested its endemic fauna and flora. The population, their local traditions, the political situation, and not least the details of the country's geology, remained vague in the few non-French-speaking sources available to me. Even a travel guide that I found in a bookshop reduced the country to an array of nature reserves and parks designed for the casual tourist. With no direct flights to that island, except from Paris, it seemed to me as though its former colonial masters had created a curtain to hide this mysterious island from the outside world.

In February 2005, I had the chance to get my first impression of Madagascar when I was chosen to accompany the BGS Business Development Director, David Ovadia, to fetch a signed copy of the contract document and to make some purchases for the first field season, scheduled to start in June. BGS, in partnership with the US Geological Survey and a local consultant, had won a major World Bank assisted project to undertake geological mapping and mineral reconnaissance in northern and central Madagascar, an area of approximately 139,000 km^2 of predominantly mountainous evergreen forest and savannah grassland. It would be a daunting task, involving the geological surveying of ninety-eight map sheets at 1:100,000 scale, the collection of over twenty-one thousand stream sediment and panned concentrate samples for geochemical mapping, and rock sampling for petrological, mineralogical and age determination purposes. Each geologist would have to cover an area of 100 km² per day! In addition, our consortium was to undertake reconnaissance mapping and sampling over a further area of 115,000 km².

We arrived in the late evening at Ivato International Airport after a ten-hour flight from Paris. The airport looked like an architectural disaster from the 1960s, its size and design being all too like that of airports served by low cost airlines in Europe. The airport was twenty-five kilometres from the centre of the capital city of Antananarivo. We had to queue three times in the arrival hall: for a short-stay visa stamp, for passport control, and for baggage. I had the impression that there were as many Malagasy officials as passengers.

On the morning after our arrival, I had a first view of Antananarivo, a town of 1.7 million inhabitants located near the geographical centre of Madagascar. It is home to almost 10 per cent of Madagascar's population. Many of its inhabitants, living in very poor conditions on the outskirts of the town, have arrived in recent years from the rural areas of this large island of 587,000 km². In comparison to most sub-Saharan African capitals, Antananarivo has a unique appearance and flair. Built over a cluster of granite hills, which are separated by rice paddies in the intervening deeper valleys, the old town is comprised of two- or three-storey brick buildings, often with steep, decorated metal roofs. The orange-red of the houses forms a splendid contrast to the lush yellow-green of the rice fields and the ink-blue sky over the city. The architecture is slightly reminiscent of rural towns in southern France, mixed with an indigenous component. The summit of the highest hill is crowned by the ruins of the old royal palace (then recently gutted by fire but now restored) and the still intact palace of the prime minister of the old Merina monarchy that ruled the country until 1895. The 'high society' had their residences around the royal palace in the uppermost part of the old town.

A social hierarchy can still be observed today: from upper class villas on the hilltops where a permanent cool breeze keeps away mosquitoes and flies, down to the shabby shanty towns on the margins of the rice fields where the poor live in mosquito-infested huts in permanent danger of flooding.

During the next few days I made my first excursions outside the capital, purchased topographic maps and tried to improve my less than basic French language skills. Unfortunately, as I soon realised, French is spoken only by a small minority in the larger cities although it is the official language, together with Malagasy, a language of the Austronesian family with strong links to dialects spoken on Java and Borneo. The population is descended from Austronesian groups who arrived in the fifth century or earlier, and many people that I met in the capital would not be noticed as strangers in Jakarta or Kuala Lumpur.

Compared to many other countries in southern Africa, Madagascar has some advantages: no large wild animals (apart from the now rare Nile crocodile) or venomous snakes, no landmines, no ethnic nor sectarian divisions. With a long dry season from April to November it seemed that the whole field campaign would be quite easy to manage. The road network appeared to be quite dense and all areas that we would have to visit appeared to be accessible by road. The available maps dated back to the 1960s, so I assumed that the infrastructure might have even improved since then. My excursions in the vicinity of the capital showed quite narrow but good surfaced roads through open, undulating grasslands. Here and there a granitic inselberg rose out of the grassland, giving a geologist sufficient outcrop to do his work. With these very positive impressions I returned to the UK and started to draft the work programme for our first expedition. I assured my colleagues at the BGS that this expedition would be child's play. Unfortunately, I had seen only the nice bits—the difficulties would become apparent only after we had installed a full team in-country.

Food for Thought

In June our first group left England and arrived in Antananarivo—minus a significant part of our equipment and personal luggage which, it transpired, was en route from Paris Charles de Gaulle Airport to some other part of the world. This airport is probably the worst place for a traveller in the northern hemisphere. Although some of our belongings arrived during the next few days, some important items (most critically all the geological compilation maps and images) never turned up. This was a perennial annoyance over the life of the project, for it seemed to me that Paris CDG was nothing less than a black hole for luggage.

The team for our first field expedition contained eight geologists from BGS and USGS, our four Malagasy counterparts, six drivers and a cook. What we urgently needed was a group of field assistants that we could train to collect the thousands of stream sediment samples required by the project. Fortunately, a professor from the University of Antananarivo was able to send us some thirty undergraduate geology students as potential candidates who could take on this task. Surprisingly, more than half of the candidates were young ladies. We quickly formed an interview panel and selected ten of the students, mostly based on their English language skills and physical fitness. Three days later our team of twenty-nine travelled eastward. We had chosen the district capital, Moramanga, about 110 kilometres east of Antananarivo, as our first base since it was located at the crossing point of some major roads but was still close enough to the capital in case of unexpected problems. The house and garden of a forestry station became our first base camp.

One week before we were scheduled to leave the capital and start the field work, I asked the cook to prepare a list of the most necessary items of food and kitchen equipment. When I made a quick check of his list, one amount seemed to be wrong: the number of kilos of rice surely had one zero too many added.

I called the cook and mentioned the error, suggesting that the stated 300 kg of rice should have read 30 kg. The cook, however, insisted that 300 kg was correct for two weeks and twenty-nine persons. To me this was ridiculous, since it amounted to 0.7 kg per person per day. I made a quick recalculation and thought 100 kg would be sufficient, which would allow each person 250 g per day. It should at this point be mentioned that rice forms the staple diet on the island and Madagascar has the highest per capita rice consumption in the world. Malagasy people eat rice for breakfast, lunch and dinner, and if there is nothing else, they will eat it on its own. I had been told this earlier, but to me 250 g seemed sufficient for a hot meal or two. Normally, when in Africa, I would eat bread or porridge for breakfast, some handy food like fruit, biscuits or tinned fish for lunch and take a proper meal at night. Unfortunately for a European stomach, the day started in Madagascar with unsalted, watery rice porridge that looked and tasted like wallpaper glue. For lunch our cook would prepare tasty sandwiches, a delicacy for us, but not so for our Malagasy colleagues. Whenever they found the opportunity, they bought themselves a bowl of rice with a piece of beef or chicken in a village at lunchtime and passed over their sandwiches to the local children.

Washing Lines

During the first two weeks a working routine was developed. In small groups of three or four persons, comprising a geologist, two students and occasionally a counterpart, we explored the area on foot, bicycle or four-by-four vehicle. The geologist was responsible for recording the outcrops and taking rock specimens suitable for later detailed examination, while the students took stream-sediment samples that would later be examined for heavy minerals of economic interest. The humid eastern part of Madagascar is characterised by weathered rock up to forty-metres thick, and fresh rock exposures are usually restricted to the river valleys. Wet stream-sediment samples were packed in manilla paper Kraft bags to be air dried, ideally, at the base camp. Moramanga, however, is located in a small basin immediately east of the footwall of the high central plateau (indeed, it appears to be a little known or publicised rift valley), and although we were in the middle of the dry season, this side of Madagascar is exposed to the trade winds which result in year-round precipitation along the eastern escarpment of the plateau. To gain some space for drying the samples, Chris Johnson, our geochemist, bought a gazebo. I procured about twenty metres of washing line and some pegs, which would allow us to attach the wet sediment-filled paper bags to a series of strung-out lines. On the evening of the third day we had everything arranged to dry the incoming samples, even in the permanent drizzle of Moramanga. But when Chris and myself inspected our handy-work the next morning, we had an unexpected surprise. Our sample-drying facility had been taken over and was now full of female underwear. The girl students had done their washing during the night and used our conveniently erected washing lines. I assured Chris that I would find him another twenty metres of line.

Roads to Nowhere

As the project progressed it became clear that the roads depicted on the topographical map had little in common with the road system now in place. Large parts of the road network that had existed at the end of the colonial period were now impassable. Lack of maintenance, broken bridges and landslides had in many places transformed what had once been decent roads into little more than narrow footpaths. The reason for this sorry state of affairs was clear enough. Between the mid-1970s and 2001 Madagascar found itself in the hands of the 'Red Admiral', a left wing dictator who drained most of the country's wealth into the pockets of the ruling elite. This corrupting influence together with a crude Marxist ideology had ruined the economy, and Madagascar, once the crown jewel in the French colonial empire, became one of the poorest countries on earth. In the mid 1970s the Malagasy currency, the Malagasy Franc, was still pegged to the French Franc. By the 1990s inflation was at double figures and made imported industrial products, machines and spare parts into prohibitively expensive luxury items. No money was left for road repairs, and I later learned that on average, since the end of the 1960s, a thousand kilometres of drivable roads had deteriorated each year into footpaths. Under these conditions,

Negotiating a river crossing damaged by floods in northern Madagascar. (Photograph by W. Bauer.)

motorbikes and bicycles seemed to be the better mode of transport to the remote areas, although even these simple vehicles were not very useful in mountainous terrain.

When we tried to reach some of the more remote places another problem arose. In a country without road signs and with maps of dubious reliability it was sometimes necessary to ask any available local inhabitant for directions. In the beginning we would ask, 'Is this the road to——?' But despite a positive answer, we would all too often encounter a broken bridge or some other major obstacle. We quickly learnt that the second question had to be, 'Can we reach—by car?' Not everybody we asked knew the possibilities of a four-by-four pickup on those roads, so the third question was, 'When was the last time a motor car came this way?' If the person had to think for a long time, or if the answer was along the lines of 'When my father was still young', we knew that we had to prepare ourselves for the worst.

A Long Hike

Our daily programme was scheduled in such a way that a small team could be dropped in the morning at the last place that was accessible by car and from there the geologist and his assistants would walk often over a distance of twelve to fifteen kilometres. In most cases the same distance had to be hiked back in the afternoon, which limited our working radius from the base camp. After a few days working out from the camp we would cover the easily accessible parts of the current map sheet and the two-day hikes would then begin. I did the first of such hikes accompanied by two students and a Malagasy counterpart. The starting point for our hike had been explored two days earlier where we had encountered a very narrow bridge, made of a few slippery trunks across a muddy twenty-five-metre-wide river. Two days later we set out with our sleeping bags and a two-day provision of food and we were in good spirits. But when we arrived at the bridge, we found it destroyed. Not damaged by a flood or other natural means, but vandalised. We could see that the plant fibres which had been used to fix the bridge had been cut by machetes before the trunks had been dropped down into the river. The river was deep but it was flowing quite slowly. I suggested we might swim across but one of my companions couldn't swim and the other two mentioned that such rivers might contain crocodiles. However, just at that moment a fisherman came down the river in his canoe. For a small banknote he took us over to the other bank of the river. We also asked him to inform the people in the next village that the bridge had been destroyed so that they might repair it.

Continuing our hike we made good progress and after crossing the river valley we reached high ground where the path continued along the watershed. A footpath in Madagascar is in no way comparable to a European hiking trail. The width of a path here is just sufficient to place two feet next to each other, rather like walking a tight rope. In addition, Malagasy people obviously like shortcuts so that each slope is taken directly. When such a path becomes wet, it can be a very slippery mess. In these cases my Malagasy companions would take off their shoes and walk on bare feet, clawing their toes into the mud. That was not an option for my soft feet, and I landed more than once on my backside.

By lunchtime we had reached open grassland where an old man and a young boy crossed our path. My companions asked them the way to our intended destination, whereupon they pointed to a hardly recognisable path going downhill. My compass and the GPS indicated that we should continue on the current path and not downhill. After a short discussion with my Malagasy colleagues, we followed the path that had been indicated by the locals and ended up in a wide valley that was occupied by a swamp. The onward path was marked every twenty metres by a bamboo pole with some grass at the top. The path itself was underlain by wooden planks but these were some twenty to thirty centimetres below the water level. A slippery balancing act ensued—one wrong step and we could end up to our hips in a stinking swamp. We emerged wet and dirty from the valley and the path then climbed up to a ridge and led us in the direction in which we had been heading before being directed into the swamp.

Late in the afternoon we reached our target. The houses of the village at the end of the path were scattered over a large area between light green, terraced rice paddies, crowned by dark green trees along the ridge crests. No villagers were visible and we couldn't see a school or a church, which normally mark the centre of such a settlement, so we walked towards the biggest house. Suddenly about twenty men in two groups approached from different directions and surrounded us. They didn't look very friendly and were armed with short spears. One of my companions touched my shoulder and pointed to a member of the group who to my surprise was recognisable as the elderly man who had earlier directed us into the swamp. We lifted a right hand indicating that we were not armed and came in peace. Three of the men came closer and started to negotiate with my Malagasy companions. A long discussion ensued which I couldn't understand. After twenty unnerving minutes one of my companions told me that the village men couldn't decide whether to let us stay here. Strangers were not welcome in their community. We would have wait until their 'king' returned.

We sat down, watched mistrustfully by the villagers. My three companions remained calm, so I was also persuaded not to worry—the worst that could happen would be a night outside on our way back. After a while the 'king' appeared: a tall, lean man in his mid sixties. Again a long discussion ensued and I detected several times the use of the word *Frantsay* (Frenchman). Then suddenly, everybody became very relaxed. Later my colleagues told me that the villagers had accused them of leading a Frenchman to their village. When it was explained that I was in fact German, not French, they became decidedly more friendly. Our adventure was understandable only in the light of a special chapter of Malagasy history.

In 1947 the area around Moramanga was the centre of an uprising against the colonial masters. The uprising was brutally suppressed by French troops and many Malagasy were killed in massacres after the event. Families fled into the remote mountains south of Moramanga which were never under the full control of the colonial troops. These villagers were the descendants of those families and had been taught not to trust strangers.

That evening we also learned that these same villagers had destroyed the bridge at the beginning of our traverse after they had watched us inspecting it some days earlier. Likewise the footpath through the swamp was a ploy to discourage us from continuing on our way. Now, however, we had permission to stay overnight in the village and take rock samples in the vicinity. One of the villagers took us to his house for the night. We bought a large cockerel for our dinner and the wife of our host cooked a big pot of rice which we shared with the family. As the house consisted of only a single large room, our sleeping place was confined to one corner where normally the geese resided for the night. Some cooking pots, dishes, cutlery and mats formed the furnishings. Grass bags hanging from the ceiling constituted their wardrobe. The village had neither school nor medical services, the nearest school being six hours away on foot. That night my companions had to tell our host all the news from the outside world—any story was a welcome diversion in their simple isolation.

In the morning we thanked our host for his hospitality with a small money gift. Two young men were selected to be our guides and with their help we quickly found some rock outcrops and small streams to sample. After we had completed our job, they showed us the shortest way back, without the detour through the swamp. We had successfully completed our mission, with many new impressions to take back from that remote community, and a few itching flea bites after a night spent on a sleeping place for geese.

Forgotten World

The 'last outpost of civilisation' in Madagascar is usually the terminal halt of a bush taxi. These taxis, mostly old Toyota and Mazda minibuses that can carry around twenty people, form the backbone of overland transport. A walk of more than one day from such a terminal halt becomes an expedition. Food, geological equipment, tents, cooking gear—everything has to be packed in loads suitable for porters. Once you leave the drivable roads you enter a long forgotten world. The people in these remote areas have for generations followed the same rhythm of sowing and harvesting, birth and death, sometimes interrupted by circumcision ceremonies, the *famadihana* (a body transfer of the ancestors) or the arrival of strangers equipped with large hammers!

On one such expedition I had already spent half a day without finding a single outcrop. Only thick vegetation, interrupted here and there by rice paddies, lined the way. Suddenly I spotted in the middle of some rice fields a huge rock which looked *in situ*. I followed the small earth dams between the individual rice paddies and armed with a big sledge hammer I headed with singular intent toward the rock. I had almost reached my target when I saw in the distance a local rice farmer waving with his arms and running across the flooded field towards me. He cried, 'Vato masina, vato masina,' and seemed to be extremely upset. When I looked back to my Malagasy colleague, I saw him also hectically waving his arms in a sign for me to come back. When the rice farmer arrived, we learned that this rock was a holy place where they worshipped their ancestors. I had almost committed sacrilege. As a European one may smile, but what would we think if a tall African with a hammer walked into Canterbury Cathedral in order to chip a piece of rock from the church fabric for his collection?

Finding a Family

In Madagascar large families are common. The family is still a core feature of the society, and according to their tradition a man has to have a family. When I came to Madagascar, I was a happy bachelor. On the first day of our fieldwork, one common question from my lady students was 'Are you married.' The more crafty among them would ask, after they had heard that I recently moved from Germany to England, 'Does your wife also now live in England?' Such questions should have given me a warning that my time as an independent man might come to an end quite soon.

On my second field season, later in 2005, we had to cover an area in northern Madagascar near Ambilobe, the home town of one of our counterparts. On a Saturday evening he

The head of a rafting expedition on the Mangoro River, central Madagascar, provides medical aid to a local villager. (Photograph by R. M. Key.)

suggested we visit the local discotheque, a good opportunity to relax and meet some of his family members. I agreed to join him and before going to the dance we picked up his two sisters, one of them carrying a little baby. The baby was dropped at the house of the grandparents and we spent a nice evening in the discotheque with the young lady that I assumed to be the mother of the baby and therefore in a formal relationship. Some weeks later we had finished our stint in the field and returned to the capital. On the evening of our arrival, my counterpart called me and mentioned that one of his sisters was back from a trip to France, and would I like to join them for dinner. I was surprised to see the young lady from the discotheque in Ambilobe again. During our dinner I ask casually, where she had left her baby during her trip to France. She seemed confused, then she laughed, explaining that it was her sister's baby. After we had solved my misunderstanding we had a wonderful time and at the end of the same week we became engaged and nine months later were married in Diego-Suarez at the northern tip of Madagascar.

The Madagascar project lasted three years. We did what was expected of us as geologists, but we also repaired broken bridges, transported injured people to the next hospital, helped occasionally with our medical box when first aid was needed and travelled thousands of kilometres by car, on bicycle or motorbike, by boat, or on foot, and on one occasion even by ox cart. Ordinary Malagasy people turned out to be as supportive and friendly as anyone could imagine.

Most logistical problems were solved with the kind help of our counterparts. They formed our link to the local population and carried a lot of responsibility for the smoothness of the field operations. We had many difficulties, accidents and tropical diseases to overcome, but the lasting result was a modern geological map that, hopefully, can help to attract foreign investment into the mining sector. For me, my time in Madagascar literally changed my life.

Silver Salvers and Slug-Eels
Bob Thomas

In 2003 BGS, in partnership with the Norwegian Geological Survey, won a contract to geologically map a substantial part of Zambezia Province in northeast Mozambique. This work involved two field seasons, each requiring a team of six geologists. The teams were a disparate group: over the two seasons they comprised two British members (myself and Louise Hollick), two Germans, a Spaniard, an Italian, a Belgian and a Lithuanian. This was sometimes an incendiary mix when it came to geological and sample selection matters, but otherwise we made a remarkably harmonious group, with lifetime friendships forged.

Most notably, our accommodation was a series of wonderfully ingenious bush camps set up and managed by a Mozambiquan company called Eteng. The Mozambiquans are extremely well versed in bushcraft and after a couple of days all manner of comforts had been erected in the camp, including large tables made *in situ* from Msimbiti sticks woven together with Mpanda bark and constructed at a comfortable height for sample examination, lower tables by our tents for washing and shaving, and palm-tree loungers for the odd spot of relaxation. The ablutions were an absolute delight, each cubicle taking the form of a spiral maze with a pot of gold in the inner sanctum and a large white flag to signal occupancy (or surrender). The showers were a battery of large brown plastic funnels, each evening full to the brim with *agua quente* (hot water) and floored by comfortable raised planks of *geelhout* to keep dainty feet out of the rich, red African mud. On many balmy evenings the sounds of lusty Lithuanian folk songs or crooning Italian ballads could be heard emanating from this veritable pleasure palace.

On long field expeditions, deep in the bush, food becomes an important and much discussed subject. Our Eteng camps

Above and right. Anyone for luncheon? Boiled rodent and burnt slug-eel, Mozambique. (Photographs by G. Motuza & R. J. Thomas.)

'Shark's tooth' inselberg, Mozambique. (Photograph by R. J. Thomas.)

were managed by a splendid fellow called Carlos who looked after our every comfort. We had good food in the camps, mainly based on the carcasses of either goat or fowl, and served in a huge mess tent on cloth-covered trestle tables by an immaculate waiter on a silver (looking) salver. At regular intervals Carlos would disappear for a couple of days to the coast unannounced, but would always disarm our chagrin by returning with large quantities of delicious fresh *prauwns* (prawns) and ripe mangoes, bananas and pineapples for a special feast. Daytime forage was often less palatable, with boiled rodent and burnt slug-eels frequently proffered by the local populace if we arrived at the kraals around lunchtime.

The Mozambiquan countryside is truly spectacular in this region, with its Proterozoic gneisses forming low whalebacks intruded by Pan-African granites which have been eroded into glorious sharp, towering inselbergs. Our particular favourite was the 'shark's tooth'. Some particularly exciting and significant Pan-African metasedimentary rocks were discovered, which not only proved crucial to our understanding of the geology of the area, but also gave rise to some very characteristic beautiful inselbergs with large perched caves. All in all, a fantastic place to work.

Jungle Book—Excerpts from a PNG Diary [1]
Bert De Waele

Sunday 11 May 2008, Port Moresby, Papua New Guinea. I've been in Port Moresby for fourteen days now. That's quite a lot more than originally planned! We were supposed to leave for the field

---

1 The following record derives from a project undertaken jointly by BGS and Deutsche Montan Technologie GmbH between 2006 and 2011 (Geological mapping and mineral potential assessment of the Highlands of Papua New Guinea), with funding from the European Commission.

area last Monday (fifth), but because of logistical delays, the departure has been delayed for a week.

Port Moresby is not the nicest place to stay. It is a large sprawling prison of expatriate flats and apartments, where social interaction happens entirely in clubs, accessible by invitation only. Actually, I've already figured out that having a white skin automatically earns you the right to most clubs, although I think that many long-term ex-pats feel too guilty doing it that way for long and eventually sign up. Interaction with the local PNG people is largely limited to the guys at work. From what I've seen, most seem bright and funny, and they all have a good sense of humour. I'm quite keen to be in the field with such a bunch.

Wednesday 14 May, 16:30 hours, Mauwol village. Yesterday evening, our helicopter arrived: a white and blue machine with the name 'Islands' on it. The company is owned by a former minister in the PNG government, who is now active in the opposition. We were told that, even though the helicopter was now on site, we still would not be able to use it for lack of kerosene, which was en route by truck from Lae. With a landslip on the highway, and no contact with the truck, we were unsure if it would arrive anytime soon. As a result I decided to try and plan a series of short traverses in the region of our base camp at Kumbareta Mission (also known as Bayer Mission), to cover for this eventuality. The only problem with that, I was told, is that two communities, one around Kumbareta, the other just to the north of us, are at war. Reports claim two people killed by machete, and one critically wounded by shotgun, currently fighting for his life in a hospital in Mount Hagen. The recommendation, therefore, was to stay away from these particular communities, and stay out of trouble. That immediately ruled out a few possible outings, while the road we had taken for a previous familiarisation trip had since been rendered unusable because of broken bridges and a landslide which would prevent access to the NE of the mission. In short, without a helicopter we would not be able to do anything meaningful.

All our planning efforts were shortcut when, just before dinner, the truck with kerosene arrived. I immediately put out the maps again and convened the geologists to discuss our new options. We soon reached agreement on a series of traverses up north, starting with the highest priority targets. Dinner tasted a lot better now that all our equipment was in place to allow the start of our work.

The helicopter is a six-seater, but Eniko (my PNG counterpart) and I are the only two people in it (plus the pilot). The pilot is a Papoe and speaks Pidgin, which is handy, I guess, when you work in PNG. I only have to indicate on a map where I want to go, and the next thing, we are off! Flying over the terrain north of the mission it becomes overly apparent how remote and inaccessible this region really is. Below us is a deep canyon, carved by the Bayer River, and then we fly over some more flat-lying ground around Ruti Mission, underlain by younger volcanic rocks related to the eruptions of Mount Hagen and its ancillary domes. North of that the real highlands start: from three hundred metres high near the Yuat and Jimi rivers, to three thousand metres on the top of some mountains. This is really rugged terrain, with rainforest all over, speckled with a few small-scale banana plantations and small villages. As we move towards our target area, the villages disappear almost entirely, leaving only rugged mountainous terrain with the occasional two or three hut village. Why people choose to live in these remote locations is beyond my comprehension.

After about a fifteen-minute flight we locate the river we want to work down, and move further up the valley in search of a suitable landing area near the headwaters. I switch on my GPS to make sure, and we are dead on target. The pilot has a better eye than me and spots a few potential landing sites. My preferred one is a small village of five huts, perched on a ridge in between two impressive waterfalls. The pilot makes a slow approach to get a better look, and we see about thirty or so villagers already waving in excitement, pointing at an open area on the ridge suitable for landing. Mist is rolling in, so the pilot decides to make another circle and wait for the air to clear. We set down and quickly get ourselves and our luggage out. I give a thumbs up and the chopper leaves with a wave. Hopefully we'll see him back in three days at our pick up point.

We are both immediately hemmed in by the villagers, who are almost beside themselves with joy. I literally get embraced by scruffy old men with red-brown teeth, and have to shake hands all-round. The villagers are mostly dressed in vegetation. A string, made of some bark, is used as a belt, in between which leaves are put to cover their privates. Some have pieces of carved wood or bone in their noses, and some have painted faces, or hair decorated with flowers or green moss. I feel like I am Robinson Crusoe meeting so many Fridays in a deserted corner of the Earth.

As the commotion dies down a bit, Eniko starts chewing a betel nut and explains the reason for our visit. He gets the undivided attention of everyone, and I give out a few printed folders explaining our work, one in English, which nobody reads, and one in Pidgin, which at least a few can read. Most people here, men and women, are smoking cigar-like contraptions. Most are also chewing the betel nut with lime, which results in some serious spitting all around. The colour of their teeth attests to the continuous use of tobacco and betel nut.

Eniko's discussions lead to the allocation of a house in the village with three rooms for us. The house is built on poles, and inside there is a central hearth, while around the sides there are reed mats to sleep on. The house can actually be locked with a small padlock, so we can safely leave all our stuff in the hut while working. Eniko has explained our plan and we are allocated two guides to do some work north and northeast of the village. We set out from the village, and are accompanied by some twenty people for the first kilometre, until, after two outcrops, they get the idea of what we do. Then our entourage dwindles to a handful of people, who accompany us up the streams and valleys. As I choose more inaccessible routes, the bush knives come out, and the guides have to begin hacking a way through the bush. The terrain is excruciatingly difficult, both steep slopes, dense vegetation and slippery, muddy paths. When we finally make it back to the village our small loop looks pathetically small on the map.

Supper consisted of a multi-course meal. It started with some roasted maize, after which I was given a sort of soggy 'biscuit' made from taro-roots and leaves, which tasted alright, although I would probably not have eaten the whole thing if I had been able to see it. Then came a cucumber, and then the main course, rice (ours) and a village chicken which I bought. The end-result was a totally stuffed geologist ready for a well-deserved night-rest. I slept on the floor itself, not wanting to bother about the mattress we had brought. In fact, I slept so well that I decided to leave the mattress in the base camp on future trips.

15 May, 09:00 hours, Mauwol village. We'll be setting off soon, after lunch, downstream, perhaps to reach the Yuat River. Eniko expresses his doubt that we'll be able to make it that far (thirteen kilometres in a direct line on the map), and thinks we'll be sleeping in a village somewhere half-way this evening. We get four porter/guides from Mauwol, and take the slow trip down, occasionally cutting through the bush where the path gets obscure. Because of the hard work, steep muddy slopes, and slow progress, we make regular breaks of twenty minutes or so to allow the guys to chew some nuts or smoke a cigarette/cigar.

At the end of the day we finally reach an open area with a large coconut tree, which appears to be the abandoned site of a village. The end-destination is still a kilometre or so away, but we decide to get a short rest and sample some of the coconuts. One guide clambers up the twenty-metre-tall tree, and drops a few large nuts, which eagerly get chopped clean and opened. The brown nuts have ample coconut meat inside, but less juice, while the green ones are full of juice, with little soft meat. After that welcome break we walked another hour to reach the village, just a few huts in among the rainforest.

A house in Papua New Guinea used by the team as an overnight sleeping place; to the left of the small tree is the part of the house reserved for pigs. (Photograph by B. De Waele.)

It was almost dusk as we arrived at our next sleeping place where we greeted the house owner and his family. They had just cooked their evening meal of sweet and Irish potatoes, plantain banana and pork meat, which we were served without question. The hospitality in these remote communities is really phenomenal! It started to drizzle, and we were invited inside, and it was then that I realized that half of the house, which I thought was quite big, was actually occupied by pigs. Luckily there's a wall between the pig and the human quarters, with the pigs situated at the lower end, so that any effluents run down slope away from the main house. Eniko and I got an elevated spot on the far side of the pig-section, and we brewed some tea and cooked some fried rice and corned beef. We only ate a little of that and passed the food to our hosts. The number of people had by that time swelled to twenty-one, of which eight were children. The sugary, milky tea was passed around, and I could clearly see from their faces they had not tasted it before. The rice, also, went down very well, especially with the children who were scooping handfuls of it from their banana-leaf plates. It was a joy to watch these children lick the greasy rice from their banana leaves and sip the sweet tea. I was very tired, and as most guys started lighting up their cigars and chewing betel nut, I dozed off.

17 May, 07:40 hours, village next to airstrip of the Baptist Mission. Yesterday took us through lots of poor tracks in the rainforest, and via two villages to our exit point near a small airstrip we had spotted from the helicopter on approach. Along the way, we lost two of our porters from Mauwol, as they felt unsafe entering the area of another Wantok, especially during the upcoming council elections. We replaced them easily in the first village we passed, and added another guide from another village further down the slope, who knew the people of the villages near the airstrip well and would act as our negotiator and guide. This kind of situation seems rampant in PNG, where free movement for people across the various tribal areas is simply not possible for all sorts of 'political' reasons. I am unsure whether this is due to ancient rivalries, or because of the inherent feeling of ownership of the land, which appears to go much deeper than that experienced by people outside PNG. What I do know is that this inbred xenophobia stifles local economies, and makes the trade between various regions or Wantoks near-impossible. This is the reason, I suspect, that here in PNG, one does not find small grocery shops in every village, because the supply chain needed for that kind of economy is hampered by these land issues and rites of passage.

In each of the two villages we passed we had to spend some time to explain. This also is the customary thing. When planning for work, the loss of at least thirty minutes every time one passes a village has to be factored into our calculations. Each explanation takes Eniko at least ten minutes, and in most cases we were sat down and offered some cooked bananas or groundnuts. What is nice to see is that most people to some extent understand what we are doing, and are excited by it. I guess they all realize that our information may in time improve their situation if exploration or mining companies come in.

After a long trek through the forest, we arrive at the Baptist Mission near to an airstrip where we expect to get picked up next day. As soon as we enter the village itself we are greeted by a colourful group of people, some one hundred or so, each one shaking our hands, smiling broadly to show off their brown-red rows of teeth. We get overwhelmed by all the attention and sit down on a tree until the commotion has died down enough for Eniko to make his introduction. This time, for some unfathomable reason, it only takes us some twenty minutes to be allocated a house, elevated on long stilts, with three rooms. Eniko and I will share one room, while the five porters will move into the remaining rooms. On the walk to the house I notice a lot of pineapples, so I ask Eniko to arrange a few for a short snack. As we sit down for our pineapples I finally have time to look at the colourful attire displayed by these people. Most men have elaborate head dresses of feathers, moss and flowers, and some have also taken to painting their faces. They were dressed up because of the council election taking place that week. Apparently there are meetings all over the place, and the people are all getting ready to vote. Voting seems to be a very important thing for them and they take it all very seriously and are in a festive mood. Even so, Eniko tells me that during election times this festive mood can sometimes turn into violent rage.

As I was getting hungry, I ask Eniko to try and find some food (chicken or pork), and he sends one of our porters away on a discovery tour. Within five minutes he returns with the back half of a pig that will set us back only ten Kina (two Euros). Apparently there have been a few *mou mou*'s prepared for the council election, and cooked meat is in plentiful supply. We settle inside and start carving nice juicy slices of pork meat to fry. A little later, the house owner's wife comes in with a full pot of banana, sweet potato (Kaukau) and greens, which makes our meal complete. With a full stomach I retire to bed, knowing that tomorrow we will be picked up by helicopter.

Just this morning, we had a breakfast of sweet potato and bananas cooked by the house owner's wife. Then we moved to the airstrip with our luggage and I made a call to base to see whether the helicopter would be ready. At ten, we got confirmation we'd be picked up in thirty minutes. Meanwhile I started talking with a ferociously decorated man who spoke a bit of English. He explained to me that the airstrip was made by the Baptist Mission, and that every Monday a plane arrived to bring medical supplies for the medical post here. There was also a small Baptist church, but no school. For schooling, children would have to move out to Ruti Mission, some thirty-five kilometres away, a solid three-day walk. I talked to him about the idea of community schools, and that he, for instance, could teach the local children some English and Pidgin, writing and reading skills if he wanted to. He understood and said that he'd think about it. I said that the council elections would be a great time to promote such ideas, as education is the cornerstone of society. He simply laughed and thought I had made a joke. So, even though election time is important to them, they seem to give little credit to the value of a councillor. He said to me that the man who was standing for election here does not speak Pidgin or English himself, so would not be interested in putting up a school.

Suddenly the thud-thud of the helicopter becomes audible, and in a flash, the rugby stops, the field gets cleared, and the dressed up throng moves to the sidelines to watch the helicopter. In fact, there are so many people gathered there that I clearly don't stand out enough for the pilot to see me, and to my surprise, rather than landing, he turns around and sets off to the village where we had started. Everyone, not the least me, is astonished, but we move the bags onto the strip having decided to stay there until he returns. Sure enough, five minutes later he's back and after hovering a bit to see whether we are there, he spots us, and finally lands. We get in, and I ask him whether we can take two of our guides, both with damaged feet, to the village. He agrees, and the excited guides get in. This must be the moment of their lives, flying over the terrain we have walked through, amazing as it is, to land in their village. The mix of terror and excitement is great to see. Where we land, the villagers have made a helipad. The guides get out, and we warmly shake hands with them and with the villagers who had taken care of us three days previously. When we finally get back to Kumbareta Mission I can have a shower and then to bed. Nothing beats a hot shower after four days in the rainforest!

Monday 19 May, Kumbareta Mission. We are ready and waiting for an available helicopter flight to take us to the starting point for our second traverse, which is planned to last for three days starting from a small locality called 'Fankafank', at an elevation of around 1,400 meters, and descending through the rainforest to the triple junction of the Lai, Jimi and Yuat rivers (at three hundred meters), where there is a small airstrip called Mamusi, that will provide an excellent pick-up position.

Delayed by poor visibility caused by low mist, we finally leave at around 12:00, and it takes us a good twenty minutes to get to the chosen spot. As before, the terrain looks precipitous, with a few high waterfalls and deep gorges that will make life difficult. Fankafank is positioned on a long ridge, partially cleared to make space for a couple of huts, a small church (also just a hut), and a small elementary school. Because of the school there is a good landing spot, but in contrast to the previous situation there are hardly any people to welcome us here. This is later explained by the fact that on the morning after there will be local council elections here. Almost everyone was higher up the slope at a meeting to discuss the impending elections. Only two men and a few children turn up and take us to the head teacher of the small school, who seems to have preferred staying out of politics. He welcomes us with open arms, and Eniko explains what we will be doing here. Rumours about us have already reached this remote village, so he is not at all surprised that we have come. As we are being allocated a hut to sleep in, more people turn up and we have to explain our presence again. Since it is only 13:00 hours, we decide to do a small traverse up the slopes, before settling down for the night in the hut. We are allocated a few enthusiastic guides, but as we depart, are followed by three children and four extra adult guides.

The walk takes us through a stretch of rainforest, where we come across a stream the bed of which is covered in travertine rock. I ask where the water comes from, and they say it simply appears from within the mountain. They seem surprised that I would know this from merely looking at the riverbed, but I explain that the travertine means there is a lot of dissolved carbonate in the water, which only occurs where there are limestone and karst phenomena (dissolution of limestone in 'acid' water). I say that I want to see the source, so they take me upstream. The travertine is very easy to walk on, providing an excellent non-slip surface, so we make good progress, and discover a few very picturesque travertine falls. After climbing some one hundred meters, the guides take us away from the stream and we reach a small hut where an old man lives. From the way everyone greets the man, I suspect that he is the father of a few of those guides, and that this is just a courtesy visit we are making. We take a short break, and then press on to see the source of the small stream.

They take us along a small path climbing up the slope, and sure enough we reach a place where an impressive volume of water simply appears from under the ground. Above the source there are the remnants of an earlier stream, indicating that the karstic source must have been higher up the slope at some time in the past. When asked, the guides do not remember when the source could have shifted from the higher to the lower level, so it must have happened quite some time ago. A bit further on we find a similar, but even larger source, with a larger fossil stream indicating that again this water once sprang from significantly higher up the slope. I explore a few small cavities in the limestone, but they all end in muddy rubble, indicating that roof collapses have closed access to the underground caves. As we walk further along the path, the front guide peers down into a small crevasse in the limestone, and then back at me. I also look into the hole and am surprised to find two human skulls and an assortment of other bones. Eniko, who was less startled than me, tells me that long ago the people would simply deposit the bodies of deceased relatives in caves, rather than burying them underground. He asks the guides if they know who the bones belong to, but they say they don't know and that they have been there for as long as they can remember.

When we get back to Fankafank village, we stumble upon the election team who have just arrived. These guys have the unenviable task of walking from village to village within the voting district to organise and collect the votes from the people. They are proudly standing next to their two election boxes, and tell me that they will be spending the night here in Fankafank to organise the elections the next morning.

Supper comprises rice, sweet potato, plantain banana and

some greens. After that the pastor comes in with a guitar, and a bit later the six election officials. We talk a bit in English, but as the conversation goes into Pidgin, I take the guitar and play a few tunes. Our companions discuss matters long into the night, talking politics I think; so I doze off long before they take their leave.

In the morning, after a breakfast of sweet potato, banana and leaves, I go up to the election ground to see what is happening. The officials have erected a circular arena with a piece of string. A clearly marked area for the observers lies within it. There is also a makeshift election booth, made out of cardboard, a registration table and another table for handing out the voting strips. I get shown around proudly by one official, and see that the electoral roll for the district lists 306 eligible voters. There are six candidates, whose names and numbers are posted at the entrance of the arena. The way this will go is that when voting starts, each name on the voters list will be called, and that person will be accompanied by a witness who can read and write. Then the finger of the voter gets painted, and the name ticked on the list. The voter is given one voting card, which is brought to the polling booth, where an official records the choice of the candidate. The witness must see to it that the official records the wishes of the voter correctly. Then the voter and official exit the arena, and the vote is cast. The observers simply make a tally and look on to see that there are no irregularities. As we wait for more eligible voters to turn up, there is a commotion at one side of the field. An old man has turned up, painted white with ash, and carrying a spear and a bow and arrows. He shouts some words and makes threatening gestures before eventually being calmed down by one of the officials. It is explained to me that the old man is the son of a previous traditional leader and always makes a theatrical entrance to create a good impression, and, perhaps, to honour his father.

The election itself starts with a prayer, then a speech,

translated into local *tokless*, explaining the importance of the election and how it will be conducted. Voters then start, one by one, to stream through. I decide to go down to the house and wait out the voting there. We will need a few porters/guides to accompany us on our onward traverse, but will have to wait until they have cast their votes.

In the house I start talking to the pastor, who tells me a story of a young man who lives in the area and at one time in the past was sought by the police. He climbed up to a cliff that can be

A villager, painted with ash, poses with his wife and children, Papua New Guinea. (Photograph by B. De Waele.)

seen from the village, and went down into a hole below the cliff, using a rope. He found first one *cuscus*, killed it and put it in his *bilum*. Then as he descended further he found another *cuscus*. He then started a fire with a torch and went deeper inside, where he found a road. He stayed there, surviving on his caught *cuscus*, and only came out again three days later. This story tells me that there are caves in these cliffs, perhaps worth exploring.

Slowly the voters descend from the field, and we get ready to depart for the next village down the slope. The painted old man actually lives close to that village, and tells Eniko he can escort us all the way down to the airstrip. The day now consists of an arduous walk down to the stream at 1,200 meters, followed by a slow climb up the slope to about 1,800 meters. Luckily, half way up the slope, we can take a break at the hut of the old guide, who introduces us all to his wife and many children. Two of his children have sores on their legs, called 'one kina sores', as they are perfectly circular. The sore on the smallest child of perhaps a year old, looks very nasty, so Eniko digs out our medical gear and treats both children with antibiotic and antiseptic creams and bandages. The old man prepares us a village chicken and greens, which we share among us all (seven people). His house is fenced by a wooden barricade, outside of which he keeps some twenty or so pigs. Old as he is, he still grows all sorts of stuff in his field as well as raising pigs.

After lunch we climb again and reach the summit (1,800 meters) at around 17:00 hours. Just before the summit, the two leading guides suddenly drop their gear and rush off along the slope. They have seen a wild bush fowl, which they fail to catch, but have found its nesting mound. By the time I get there they have started digging into the nest in search of the eggs. Sure enough, some five minutes later they find one large reddish brown egg. The guide tells me that sometimes these nests can contain more than ten eggs, but they are unlucky this time.

We carry on, descending the slope now, to reach our village. As suspected, light has all but faded by the time I arrive with the lead guide. I sit down, exhausted, as the guide sets off in search of the people, who are obviously already in their huts, perhaps even sleeping. After a few minutes, sounds start to emanate from the direction in which the guide had disappeared and I am soon engulfed in a mass of curious and excited people.

It is fully dark now, and the villagers have thoughtfully brought a large plate of cooked bananas and some sweet bananas, which are eaten rapidly by our team. We are then allocated a hut and settle in to brew a large pot of tea. Everyone is tired, and we soon drift off to sleep.

Wednesday 21 May. Morning comes and we set about making some breakfast of rice with corned beef. Outside, the village has gathered, and bananas, sweet potatoes and greens are being cooked also. Then we assemble our goods and start off again to Mamusi airstrip, some five kilometres away. A lady has decided to join our team, and walks the entire way with a baby in her *bilum*. The path is flat now, and we make easy progress, at one point crossing a large stream on a bamboo bridge. Because we are so close to the Yuat river, the outcrop is very poor, and we don't need to stop very often to record observations. We stop at a small clear stream and everyone takes a bath, after which we only walk another hour or so to reach the village of Mamusi, next to the airstrip. It is 15:00 hours now, and so I call to find out when we can be picked up. The helicopter will have to go for service next day, so we elect to be picked up today. We walk to the airstrip where I pay all our helpers, and within an hour the chopper finds us, and we fly out, back to Kumbareta for a hot shower.

Thursday 29 May, Lakamanda village. We boarded the helicopter and flew some fifteen minutes to our target area, being dropped off next to a few huts near the community of Lakamanda. The people welcomed us with open arms, as is usual in these parts, and we explained what we were planning to do. We set off with a few guides to do a short exploratory walk up a creek and immediately found some significant sulphide mineralization, raising the spirit of our guides who were already dreaming of the future mining in their village.

Back at the hut we had some time to survey our future home.

The hut was a three bedroom affair, with a nice lawn in front. We installed ourselves in the 'living room', where I spread out a reed mat and my sleeping bag. Outside, a larger cassowary bird was stalking around, occasionally chasing the dogs around the lawn. At sunset a spectacular rose coloured sky lifted my spirits as I was sitting on the lawn chewing some sugar cane and occasionally patting the cassowary as it trotted around, pecking at the people. Dinner consisted of rice and corned beef, and sleep came quite rapidly after that, with the fire slowly dying out and darkening the room.

Friday 30 May. In the morning, a large group of people had gathered outside the hut, to discuss who would get to go with us on our day's work. We cooked rice, which I ate with powdered milk and sugar, while Eniko added a tin of mackerel fish. An older man was taking the lead in the discussions, loudly proclaiming all sorts of stuff, while everyone else was respectfully listening. Eniko had said that we only had a budget for three workers per day, so the discussion centred around who the chosen ones would be for today, as well as sorting out who'd be going tomorrow. A conclusion was finally reached by 9:30, and we left with three men, three boys and three dogs. We followed river courses the entire day, slipping on the wet rocks and fallen logs, until, in the evening we reached a spot of the river where three guys were preparing a traditional fishing exercise. They had dammed off a part of the river, and poisoned the water upstream, and were waiting for the fish to get disoriented enough for it to be possible to simply pick them up from the water. We settled down on a few rocks and watched the spectacle. Sure enough, after some twenty minutes, the fish started to get 'drunk' and children began to pick them up and throw them in a pond for later collection. Sizes ranged from thirty-centimetre fish down to small three-centimetre-long yuppies, but all were collected for eating. The dogs we brought also had a field day, jumping around the river course pouncing on the now partly floating fish.

Back home, I was surprised to find food ready for us. Eniko had bought a quarter of a pig yesterday, and ordered it to be cooked with banana for our return. There were also assorted greens, which made a very palatable dish. The meat was shared among all the men present, our guides and boys, and the family of the house as well as the neighbours, and soon everyone was gorging on the pig meat. There's nothing more satisfying than seeing everyone enjoy a good meal, with especially the children smacking their lips as they chewed the pork.

Saturday 31 May. Kau kau is boiling, as is the rice. Outside, I hear the same old man giving his, apparently daily, lecture to the gathered crowd. When we get outside to put our boots on, three new guides are ready for departure, and unsurprisingly, the old man is one of them. The day then consists of quite a lot of solid marching, as I want to reach some far-flung area of interest north of the village. Most of the trek passes through secondary forest, some of which needs a bit of trimming with a machete. The river courses, when we get across them, are all treacherous slippery affairs, and we fail to cover large distances within them, so often leave the course to try and cover some distance before re-joining the river to look for outcrop. It is quite late, and dusky, by the time we get back to the hut, but luckily, banana and greens are cooked and ready when we arrive so that we can immediately cook some tea and eat our meal. We're all knackered, but sit outside for a while to reflect on the traverse. I call base and arrange for the chopper to pick us up tomorrow.

In the morning, Eniko and I cook up all the remaining food from our bags. Our food supply consists of two kilo of rice and a few tins of fish. Breakfast therefore caters for our neighbours as well, and is well received. Banana leaves get brought in, and some twenty or so 'plates' or rice/fish dished out. Soon everyone is smacking away and drinking pots of tea. Then I call base to find out when we'll be picked up and am told that it'll be around 11:00. We move our stuff to the landing area, which has been cleaned up yesterday by a guy, and wait for the tell-tale 'chuck-chuck' sound. The chopper arrives on time, and I signal him using my mirror. The pilot dishes out candy to all the children, and we offer a lift to two blokes, one with a large bag of coffee. Then, off we go, to Kumbareta Mission, for a hot shower and some well-deserved rest.

Did you Bring Anything for Your Head?
Richard Ellison

The above question was one that came to have significant meaning.

An aspect of the project to complete the geological mapping of the entire United Arab Emirates was to journey to the Arabian Gulf islands about ninety kilometres offshore. Qarnain is one of these islands, a tiny blob about two kilometres across and up to fifty metres high, formed by salt which encases various lumps of basement rock brought to the surface in a narrow pipe-like tube from a depth of about eight kilometres. I was to travel with BGS colleague Bob Thomas during our eight week field season in October 2011.

Arrangements involved the absentee Sheikh landlord and various intermediaries, the lowliest of whom was Abdullah, a local Iranian fisherman who was our main contact. Unfortunately he spoke limited English and our Farsi is non-existent. We waited for a sea forecast of less than three-metre 'waves' and after several mobile calls of increasing volume to establish understanding, a rendezvous was set for the following day.

A 5 am start on a windless morning which broke into a classic emirates cloudless day entailed a 120-kilometre-dash along the coastal highway, dodging buses crammed with migrant workers.

Arrival at a remote jetty through a security gate with an armed Ghurkha guard seemed incongruous. But the Sheikh had to be protected, even though he made only one visit each year to the island. A second person emerged from the ramshackle guard hut. He looked an unlikely fisherman, and turned out to be another Abdullah who spoke perfect English with a public school accent, dressed in designer denims, ironed white shirt, leather bomber jacket and cool shades. Welcomes all round, and relief that our native tongue was to be the currency of the day. He beamed 'I would like to introduce you to my friend Abdullah' (just to add confusion, a third Abdullah) 'who will be taking us to the island today. Oh, and did you bring anything for your head?'

The reason for the question soon became apparent. Abdullah 3 was introduced as the UAE offshore powerboat racing champion and he was going to transport us in one of his new boats. Around a low promontory the three three-litre motors on a sleek open-top monster were thrumming in anticipation and straining at the leash.

This machine was going to project us to the island in less than forty minutes. Abdullahs 2 and 3 were going to test the brand new engines, but they 'might not' reach full speed of 100 mph. We were ushered into the plush white leather bench passenger seat behind the two Abdullahs who had donned full-face crash helmets for the journey. Our head protection was provided by our battered BGS-issue sunglasses. At 40 mph we pushed out beyond the glassy waters of the protective headland into a one-metre-high swell over which we powered with gentle lurches and dull thuds. Co-pilot Abdullah 2 turned around, shouted a rhetorical 'no problem', and gave a thumbs up. We sank lower into the leather seats, cheeks flapping wildly, nostrils flaring widely in the violent wind as 60 mph was reached. It was at this point that an untimely end became a distinct possibility as we entered a dense fog bank with less than twenty metres visibility—in a congested seaway littered with dhows, super tankers and oil rigs all around. Clearly Allah was now in control of the throttle because speed was maintained. We crouched lower, heads on our knees, silent in the now icy wind which wailed like a banshee in our unprotected ears.

We shot out of the gloom intact. More thumbs up and an increase in speed to 90 mph, with the boat only intermittently touching the water. Hair (what's left of in the case of RJT) was about to be wrenched from the scalp and there was a commensurate increase in cheek floppiness (flubbering?). Jowls were wrapped around the neck like a head scarf and by this time we had sunk silently to the floor. Then an enormous BANG, followed by a staccato mechanical rattle and a deceleration so rapid that the overtaking bow wave nearly submerged the boat. A drive shaft had broken. Dignity stripped, we limped for another thirty minutes at walking pace to Qarnain and a deserted inlet where a Land Cruiser, with engine running, awaited our field work. No worries, a replacement outboard would be despatched from the mainland to be fitted in time for our 4 pm return in the evening.

As the first geologists ever to map the island we had our work cut out, rushing around making as many observations and taking as many photos as we could. At the evening rendezvous the stricken powerboat had been joined by a fishing boat. Repairs had been halted and the new mode of transport took us at a more sedate speed to the mainland. The coast looked different in the starlight, mainly because it was 260 kilometres west of our point of embarkation. No matter, land transport had been laid on in the form of a dilapidated Jeep driven presumably by Abdullah 1, and from which we emerged several hours later coughing petrol fumes. A final leg undertaken in our own project Nissan Patrol completed the twenty-hour day of contrasts. And we had just failed to do a ton on water. Thank goodness.

Sand and Starlight—Excerpts from a Project Blog
Helen Burke

United Arab Emirates field season four, February 2010.
Hello from Abu Dhabi. I'm working here, along with BGS colleagues Richard Ellison, Richard Smith, Jon Lee, Andy Newell and Bob Thomas to make 1:100,000 scale geological maps of the whole country for the Ministry of Energy. We're here for seven weeks altogether.

We're working six days a week, with a weekly office day to digitise our linework. The night before a day off is traditionally barbecue night, washed down with a refreshing gin and tonic. Last week on our day off we went to the swimming beach at Abu Dhabi for a swim in the Arabian Gulf. It's the saltiest water I've ever swum in. The bottom is lime mud so it's a bit slimy under your feet. The sea was pretty warm though, and I didn't even have to tread water to stay afloat. Unfortunately, my camera swam in the Gulf before I did and it isn't at all happy now!

I was a TV star yesterday! A film crew for Teachers TV were keen to film us working in the desert. They spent three full days filming for a fifteen-minute programme! Bob Thomas and I took them to the Liwa area so they could film us doing some infilling of data points along roads and tracks, the main desert having already been covered by earlier traverses. Liwa is where the biggest sand dunes in the country are located, the mega-barchans. The film crew were keen to record us digging holes in the inter-dune *sabkhas* to see the thickness of the gypsum pan (which looks a lot like Kendal mint cake!). Unfortunately, we had to do everything twice because it took them so long to set up the shot. We abandoned work in the end, despite their assurances that they wouldn't hold us up.

The film crew had some unexpected excitement when Bob's tyre came off the rim in the sand dunes the other day. Rather than offer to help, they reached for the camera to catch it on film.

Luckily their driver helped to get the tyre back on. Jacking the car up on sand was no mean feat, but they managed. There was a kilo of sand in the tyre when it went back on though, which made driving on roads interesting. Yesterday, I got stuck in soft sand (again!) and their driver had to pull me out, but he wasn't allowed to do this until they'd set up the camera to catch it on film. There went my pride. The tow rope snapped and rebounded into the car, smashing the brake light, so I've been over to the car hire company workshop today to get it fixed.

I spent Valentine's weekend on a three-day 140-kilometre long traverse across the desert. I'll remember it for the rest of my life. Jon Lee and I went in a three-car convoy with a guide leading the way to pick the route. This was my second traverse, so I was getting used to the driving by then. I gaffer-taped a camera to the dashboard to video some dune driving. The 'dash cam' footage looks like a computer game, it's just like being on a roller coaster. Being perched at the top of a big dune reminded me of Oblivion at Alton Towers. Don't Look Down! The avalanching sand makes a thundering noise as you drive down the dune face, and you can feel the whole dune vibrate under your feet if you stand at the top when someone drives down.

We had clear skies at night and the stars were amazing. I've never seen so many. The sunsets were spectacular as well. Not surprisingly, I have lots of photos to bore people with when I get home! The other traverse team of Richard Smith and Bob Thomas weren't so lucky. Richard's car face-planted into a dune as he came over it, the radiator smashed with the impact and the air bag went off. Most importantly, Richard is absolutely fine, but the car is still in the desert awaiting recovery, twenty-five kilometres from the nearest road. It was a stark reminder to us that there's a harsh side to the beauty of the desert. A six-strong recovery team took three days of toiling to drag the car out of the desert.

4 March. We've spent our last week of the current field season gathering samples of the various formations we've been mapping and we've packed up all our kit and put it into storage ready for the next field season in October. The samples are now crated up ready for shipping to the UK for dating and heavy mineral analysis to determine their source area.

Yesterday three of us went to map Zayed Military City, just off the Dubai road. It had taken the whole field season to gain access, so we couldn't miss the chance. We divided up the area between us and went in with soldiers as chaperones to keep a watchful eye on us. I was stopped at the gate, after we'd already got clearance, but the others sailed through ahead of me. One of the soldiers opened the passenger door and didn't like seeing my tablet PC on the seat. Thankfully, the soldier who chaperoned me was in the car behind and explained what I was doing there. I spent the next few hours driving along tarmac roads, stopping off every two kilometres to make observation points and take a closer look at outcrops.

There were no roads in the southern half of my mapping area and I was a bit concerned about making a traverse across the dunes, given my past experiences of getting stuck, especially as my tow ropes had been taken for storage, but I needn't have worried. Thankfully, after all the rain we've had lately, the sand was pretty well compacted, which made driving over it much easier.

While I was driving over the dunes I disturbed some gazelle and birds that looked like curlews, obviously making the most of the fact that the area isn't open to the public. The dunes were covered in small white flowers, which must have sprung up after the rain. It would have looked like a nature reserve had it not been for two tanks parked on top of a dune.

I have to admit, I had absolutely no idea what to expect when I was asked to work on this project. I heard a few snippets from people who had been out on previous mapping seasons, but that's about it. I didn't even know that Abu Dhabi is the country's capital, I just assumed it was Dubai. This is the first time I've ever worked overseas and it's the first time I've driven on the right hand side of the road.

I've been keeping a diary of everything that's happened from day to day, and I wrote a few first impressions very early on. The first thing that struck me was the way people drive here. The 120 kmph speed limits are more or less completely ignored and people drive really aggressively, tailgating with only centimetres between their bumpers, and flashing their lights at the person in front to move out of the way. And if that doesn't work, there's always the hard shoulder. The Dubai-Abu Dhabi road has the shocking statistic of having the highest number of fatal accidents in the country. My Abu Dhabi guide book states that someone dies on UAE roads every forty-eight hours. One saving grace, however, is that lorries aren't permitted to overtake. It would be chaos if that were allowed.

I found that you can get fruit and vegetables sourced from every country on the planet in the big supermarkets (except from Britain it seems!). We've been eating Australian carrots, UAE tomatoes, Saudi potatoes, French and American apples, New Zealand cherries, Greek and Egyptian olives (Greek ones are the best by a long way!) and Spanish onions.

I've also noticed that there is very little road-kill here, which is surprising, given that even relatively minor roads have three lanes either side. Come to think of it, I haven't had many splattered insects cementing themselves to the windscreen either!

The amount of new development going up here is unbelievable. We've been staying in a district called Khalifa City A, most of which seems to be a building site. It's very easy to get lost because all the roads look the same. A lot of houses under construction seem to have been completely abandoned, yet they often stand side by side with palatial residences. The whole of Abu Dhabi is rapidly expanding, especially over towards Saadiyat Island, where the new Grand Prix circuit is. I can't help wondering who all these new houses are for.

I've found people here really helpful, especially when I've stopped at the side of the road to let my tyres down to go off-road, or to re-inflate them afterwards, despite the obvious language barrier. I must have been asked if I needed help a dozen times when I pulled up at the side of the access road to Al Dhafra camel festival to re-inflate my tyres before heading back.

I've also been given Arabic tea out of Thermos flasks, which initially I took out of politeness, only to find that I actually like the taste of it (a complete surprise, as I've never liked tea or coffee in my life!). One fond memory is being given tea by a Bedouin camel farmer and his son outside their tarpaulin hut near the end of our second traverse in the Liwa desert, and a shopkeeper in Liwa giving us oranges just because we happened to stop by.

I've felt safe working alone in remote areas, except once, when I had a dodgy offer from a camel farmer in my mapping area. He only spoke a few words of English, which included 'bed' and '10 Dirhams'. When I refused, he offered to pay on his credit card! Needless to say, Card Declined.

There are a few things that will stay with me for the rest of my life. Mainly, what a stunning place the desert is, particularly at sunrise and sunset, when the sun is low, bringing out the red colour of the dunes and casting long shadows, showing them up at their best. The night sky is unbelievable, with no light pollution for miles around. As we found with the traverses, however, the desert is a place to be respected as well as admired.

There have been a few surprises too. One is that you can get a mobile phone signal all over the country, even in the deepest desert areas if you stand on top of a dune. I've also seen countless random rubbish tips, which spoil the otherwise pristine desert. I was surprised at how green Liwa is, it's quite a sight after travelling through miles and miles of dunes to overlook a corridor of green that runs along the main road. I've seen gazelle, geckos, lots of camels (no surprises there) and spiders that would give Bolt a run for his money if you scaled them up. Just the other day I saw ospreys courting and fishing at the coast by an oil installation. My colleagues have been lucky enough (or unlucky, depending on how you look at it) to see desert monitors and a snake. One thing I haven't seen, despite warnings from colleagues who have been here before, is scorpions. That's definitely a good thing!

There are a few things that I'll miss, like having the windscreen washed every time I stop for fuel. The pump attendants always stop me from helping. I'll miss the reliable sunshine and the feeling of being the only person for miles around, where the only sounds are the breeze over the dunes and the solitary bees that seem to be attracted to my hair. You have to go to a lot of effort to get remoteness like that back home.

Now for the ultimate question: would I recommend working here to other people? Absolutely. It's been hard work, with long hours and lots of driving on sand dunes and manic roads, but very rewarding.

UAE field season five, 28 October. We're back for another mapping season here in the UAE. This time the team consists of Kathryn Goodenough, Simon Price, Bob Thomas, Jon Lee and myself, with Andy Farrant in charge.

We arrived in Abu Dhabi on Monday 18 October, which happened to be eleven years to the day since I joined BGS. After picking up our field kit from storage at the Ministry of Energy, we headed over to our labour camp accommodation at Ruwais near the coast, in the west of the country, which is to be our home for the next six weeks. It's fair to say that we all made assumptions about living in a labour camp, but it's actually much better than any of us expected. We have en-suite rooms with air con (essential in 40 °C heat), all meals are provided and they even do our laundry. There are also loads of sports facilities here. I've been in the swimming pool pretty much every night, and

I've had it all to myself for the last couple of nights, except for a dragon fly picking off stricken insects from the surface of the water.

We spent the first few days here looking at well documented outcrops of Miocene age along the coast and on the third day we went over to the area we mapped last season to look at a few outcrops together. Since then we've been working in our own mapping areas. We're working in mapping pairs, mainly for safety reasons so there's someone nearby in case one of us

Stuck in sand, United Arab Emirates. (Photograph by R. J. Thomas.)

gets stuck in the sand. Bob and myself are working south of Gayathi, which is very like the terrain where we were working last season, with increasing numbers of menacing looking sand dunes as we head south. Bob had to dig his car out on the first day but he knows what he's doing. He suggested mapping the area in convoy, which I'm much happier about. I've been sticking to tracks so far, not wanting to push my luck, but they run out altogether in the big dunes.

At the end of the first day on our own, I was waiting for Bob to get back to the road because, unawares, I'd brought with me a broken compressor and couldn't re-inflate my tyres, when a chap came up to me with a boxed gadget in his hand. At first glance I thought it was a hand blender, but then when he opened it and showed me the suction cups and plunger inside, I assumed it was a breast pump! I was just thinking why on earth would I want one of those, when he showed me the picture of a man on the pack with all six suction cups on his back. Anti snoring device? No, it was a massager for muscular aches and pains! I politely said I didn't need it and he put it back in the boot of his car and drove off.

Yesterday I was driving down a track and came across two camels lying in the middle of it. There wasn't enough room to go round them and I didn't want to startle them, especially as they had tiny babies still with their umbilical cords, so I waited patiently while they moved off in their own time. I like seeing camels and the way they regard you with an air of arrogance!

I'd forgotten how much I like the peace and quiet of the desert, and the harsh beauty of it. The dunes have a satiny sheen on them that's most noticeable around the middle of the day, when the sun is at its highest. I always had the impression that deserts are lifeless places, but that's not the case. There are loads of small butterflies with black wingtips that land on me when I get out of the car to look at outcrops. I have no idea what they feed on, I haven't come across a single flower. I also had a nasty surprise when I picked up a rock the other day and some huge ants scurried out. I dropped it straight away, thinking those ants must have a nasty bite.

9 November. We are exactly half way through our mapping season. As I type this, there's a dust storm raging outside with loads of thunder and lightning, and it's just started to rain. It's like a tropical storm and it's been building up for a couple of days. The lightning is spectacular and the thunder is incredibly loud now the storm is moving overhead.

Today was an office day to catch up with putting lines on our maps etc. We're using rugged tablet PCs running the BGS·SIGMAmobile field data capture system to gather our field data digitally and for compiling our linework (SIGMA stands for System for Integrated Geoscience Mapping). Because the maps will be published at 1:100,000 scale, we're making observation points every two kilometres above a set grid line, below which we work at four kilometre point spacing. It's very different to the 1:10,000 scale mapping that I'm used to in the UK.

Four of us went on three-day traverses over the weekend to map Sabkha Mati. As the name suggests, it's a huge *sabkha* area that stretches way over the Saudi border. In fact, more of it is on the Saudi than on the UAE side. We hired guides to scout the route for us because we expected to encounter a lot of sand dunes and treacherous wet areas; but the *sabkha* was pretty dry and we found undulating sand sheets rather than dunes, which made the driving very easy and our guides ended up following us. There was one sticky moment when Bob went full pelt into a wet area next to the Saudi border and his car ground to a halt, sinking to about half way up the wheels. He 'crocodiled' the vehicle out fairly easily and we found a way round. There was actually a substantial pond of surface water not far away, but it just looked like another mirage.

We worked in pairs during the day and met up in the evenings to camp. We're well equipped with camping stoves etc. and ate our 'just add water' food under the stars. There was very little light pollution, even less on the second night, when we camped further south. The only light pollution came from a cluster of lights at a border post with Saudi Arabia over to the west and a couple of distant towns on the coast. Bob knows loads of constellations and was pointing them out to us, but I'm ashamed to say that I can only remember a couple. We saw some impressive shooting stars, one of which broke up and scattered into tiny pieces before fizzling out altogether. I even spotted a couple of Jupiter's moons with my binoculars. We could see the Milky Way stretched out above us, a sight I'll remember for a long time.

As I drove over the *sabkha* with its red sand I kept thinking that I could be on the surface of Mars. It's completely uninhabited and there doesn't seem to be much wildlife around. We had a swarm of ten or so dragon flies around us in the morning at 'base camp two' and that was about it. Knowing that their larvae are dependent on fresh water, they looked very out of place in the middle of a vast dusty salt pan.

We've got a lot planned for the next week or so. We're going to drive to Al Ain in a couple of days and across the border into Oman to get our passports stamped again to renew our thirty-day visas, and our next three-day traverses start this Saturday. Bob and I will start ours in the southern bit of my mapping area, where the sand dunes are difficult to negotiate. Our guides won't be bored on that one!

17 November. We're fast approaching our final two weeks here. The last week has been eventful, but also really enjoyable.

Last week Bob, Andy and I spent a day looking at Miocene outcrops to make sure we were all in agreement about the different geological units where our mapping areas meet. One memorable moment was when we came across some fossilised elephant footprints in a white limestone 'pavement' that would have been soft carbonate mud at the time the elephants had wandered through. Bob and Andy decided to clamber onto the car roof for a better look at the prints over a chain-link fence that closed off the area.

Four of us went on desert traverses over the weekend. Bob and I did the eastern traverse, starting in my mapping area to fill in a few gaps in difficult dunes, finishing up 310 kilometres later at Liwa. Bob and I had Ibrahim as our guide, who seemed to take exception at a single grain of sand getting into his car. I often saw him using a paintbrush to dust off his belongings whenever we stopped to make our field notes. I even saw him dust off his pen! In total contrast, my car was full of sand, particularly in the foot well on the driver's side, where the sand in my sandals has spilled out. In fact, there was a thin coating of fine sand on everything inside the vehicle after the wind blew in sand that the tyres threw up as I ploughed the car through soft patches on the sides of dunes. Mind you, I did have all four windows open to let the breeze cool me off a bit instead of the air con. Ibrahim led the way, with me in the middle, and Bob behind. This wasn't a random order, it was because I was the least experienced sand driver and there was always someone in front or behind to tow me out if I got stuck, which I inevitably did, more than once.

I got spectacularly stuck on one occasion, which was my own fault for not leaving Ibrahim a big enough gap to go over a dune. As my car sea sawed over the crest of a particularly large *barchan* and my view changed from nothing but sky to Ibrahim's car below, I realised that Ibrahim still hadn't reached the bottom, so I braked. Believe it or not, this usually holds the car, even in avalanching sand, but on this occasion my car fishtailed and swiftly ground to a halt about half way down the leeward side of the dune. I've been assured that the angle of repose of sand is no more than 30° or so, but it feels a lot steeper when the car is dug in sideways half way down a huge *barchan* and you're sat in the down-dune side of the vehicle.

The dunes on the first day were difficult to negotiate; we had to get through fields of coalesced *barchans* that didn't allow much room for manoeuvre between them. Ibrahim got stuck after going down a dune onto a shelf of really soft sand, which stepped down again to the base of the dune, then our cars got bogged down after trying to free Ibrahim. This was at 5 pm and the sun was setting rapidly. Not wanting to go any further after we got the cars out, we decided to park up on a nearby Gayathi outcrop and set up camp for the night. Bob and I cooked up boil-in-the-bag rice and curry. After tea we took it in turns to look at the moon through my binoculars, with Bob pointing out the major lunar features, including the Sea of Tranquillity where the moon landings took place, and a huge impact crater right on the edge of the lit side. Bob recounted watching the famous moon landing live on the TV when he was in his teens, with all the tension of not knowing if they'd make it back, and the huge relief when they did.

Thankfully, the driving on the second day was really easy, and we made rapid progress across wide, fairly flat sand sheets covered in thin veneers of translucent rounded orange quartz-sand grains that glow amber in the sun. These sand sheets are separated by narrow ridges of *barchans* stacked one behind the other like fallen dominoes. We did have some thunder and lightning though, and the rain made the dunes look totally different.

We spent our second night further south, at the foot of a huge *barchan*. As this was my last traverse, and my last night in the desert, I made sure I got loads of photos of the sunset and sunrise. On the third day, as we approached Liwa, the sand sheets gave way to more coalesced *barchans*. We had about ten kilometres still to go and we could see the plantations of Liwa in the distance, but our progress was slow because it was difficult for Ibrahim to pick a route. After he and I got stuck again, and with the afternoon pressing on, Ibrahim found an alternative route that thankfully brought us out onto a sand road that led us to Liwa, then onto dirt tracks and eventually onto a road. I loved every minute of the traverse: camping in the middle of nowhere, the total silence of the desert, the spectacular sunrises, sunsets and night skies, but I was so relieved to see a road at the end of it, I could have knelt down and kissed the tarmac!

30 November. We've pretty much reached the end of our field season here. Today we're busy packing up our kit for storing at the labour camp ready for the next field season. We've spent the last couple of weeks making sure we've covered the ground in our mapping areas, ensuring that we haven't left any big gaps and that we've taken samples from the best outcrops for radiometric dating.

As we were nearing Gayathi on our way back up to Ruwais, we saw the sickening scene of a car accident that had only just happened. The crashed car was on its roof, which was caved in, facing our direction of travel on our side of the road, and the central reservation had been completely flattened. I felt sick to my stomach, but then noticed the driver staggering around in a daze with nothing more than a bit of blood around his mouth. How he managed to walk away from that I'll never know. I avoided looking into the car in case he had a passenger. Luckily a crowd of people had already gathered to offer assistance. Despite numerous public service announcements on the radio and speed cameras along the roads, people still drive way too fast here. I quickly learned, for example, that when someone flashes their lights as I'm joining a dual carriageway, it doesn't mean they're letting me out, they're signalling to me not to even think about it.

The most obvious thing I'll miss when I go home is the reliable sunshine. It's cooled down considerably since we arrived, but the daytime temperature has never dropped below the low thirties. I'll miss the peace and quiet of the desert and the stunning panoramic views of the dunes that change gradually as the shadows lengthen through the day, looking their best an hour or so before sunset. A camera can never do those views justice.

However, there are a few things that I won't miss. It always amazes me how much rubbish there is in the desert, often piled up at the base of sand dunes where there are no other signs that anyone has ever been there. I hate seeing empty plastic water bottles in the dunes as well. It's easy to lose all sense of scale in the desert. A rusty old barrel sticking out of the sand can look like the tin shack of a camel station or the rusting remains of a car from a distance.

I've seen a variety of desert wildlife, from enormous ants, to a peregrine falcon, a herd of small gazelle that sprinted off as soon as they saw the car, a smooth-skinned skink that buried itself in the sand to hide, and countless butterflies. There's plenty of life in the desert, you just have to look a bit harder to find it. One thing I haven't seen, or gone looking for, not surprisingly, is scorpions. One of my colleagues saw a cobra a few weeks ago. I count myself lucky that I haven't seen one of those either.

As this is my last 'tour of duty' I'll be a bit sad to leave. I feel very lucky to have worked here and it's an experience that will stay with me for the rest of my life. I'd definitely recommend working overseas.